"I ROB BANKS: THAT'S WHERE THE MONEY IS!"

The Story of
Bank Robber Willie "The Actor" Sutton
and the
Killing of Arnold Schuster

Donald De Simone

Shapolsky Publishers, Inc.
New York

A Shapolsky Book

For any additional information, contact:
Shapolsky Publishers, Inc.
136 West 22nd Street
New York, NY 10011
(212) 633-2022
FAX (212) 633-2123

10 9 8 7 6 5 4 3 2 1

ISBN 1-56171-051-2

Design and Computerized Typesetting by
Gessen Book Electronics, Newton, MA

Manufactured in the United States of America

To Michael-my-Mullen

and

Jonny's son Frank

The past, present, future—may it all
come together when Entering Heaven A
Minute Apart

Payback's a motherfucker!

—*Meyer Lansky*

On February 10, 1947, Willie "The Actor" Sutton, perhaps the most notorious bank robber of the century, escaped from the maximum security Holmesburg Prison in Philadelphia, Pennsylvania.

The car which took "Slick" Willie to Staten Island, New York, was driven by Margaret Moore, a longtime girlfriend, while Willie hid under a blanket in the backseat. Next to Margaret, in the front seat, was a ten-year-old boy. The child seemed like the perfect camouflage for a perfect escape. His name was Dannie Vale.

Almost five years later to the day, Willie Sutton, the #1 MOST WANTED MAN in the U.S.A., who had been living quietly in New York while masterminding a series of ingenious bank jobs, was spotted on a subway train by twenty-four year-old Arnold Schuster. At first the police took the credit for Willie's capture. But Arnold, hungry for the public acclaim and a reward rumored to be in excess of $70,000, persevered until he was finally recognized as the man who had brought Sutton to justice.

He didn't have long to savor his fame. In the cold evening wind of March 8, 1952, Schuster was mercilessly gunned down a few feet from his home in Brooklyn. The murder was carried out by a crazed member of the mob who on the one hand wanted to show "civilians," in no uncertain terms, to mind their own business and who on the other saw the "hit" as a ticket for a quick promotion in the organization.

Ironically, the murder which was meant as retribution for Schuster's turning in of Willie Sutton was witnessed by the same person who had unknowingly witnessed Willie's escape from Holmesburg five years earlier—Dannie Vale.

The Schuster murder touched off a massive public outcry and the first-ever worldwide search for the killer. To this day, the brutal slaying of Arnold Schuster has never been solved, and Dannie Vale has maintained his silence.

That is, until now.

1947

Monday, February 10

ar in the northeastern section of Philadelphia, just inside the city limits, stood an imposing square stone wall, fifteen feet thick at the base, nine feet thick at the top, and thirty-five feet high. This was the fence of Holmesburg Prison.

Ten one-story corridors extended from a central rotunda like spokes. From the rotunda, guards commanded a view of every cell block. Holmesburg was a branch of the Philadelphia County Prison, but it was no ordinary county jail. It held some of the most dangerous criminals—a Pennsylvania Alcatraz of sorts.

William Francis Sutton, bank robber, was brought to "escape-proof" Holmesburg on October 10, 1945, because he had gotten out of two other prisons before it.

Now, sixteen months later, Willie was still trapped. But his mind was fiercely at work.

"In Palestine the News Is Peace Through Force . . ." Willie "The Actor" Sutton—the Gentleman Bank Robber—always up on the day's headlines, was muttering mostly to himself, as he shuffled beside Frederick J. "Angel" Tenuto along the smelly soup alley of Holmesburg.

"I'm rootin' for them, but that's Middle East news, Willie," Angel

Tenuto answered with a voice that crackled like a low-key time bomb. "Let's get to northeastern Philly news. How we gettin' the fuck out of this rigor-mortis steel jail? Peacefully? Or through good old force?"

An imposing guard came up the mess hall corridor toward them and glanced at the two inmates. Slick Willie caught the look. It gave him the answer to Angel's heated question.

"Neither," he laughed. He poked at the shit on his tray at the jammed mess hall table. "We leave at midnight on the wings of Mazziotta money."

Willie Sutton, the Babe Ruth of Bank Robbers, left the mess hall moments later, parading past the cells of condemned prisoners, past the guarded center hub of the prison. He looked out at the corridors branching out from the center like spokes.

"I'll kill you if you try," Dr. Baldi, the superintendent, had told him when he was shipped over from North Philly's Eastern State Penitentiary. "Thanks," Sutton had said. "But I'll get out of here."

Sing Sing escape time, he reminisced. Then, North Philly's Eastern Cage—twelve of them burrowing their way out of a 97-foot tunnel like moles. It had taken them 14 months to dig their way out.

And now, tonight, "escape-proof" Holmesburg. Sorry, Dr. Baldi. The nation's magazines were proclaiming that the business of bank robbery was up 33 percent this year. I'll personally contribute to doubling that percentage before the year is out, Willie promised himself, his blue eyes lighting whimsically.

Willie, as always, would be packing a dummy pistol. But he was also bringing along a few of the guys, including his psycho killer, Angel, the man with the real *pistola*. Angel wouldn't hesitate to take you to the nearest morgue if for some inexplicable reason things went awry.

Willie's mind quickened to the recent death of Alphonse "Al" Capone, Brooklyn-born as he was. *Nato*, January 17, 1899. *Morto*, January 25, 1947. Developed syphilis behind bars. Nothing to worry about, he decided. Tonight Mazziotta mob money would win the day.

Willie Sutton banked on it when, at 2:44 a.m., with the blue light of the snowy evening filtering through the bars, he slid from his bare cot to his cell door and leaned ever so cautiously against it.

It was unlocked.

Four and a half minutes. The plan had to be executed in four and a half minutes.

After months of planning, every last detail of Willie's elaborate escape plan was indelibly etched on his mind. He *knew* that there was a sergeant and four guards on duty, plus two at the circular desk in the rotunda. The prison was undermanned and only two cell blocks were being patrolled.

Every fifteen minutes a guard walked through C block. That's where the condemned men were held. Every thirty minutes a guard walked through D block, which held men judged to be especially dangerous—men like Willie and Angel Tenuto.

Sutton rested on the toes of his backless bedroom slippers as he slithered from the cell, Angel and another of their cellmates close on his heels.

At precisely 2:45 a.m. a guard entered D block. The cells were all dark and the corridor was only dimly lit. He began the slow walk to the far end of the hall where he would punch the time clock. The double doors leading from the rotunda were locked behind him. Fifty feet farther on he unlocked a second set of barred doors.

Just then, three figures emerged from the shadows and rushed towards the unsuspecting guard. In seconds they had overpowered him. Another guard appeared at the rotunda door. Angel, with the assistance of a .38, convinced him to hand over the keys.

With the keys to everything in the place, the three convicts released two others. Then they surprised two guards in the boiler room and took their uniform coats and caps. From a storeroom they obtained two ladders. Now they were ready to check out.

Two officers were overseeing the center hub, one of them "on the take." The men made it past.

Double steel doors by the exit gallery. Another giant door between the exit alley and the Prison yard. Angel played it for real with his loaded pistol, seizing, confusing two guards by the gallery.

Willie's precision timing brought them six seconds ahead of schedule into the stormy snow mound of the yard. They stood exposed in the open area, facing a 35-foot stone wall and a machine gun perched on the top of a tower.

The searchlight zeroed in on them from the tower above. The guard in the tower wouldn't take a nickel from his mother if it meant her life. Willie, dressed like a guard, coolly waved to him. "It's okay. Everything's all right," he called and held his breath. The searchlight died in the night.

"I had that high-rise hack's forehead right in my sight," Angel whispered to keen Willie. "Go out of here with a fuckin' bang!"

"No need." Willie quickly gestured to the men to haul the two 20-foot ladders, which had been lashed together, over to the darkened wall. It was just as if he were under the warden's instructions.

The five escapers climbed the ladder. Then, they unfurled 40 feet of rope tipped with a three-pronged iron hook to catch in the wall. It had taken Willie months to make the rope out of cotton cord he pilfered from the prison looms. But now it was all worth it. They slid down the other side of the wall—the free side—and landed with a muffled crunch on the snow-covered ground. Baldi was sure to make someone pay for this, Willie smirked.

The 1947 Studebaker Champion by the curb purred for Willie and Angel. The other three men scattered, disappearing quickly into the snowy night. They'd be caught soon, Willie knew. But that didn't matter. All that mattered was that he was FREE.

The "proposed" beaver-toothed Brooklyn mobster, Hugo Duce, was driving. "Marge is waiting nearby with a rented ten-year-old 'nephew,' Willie," he said. "The nephew's Borough Park, Brooklyn's, pride and joy. No sweat." He turned on the black dial-lit radio.

Willie looked back at the dark fortress he'd been caged in for too long. Marge and the kid driving him home. It was the perfect cover. Tonight he would sleep in a nice soft bed in a room without bars.

"How's Felice?" Willie Sutton asked as he hustled out of the official clothing.

"Old man Mazziotta is . . . retired. His kid, Johnny Squint's, in charge. You remember him, don't ya, Will?" Hugo wheeled the vehicle on the thick snow.

"Johnny Squint? My special *cop-fighter*," Willie said. He was changing into a blue serge suit in the back seat, next to Angel. "Sure. Don Vitone and Uncle Frank's favorite 'son.' I remember him well."

"Angel . . . we'll change that name. Call you 'Augie.' " Puffs of cold air came out of Hugo's mouth as he spoke, drove. "Glad to meet you, Augie. You'll be staying in the heart of Brooklyn. Hey," Hugo suddenly eyed his rear-view mirror for half a second while the windshield wipers fought the snow. "Anyone ever tell you you're a dead ringer for Johnny?"

"No." Angel was dressed now in a double-breasted rust suit, rust shirt. "And I'm glad to meet you, Hugo." Angel leaned over slightly and kissed Willie's cheek. "Any friends of my *gombarda* Willie are friends of mine."

He flung the uniform from the rolled-down car window. "And may the prick who wore it drop dead in his sleep tonight," he laughed, cursing with a near frozen jaw into the freezing-night whirlwinds.

1947

It was freezing the following night of February 11, 1947, in Borough Park, Brooklyn, New York, too.

Eve Vale was lying rigid under the brown wool blanket, having a dream, one she'd been having for ten years.

The radiator hissed and whined against the chill, but the chill won. Eve shuddered. Now there were only Roscoe's thick snores trying to keep her awake.

She clawed at the sheets, gasping for breath. Slowly, she inched over to her side of the bed. She was fighting to wake up, but was losing.

If she stared at the shadows that swirled like shapeless little demons on the wall molding, she could force them to disappear.

And then it began again anyway. Out from the shadows. Her younger sister Eleanor's voice. A litany opening dark, vague, low . . . coming ever nearer to her . . . louder . . . till it blanked out everything.

There was only the voice now.

Eve shut her eyes.

"They said you were dead . . . yet . . . a tantalizing helpless . . . vision."

Eve was numb. Every pore of her body strained toward attention.

"He burst into your hospital room. Sex-crazed. Drunk. *Cop-fighter*!

"He was coming at you, whining. The stench of alcohol on his breath and skin made you choke.

"He was *codardo*. Spewing his whiskey odors on your youthful . . . virginal . . . naked body."

Now Eve was rocking in the darkness of Eleanor's arms, voice . . . Eleanor reminding . . . reminding . . . "A *ribelle cop-fighter*! Blinding—smothering you. Terror paralyzing your being.

"His rough, sweaty hands squeezing your breasts like a vise.

"Then he was thrusting himself into you. Your eyes burning tight. Your screams stifled . . . You . . . feel the warm blood trickling down your thighs.

"And the seed entered you. HIS seed. A secret. No one saw."

And Eve's body was swelling with pregnancy. Her breasts heavy, succulent haloes.

Eleanor's voice droned on. "They came for you . . . later . . . three of them. They uncover you, stare at your naked body under the sheet. Poor Eve! You are flat on your back. Immobilized. You hear the distant voices, 'Gorgeous woman . . . seventeen, maybe eighteen. Too young . . . to die.' Even in death they lust for you. They wheel you down the cold corridors. They take you to the freezer slabs, their hospital basement morgue."

Eve was whispering now, shaking her head, hugging herself. She couldn't stop the voice. She had to listen. Had to know. Eleanor knew.

"And one by one, Eve, they have their way with you . . . rub their filthy death hands on your belly, finger your still-warm nipples . . ."

"No more!"

The voice softened. "Trust me, Eve . . . we must face that night . . . we must never forgive them . . ."

She cried out like a wounded animal. Eleanor's voice rose.

"They violated and degraded you as only God can measure!"

Eve opened her eyes in terror. The sheet over her head was suffocating her. She struggled to pull it from her, throwing both sheet and blanket off her body, weeping, huddling into a fetal position, *screaming*.

"But you tricked them, Eve! You were *alive*!"

"Eve, are you awake?" Roscoe Vale was shaking her. Eve ran her hand through her thick black hair. It was sweaty.

"Get away from me," she whispered. "Don't touch me!"

Roscoe rolled over but watched his wife sob hysterically. He couldn't take it anymore. He felt helpless. A normal woman would let her husband take her in his arms, comfort her.

Not Eve.

He left her side and walked to the window. Why did he put up with this?

"The nightmare again," was the best he could do.

She ignored him, as he knew she would.

"Where the hell are you going now?" he snapped, as he watched her silently uncurling herself and getting up fully from the bed. But he already knew where she was going. The light from a streetlamp was seeping through the room, uncovering the curvaceous outline of her firm-fleshed body, the luxurious breasts and hips, the well-formed flanks, and he suddenly hated her for tearing him up between disgust and desire.

He had tried his best. He had put up with this madness for years. With her cold, indifferent rejection. Now he felt used.

He had a right to live, too.

He lay back down listening as she went into the living room.

He could imagine the fragrance of her long, rich black hair and her loose breasts under the skimpy lavender camisole as she leaned over the living room couch to whisper to Dannie.

Does she think I don't hear her?

Her full breasts would be brushing against Dannie's chest as she gave him the hungry little kisses Roscoe yearned for.

"Wake up, Dannie."

The nightly ritual.

I won't live like this much longer, Roscoe told himself.

"I love you, Dannie. Wake up. Mommy needs you. It was so cold and snowy. You were gone the whole night last night. I *missed* you!"

Ten-year-old Dannie Vale heard her. He felt her body kneeling over his on the sofa-bed even though his back was to her. She was . . . walking in her nightmare but he wouldn't turn over. He didn't want to kiss her back. He couldn't bear to look into those tormented green eyes.

"Dannie, please." Her hands were rubbing his back.

His muscles were stiff. He pretended to be sound asleep.

"I need you, Dannie."

He felt himself choking. Why did his mother always make her need sound like a fearful curse?

1948

If you were a young girl in 1948 and you wore slacks, you were either too poor to afford a skirt, too sloppy a dresser to care about decency, or just a plain tomboy. Either way, "No young girl should be dressed like that." Dannie sat beside his mother, Eve, and heard her words as the subway train burrowed its way in downtown Brooklyn.

"It's crude, it's vile, it's an open dare to a young boy," his mother continued, the train thundering underground.

"She invites the Devil in them." Eleven-year-old Dannie Vale was attentive to his mother's exhortations, but as he bounced lightly with the swaying of the train, keeping in tune with his mother's talking, he kept watching the young girl she was talking about.

It was easy to appraise her—and safe, too. She was sitting on the ninety-degree-angled, yellowish straw-woven seat chatting, giggling with two of her dress-clad girlfriends. She was a redhead knockout.

He caught sight of her half-turned back and, when she turned once in a while to catch his look, her sparkling freckled face.

She had blue "come hither eyes." That was the "neat" expression they used in his Borough Park neighborhood. He wondered what neighborhood she was from.

"She's straight from a tease factory." His mother was as grave as ever.

He took his eyes from the girl, and sat acutely conscious of the men in the subway car. Their eyes on his mother. From atop folded newspapers, gaping from strap-hanging stances, filled with hunger and wonder. He outstared them, his mother seemingly oblivious. He lowered his eyes to his short pants. Not knickers gathered at the calves, but loose-fitting homemade hemmed cuffs that never touched or covered his bare knees.

And he concentrated. On his toothache, which was gnawing at the right side of his face. At least it wasn't like it had been before he boarded the train. It could be the homemade toothache remedy of his mother's that had toned down the twinging pain. Rye whiskey. Not swallowed but held bubble, cheeked on top and around the aching molar.

But no matter how he geared his concentration in different directions, or tried to shift his consciousness to different things, he sat ashamedly self-conscious most of all of one thing: the excitement the girl across from him had caused—inside his short pants.

If his mother noticed, she'd probably have two saints hold him while a third cut it off. He gulped, trying his best to dismiss it.

The blue-eyed redhead was just another girl. One of dozens that had caused him excitement since he had turned eleven December ninth of last year.

The train bounded into the Pacific Street Station. He felt his mother's hand in his, and recoiled from the grasp. The three young girls eyed him, and his face went down from . . . shame, his eyes on the redhead's shoes—white leather Prima Ballets.

The chesty redhead turned toward him, laughing to her girl-friends, "He's a 'creamer,' that short pants one." His mother had stood up, again grasping his hand, the train bumping in a forward-backward motion, stopping, its rubber-edged doors hissing open.

His face was flushed fit to boil, yet he couldn't help but be aware of the male stares his mother took from the train with her. She was a built-in tease factory whether *she* knew it or not. He held a clog in his throat, watching the three adolescent girls walking in front of him along the dirty-brown cement platform.

Gone.

The dazzling redhead was gone, lost in the Saturday throng. He let his mother tightly hold his hand as they ascended the steep stairwell up and out into the summer sunshine of the downtown corner of Pacific and Fourth.

Dannie squinted from the sun's glare, his free left hand going up automatically as an eye shield. Then he spotted the pudgy, sun-glassed man and four other men, among them one who was stout, balding.

Gretti. Dannie recognized him from Pete's Radio Store hangout in Borough Park. One of Johnny Squint's buddies. Gretti had been caught off guard for that instant, and Dannie's mother, Eve, had been the cause of it. He had stood nearly poised on his toes, the armpit sweat showing through his white-on-white silk shirt, his usual drab pallor livening at the captivation . . . the bewitching sudden sight of her.

But he caught himself. Turned on his black patent-leathered toes, quickly whispering to the pudgy masterful man before Dannie had a chance to wave hello.

Strange guys, Dannie thought as he watched all five of them turn down Pacific Street to a waiting, chauffeured DeSoto.

But then again Johnny Squint had a lot of strange friends. Dannie dismissed it, squinting up at the tallest building in Brooklyn, the Williamsburg Savings Bank—the dental lair.

"If you would have spoken to anyone in that *banda*," his mother's green eyes sparked, "I would have slapped you silly!" She dragged him hurriedly across Atlantic Avenue toward the bank. "That bulldog one. I've seen his bullfrog picture in the newspapers. He's the worst of that lot." His left hand was being clawed by her long fingernails. "They were your Johnny's companions! Your evil idol!" She practically swung him up the curb.

Dannie remained closed-mouthed. He could never win on the subject of cop-fighting Johnny "Squint" Mazziotta. *Not with her!* But he yanked free of her fierce grip, soothing the nail marks on his palm, wondering now what Gretti had said in the ear of that bulldog powerhouse of a sunglassed man.

After the dental stint—where his mother had insisted that she stand pat right behind the dentist during the drilling—the BMT Fourth Avenue Local roared back toward the 36th Street Station, Eve sitting snugly beside Dannie.

Homeward bound, Dannie had missed a chance at a scrumptious Nedicks Hot Dog lunch. The right side of his mouth was stuffed with cotton held over the filling in his mediciny tooth.

His single Aunt Eleanor had paid the extra money for the laughing gas so he wouldn't have to feel the pain of pinch-needle injected Novocain. His mother shifted even closer to him, crossing, then uncrossing, her barely-above-the-knees skirted, tapered legs. He tried to move away, but there was no place to go. His body straining against the half steel, half window wall of the whizzing train, he listened and glanced out at the tracks, girders, and dirt-caked underground tiles.

". . . And your Aunt Eleanor wouldn't hear of you suffering needlessly," his mother was praising her only sister. "She would have been here herself today, but you know that her job is so demanding."

That's all he needed. Dannie half-closed his eyes, thinking. His gorgeous, temperamental Aunt Eleanor. She'd slap the dentist's face silly till *he* needed a dentist, if he had dared make her only nephew wince with the slightest bit of pain.

Slapping. Dear Eleanor's favorite pastime. She had banged him around like the speed bag he used now and then in his Public Grammar School's gym, whacking him at her whim since he couldn't remember when. That is, when she wasn't plying him with expensive underwear, school shirts, giving him "loving caresses," and taking him up to Yankee Stadium or a rollicking Brooklyn Dodgers game. Dannie squeezed in his seat, half-facing his mother. "Mom. Could you . . . ask Dad or Aunt Eleanor for money for . . . long . . . pants?" He was squeezing out the words, tongue holding the cotton over his tooth, gulping, anticipating her reaction.

A stunned Eve Vale inhaled so deeply that the provocative heave and sway of her bloused bustline brought her twice the usual attention from the males in the train's car. "You what?" She had turned to Dannie, half up on her seat. "Long pants?" Her green eyes turned from spicy sex to crackling firebrands.

"That little redhead. That's what caused this. She called you a creamer in short pants, giggling at you."

Dannie sat still, looking down at his blue Thom McAn shoes, hearing his mother go from castigation to lamentations.

"That one with the trollop slacks. She should live so long to have the dashing looks of yours within a mile of her with her invitational attire. Dreamboat, that's what she meant."

His mother's hand was fidgety, truculent, "nursing" his, the cove of her chartreuse skirt too close for his comfort.

"Your father barely has 'needed' money. Eleanor would not hear of it at your age. You have wrong ideas, that's it. Would long trousers make you feel like a grown man? Would they make you *act* like one?" His mother's sobs made the scene a stadium of onlookers instead of a train ride. "There'd be a double suicide if you committed the act of fornication at your age. Your aunt and myself. And, Daniel, you know what I mean." She was forcing his sore hand even further into her sultry lap, the train pulling into their station.

He purposely held her vibrating hand, safely, out in the open as they walked the three blocks to Fourth Avenue and 39th Street to wait for the uphill trolley car—the long way home. Eve could have switched at 36th Street for the West End Line to Ninth Avenue. But did she want to pass Johnny's headquarters?

He permitted the hand-holding now out of exultant gratitude for being clear out of sight of those people on the train. Their eyes, looks, stares saying that he was a MAMA'S BOY!

The trolley began its wheel-screeching, uphill trek toward his house. His mother, sitting tight beside him, fondling his hands in the heated inlet of her taut skirt, switching then to the burners of her skirted thighs, began *again* about the audacity of his asking for long pants, this time going into the low-life *maggiore* he wanted to impress with them.

"Those disgraceful mobsters. They're ghouls. They desecrate the living dead." Dannie took in her verbal blasts at dastardly gangland. His mind and loins, however, were drifting to the pretty bundle of a redhead. Suddenly, past the trolley's side window and horizontal protective bars, he saw Pete's Radio Store, on the corner of Eighth Avenue and 40th Street. It was Johnny's gambling, book making headquarters—the Men of Action corner. It passed him by as the trolley car churned the one block to his three-story apartment house.

Twilight time, Dannie stood, waiting for his "reward."

He was spruced up in his form-fitting, powder blue Manhattan short-sleeved shirt. And matching short pants.

He had a "date" with his bitchy, blue-eyed Aunt Eleanor. He recoiled shamefully at the thought. She'd take him to a movie, *The Street with No Name* with Mark Stevens at the downtown RKO Albee, as a reward for his "brave behavior" at the dentist's office today.

He looked up at his Borough Park apartment building. His mother was in her second "fashionable" change of the day, and his father, Roscoe, was readying himself for his night watchman's job. Roscoe had, of late, been openly sarcastic about the Twin Sirens—Eve and Eleanor—Eve a zesty fashion freak, and Eleanor a taunting sybaritic screwball. Dannie gulped, shrugged, hunching his shoulders toward the nonsectarian Greenwood Cemetery.

The cemetery—the biggest in Brooklyn—was on his left, diagonally about three furlongs along the Ninth Avenue incline where he waited. Furlongs, he knew that racetrack talk from being trusted around Johnny and his men. Dannie was smiling widely now on his forlorn corner.

He glanced to his right, up Ninth Avenue. Hey, that was Hugo Duce with the wide-brimmed fedora . . . and Johnny? . . . or maybe that fellow Augie with the out-of-town accent, standing outside of Walt's All Night Diner.

He took a step forward, glancing sideways at the gabled Ninth Avenue Train Station. Aunt Eleanor would be late, dressing, primping, filling her sensuously proportioned frame to the make-them-want-to-rape-her hilt. He crisscrossed 39th to Walt's.

He sidled by the two men, on the sidewalk, not a dozen feet from them.

Buck-toothed, fedora'd Hugo Duce gave Dannie a wary wave hello.

Augie, it wasn't Johnny, winked a sincere, zany hi. Dannie grinned sheepishly, trying to mask his dejection at it not being Johnny Squint himself, in the flesh.

Dannie, by curbside, leaned against the five-foot-high, army-tan, metal mailbox. He spotted the discolored face of Al Rispone; the sleek, greasy-pencilled mustachioed Tony-boy inside Walt's.

The two-way, Ninth Avenue evening traffic buzzed by, while Dannie, out of earshot of the two men on the sidewalk, watched them counting wads of cash.

"That's the 'Break-Out Kid'?" Augie Tenuto commented while counting out mostly ten dollar bills—the pony "take" of the day— most of it Johnny Squint's. "Why'd that balding motherfucker Gretti tell that other madhatter cocksucker Al-bert about it today?" Augie stopped counting.

"Johnny's downtown South Brooklyn with Anastasia now." Hugo Duce pocketed three loose stacks of hundred dollar bills. "He'll iron it out. Uncle Frank's with him. No sweat." Trickling beads of sweat ran from under Hugo's black fedora, down along his temples.

Tony-boy and Al Rispone exited Walt's. Tony-boy, swinging a long key chain, glanced over at Dannie by the stubby mailbox. "That box was a foot higher it'd be coffin perfect," he laughed.

In the split-second berserk reflex of Augie's elbow heading for Tony-boy's pencilled mustache Hugo Duce had cut in. "*Stat dha zeet*, Tony-boy!" Hugo said sharply. "While Eve Vale is walking in life's parade, that kid stands! You wanna repeat that casket shit to John?"

Powder-keg Augie fumed inches from Tony-boy, Hugo Duce's hand on his pulsing arm.

Tony-boy looked away nervously, down Ninth Avenue, spying "mysterious"—Eve's lusty sister—Eleanor Cross. Dannie, watching all four men now, suddenly followed Tony-boy's glance. Oh, God, Aunt Eleanor. He dashed for his corner house, she'd kill him for being late. He ran like all hell. She'd kill him for fraternizing with "*abile* killers!" He made it to the sweetly scented, baby-pink sweater of hers, and caught an open right-palm smack! on his healing cheek.

Augie Tenuto looked on from the distance. A kid who helped him and Willie "The Actor" break out of prison being knocked down by a raving broad. What a crime!

Tony-boy, snazzy in gray sharkskin attire, index finger staccato swinging his key chain, calmer now, was looking beyond the aunt-nephew bullshit scene. *Albert Anastasia*, the Lord of Lords in the Outfit's real chain of command, cut and *buried* any 1947 escape "rented-nephew" *links to him*! He smiled uneasily, gazing at the tall, black iron pikes of Greenwood Cemetery, which stood in direct view.

Dead ahead.

1949

Autumn.

Dannie looked sharp in his maroon mambo jacket as he walked down 39th Street, rapturous, feisty Aunt Eleanor banging in his brain.

Last night she had sworn to him on *Adoshem*. He hadn't known what that meant, or even what language it was.

She had done more than that last night. He walked down toward the deserted Bush Terminal Pier, trying to make out the shrouded Staten Island across the darkened Narrows. He could hardly see it through the fog over the tail end of the Hudson River.

Crazy, moody Eleanor. He lingered on the dank waterfront terminal. All because he had come home a little late.

Nutty bitch that she was—he wished he had called her that to her face.

She had been waiting for him, standing like a shrew by his house, the evil fire and ice temper of hers ready to lash out.

And she was shrewd. The times she had won him over after her tantrums made him *positive* of that.

She had blocked the entrance to his doorway, standing with her hands on her hips. Hips that could send you cross-eyed when she shimmied in sultry skirts.

She blasted him verbally. "Where the hell have you been? You have me, your mother upstairs, wild with worry!" Her goddess blue eyes had blazed her touchiness, while her hands had dropped from her hips. That had caught him off guard, and she had swiftly smacked him full on his left cheek, his head snapping backward.

Damning tears had fallen down his cheeks, by the corners of his mouth.

And then, she had taken him to her. Pressing him firmly against her King's Ransom shaded skirt, engulfing him airtight-close to her low cut, busty cardigan, feeling her silken black hair cuddling his face. "Why do you make me do this?" Her breasts were pressed firmly against the side of his face and he thought he could feel the bountiful swollen nipple of one of them indenting his right cheek.

He had broken away from her, calling her, with stinging wet eyes, "a savage that God would curse."

She had screamed fit to kill, retorting with, "I swear on *Adoshem* that you'll rue this day for cursing me." He could hear her plain as day, now as last night. "I swear it on your father!" Her words had been like eerie promises on deserted Ninth Avenue. They faded now in his mind as the sound of a car motor running reverberated close behind him.

Scared, he spun around.

He squinted . . . WOW! It was Johnny, beeping the horn from behind the wheel of his brand-spanking-new Plymouth convertible.

"Over here, good lookin'," Johnny Squint waved.

Dannie ran the twenty feet to the car.

"The older kids on the corner by Fiola's told me they saw you stumbling this way. What's on your mind, Dannie V.?" Johnny narrowed his eyes, waiting for an answer.

Dannie remained mute.

"Get in. We'll discuss it over a hot *antipasto* at Fiola's. Get in, son."

That was a magic word to Dannie. Son. Only a word, but it held magic for him. He hopped into the wide open-topped convertible.

Fiola's restaurant-pizzeria was smoky, jammed with evening customers, and sure-footed, imperious men, impeccably dressed, filtering in from Pete's Radio Store diagonally across the street.

Despite his *rimbambire* knickers, Dannie sat bursting-proud within himself. He felt "mannish" sitting beside Johnny in the brown leather booth by the neon-lit window of the restaurant.

Entering neighborhood bar patrons, the teenage toughies outside, and passing night people were all seeing him so close, so chummy, with Johnny "Squint" Mazziotta, the roughest cop-fighter and biggest bookmaker in Borough Park. Dannie munched on the stuffed peppers, also devouring, in kaleidoscope-fashion, the scene that surrounded him.

Friendly, gabby Reb going on about Pawtucket Rhode Island Races. The Atlantic City Track and how it was fixed. "You had to guess who the winner was in each 'boat race' there."

Mean-eyed Little Mike commented on legalizing punchboards and on slot and pinball machines.

Fungi-faced Al Rispone grimaced about that double-dealing Mayor bastard. Uncle Frank's hand-picked choice.

A wisp of a man came in, embracing granite-armed Johnny Squint. Dannie thought that the slender fellow looked familiar. They addressed him as Lynch. A regal man with a long nose and expensive gray fedora entered unobtrusively, firmly grasping Johnny's and the slender fellow's hands, in turn.

"Uncle Frank, *conveniente*, Dannie V." Johnny smiled cordially, making the introduction.

"*Mio piacimento*," the fedora'd Uncle Frank graciously extended his hand.

"*Mia piacere*," Dannie blushed, thinking he'd drop dead on the spot *in his knickers*. He stood, heartily shaking "Uncle" Frank Costello's firm right hand, thanking heaven that Johnny had schooled him in Italian since he was six years old.

After a noisy, jukebox blasting, men-exchanging-money half an hour, Johnny Squint flexed his diamond-studded Lucien Picard wrist watch.

"Mother of Mary and Jesus Christ," Johnny was peering at the watch's face. "Dannie, do you know how late it is? Your mother's got to be half out her mind by now. Holy Toledo! She'll nail us both to a cross. Scat! Fly home!"

Dannie raced to 39th. He had wanted to talk to Johnny about . . . girls. He knew Johnny must have plenty with those rough good looks of his. He made it in record time to his apartment building.

A *friend*. He had *friends*. He took the building's three flights of steps two at a time.

1950

March 8

The Money Store. Manufacturer's Trust Co. Bank. The Borough of Queens, New York. Willie "The Actor" Sutton, America's Most Wanted Man, was not altogether acting today as he stood curbside on Queens Boulevard, watching the front door of the bank, twenty feet diagonally to his left.

He stooped, patting the porcelain face of the toy doll tucked under the pink blankets of the baby carriage he was rocking. Keep the kid warm, he thought. His cool blue eyes read 8:27 a.m.—three minutes before the Money Store's unofficial opening time. He flexed his left wrist, the Bulova watch disappearing beneath his Brooks Brothers worsted-suit sleeve .

It was cloudy, but kind of warm for the second week in March. Willie clocked Angel Tenuto, six feet from the door.

"Stand still, ya fuckin' mutt," Angel flared with his back pressed against the cold brick, he kicked at the leashed and collared dog-catcher's-dream of a Doberman pinscher. "1950's gonna be a big year for you, you growling Ludwig motherfucker. *Ya gonna die in it*!" He promised.

Angel/Augie, a.k.a "St. John," was about to reach into his expensive suit, clutch his brown Lugar and blow the frothing short-haired's cock off, but he restrained himself. Had to. Willie had planned every detail of this heist for four, shut-in months of nights.

The Doberman was nipping, biting at Angel's Dorset English shoes and yelping. "This black scrounge's prick's comin' off today," Angel mumbled. He waited for James Wetson, the sixty-two-year-old guy with the key to the bank, according to Slick Willie. Thinking about the heist, Angel actually smiled down at the whimpering dog.

Morose, bespectacled Tommy Kling stood on the sidewalk waiting four minutes now for this custodian Wetson and all the employees who would follow him into the bank before it opened for business—officially, at least—at 10:00 a.m.

Number Nine on the Ten Most Wanted List, he reflected sourly. Tommy "Mad Dog" Kling was about to slide his tinted eyeglasses up his huge flaring nose, but he stopped himself. Willie had warned him that the habit was one of his trademarks, and there was no need to move them today anyway. They had been glued to his shaggy, sideburned, wrinkled kisser this morning, so he couldn't move them even if he tried.

Look at that, pencil-drawn mustachioed Willie, Kling thought. Calm, breezy, keen, free and easy, man. And the Guinea, psycho Angel, never too far from the Master, arguing with that goddamn dog. A phony seeing-eye dog I was supposed to use. He caught himself checking out a young broad passing by. He could go for those big knockers on her, that sweet bitch. He eyed an old hag with hefty flanks, about 70, but still fuckin' material below the neck as far as he was concerned. He gazed across heavily trafficked Queens Boulevard.

Stocky, shaky Venuta. Oscar the Syrian from Boston. Both backup men across the thoroughfare in Brooks Brothers patterned outfits—Willie's ploy—and holding portmanteaus, as cunning Willie called them. They really seemed like two Madison Avenue business suit types with those brimmed tight fedoras on. Tommy spotted a pretty blonde crossing the street. He'd have the *gelt*, the *mazuma*, tonight to play that Broadway game. With Willie Sutton running the show, it worked every time.

Kling suddenly glanced to his right. Angel was swiftly shoving a fellow into the bank. It was Game Time.

8:30 a.m.

Without firing a shot, Willie Sutton owned another bank. Police Commissioner O'Brien was going to get a nice message long before the day was up.

Willie, standing by the shield-like frontal partitions, nodded to

Angel to chain up Mr. Wetson by the vestibule, and reminded Kling to patiently wait by the nearby exec's office, with the coated glass partitioned doors, for sixteen employees. And a postman.

Angel chained the chunky custodian doggy-style, legs up, head down, "collared" back to the hindlegs. Angel felt like Poncho Villa. He had to practically undress himself from the waist up to get the four leashes from across his bare chest.

There was no need for Willie to study the inside of the bank today. He knew every inch of it by heart. His precise painstaking surveillance with his photographic mind for 119 days paid off. He quietly began rearranging the many chairs he would need for the company to come.

"Are . . . you going to rob the bank?" Wetson struggled. His eyes were bulging.

"No, you stupid motherfucker. I'm here to audit." Tenuto was going to make this guy eat the fuckin' real Lugar if he didn't shut up.

"Two comin'," Tommy whispered. He readied his dummy pistol.

By the time the two employees were in the bank they were ogling Wetson, and Angel's steel Lugar. Caught! Trapped! Both of them.

"Sit down, please," Willie beckoned them. "Teddy. Jimmy. How's Ozone Park? Jackson Heights? The subway's on time today?"

The two tellers were stymied, their facial expressions asking in unison how in God's name this . . . robber . . . knew their names, where they lived?

"Your telephone operator, Mrs. Heffer, will be joining us shortly," Willie smiled. "If you two gentlemen, and Mrs. Heffer, behave correctly, then by ten to ten this morning, before the bank opens to the public, no harm will come to you, nor to any of the others—your mailman from Hollis included." Willie patted their shoulders gently, in turn.

They sat mesmerized, nodding their compliance.

One by one the bank clerks appeared for work and took their seats under Willie's tranquil control.

"Hey, Nick," Angel ribbed the sixty-nine-year-old mailman whom he had corralled. "Got any mail for me this morning?"

The mailman smiled, while Mrs. Heffer, the telephone operator from Glendale, pretended over the telephone that today was business as usual, Willie intimately prompting her.

"Come on, Nick," Angel kidded. "If I asked you if there was any mail for me, why didn't you ask me my name?"

Nick didn't smile this time, Angel's Lugar looming barrel *ready*.

The mailman shifted slightly in his chair, sitting stiff, mute.

"Ahh, you're shy," Angel actually smiled, making sure Willie The Actor did not see that the Lugar was *no dummy*. Willie didn't like guns.

Willie's timing was perfect, and when the vault alarm shut off automatically at 9:00 a.m. Willie escorted the two bank officials to the vault. "Please open it," he instructed.

They did. Quietly, quickly.

"Howard. Anne. Dan. Unlock your teller boxes."

Angel watched The Actor work, his eyes riveted on the green being gathered and stacked into the blue silk bag. Ahh, Willie, he thought, My Main Man on Earth, you got it down to a fuckin' science.

9:45 a.m.

Five minutes to exit time. Angel took his cue from Willie and marched all seventeen of the bank clerks, telephone operator, mailman and executives down to the basement. He fuckin' warned them—No!—he promised them that if they didn't sit tight for twelve fuckin' minutes there'd be hearses in Hollis, Ozone Park, Jackson Heights, all over Queens in twelve fuckin' hours.

Mr. James Wetson, who was half-dragged down to the basement, asked timidly if he could be untied.

"They'll do it for you," Angel said. "I got a date with a Doberman."

The three robbers left the bank with close to $64,000 in mostly tens, twenties, fives, and singles, as Willie Sutton had known they would. Willie walked brazenly around the block to the waiting blue Studebaker, holding the silk bag loosely. He was gone within twenty seconds, making it to the predesignated bus stop in twenty-four seconds, parking, alighting sixteen seconds later from the car onto the appearing bus.

Angel climbed into the back seat of Oscar the Syrian's Studebaker. "Where's that fuckin' dog that bit me!" he was squeezing the Lugar's handle hard.

"Angel, are you nuts?" Oscar drove toward the subway station. "We just pull off one of the neatest, sweetest bank heists since our last one," he laughed, "and you're asking about a freakin' stray? Settle down. We split the loot late tonight."

"Fuck you, you A-Hab motherfucker!" Tenuto fumed. "Pull up!"

Angel had practically ripped off the Brooks Brothers "bullshit" suit jacket and slid into a greasy Mackinaw. Donning a baseball cap, he pulled off his putty nose and jumped out of the car, leaving

Oscar stunned, at the wheel. After four scouring, precious minutes, Angel spotted the black bastard of a mongrel.

"Come to Daddy. Come to Daddy, now," he backed up, luring the mutt into an apartment house alleyway. The Doberman growled, leapt for him just as Angel dropped to one knee, ripping two slugs into the canine's belly. He peered up at the apartment windows, stowing the Lugar under his jacket.

Angel stepped over the bleeding dog, making it to the train station in two and a half minutes. He was on his way to Brooklyn to see his "Rabbi," Johnny "Squint" Mazziotta. He let the grinding El lull him to sleep, while peeping beyond the brim of his Phillies baseball cap at the groggy strap-hangers. Ahh, it was a hectic dog's life, it fuckin' was. Though everything had gone so well, he was more than hazily wondering why Willie, the Master of Disguises, hadn't made-up for today's big robbery.

Another trip over the choppy narrows for Willie The Actor. He stood on windy Whitehall Street's dock in downtown Manhattan.

Willie had changed into a short plaid jacket and sailor cap in the transit toilet—a nickel in the slot door for security—and had secured the money to his body in money belts. The ferry taking him to Staten Island would arrive in four minutes. He wondered which of his mug shots they would print along with the news of the bank hold-up.

His blue eyes glinted at the crowd around him waiting to board the ferry. New Jersey, southwest, to his right, the Statue of Liberty, dead center, in the harbor, Staten Island in the hazy distance. He might as well be invisible. He boarded the ferry, along with the vehicles and the rest of the passengers, and stood on the top deck, leaning against the ferry's rail as it creaked its way against the rotting wooden piles, beginning its familiar trek across the Hudson.

Invisible. Who had noticed him casing the Manufacturer's Queens bank for four months, dressed as a sanitation worker, a Catholic nun in full regalia—his mother, Mary, in Brooklyn would die of shame if word ever reached her of that disguise—a policeman, a padded-fat carpenter in overalls. Nobody had really noticed him at all, opening accounts, following the tellers home, getting their names, their plate numbers, clocking the Money Store's schedule.

He had left nearly $14,000 in coins in the bank. Too heavy, bulky. What the hell, Willie thought, he could well afford that. Ever since Johnny Squint arranged his escape from escape-proof prison 37 months ago, Willie had hauled in over six million in nine states. He didn't bother to figure the exact price he was paying to Johnny's

"Uncle Frank" Costello's Group or Madhatter Albert Anastasia's Crew. It was worth it.

Tonight, on his bleak Staten Island, his new isolated, marshland "prison," he'd split with Venuta, Oscar, Kling, and Angel. Angel would take the usual 30 percent to Borough Park. The loot would wind up with Uncle Frank and Mr. Murder Inc., Albert. More like *in* Mr. Albert Anastasia's *deep pockets*.

And Willie figured later he'd be able to take in a movie with Marge, or maybe Fran. He wanted to see *Borderline* with Fred MacMurray and poignant Claire Trevor.

The split took place at 9:10 p.m. As usual, there were no gripes. Oscar kissed Willie's lips, hastily going on his merry way to Providence, Rhode Island.

Venuta had stowed the baby carriage, and Kling had returned the Studebakers to Land Drive Rent-A-Car on Broadway. No problem. Thanks to the "Underworld Ambassador" Uncle Frank Costello.

By 9:35 p.m., Willie and Fran were at the movies. No harm had come to anyone today. No use hurting anyone. I could never hurt anyone, Willie thought. He was uncomfortable in his weathermen shoes. Backless, noiseless slippers were more his style.

"Chestnut silk," Fran whispered in his left ear, her teasing hand, fingernails fondling the back of his neck and slick hair.

"Watch the actors," Willie smiled.

He cabbed her back home to her boarding house in Stapleton on Bay street and legged it toward the Willowbrook State Hospital and Farm area.

He'd buy Fran a car, he decided, just as he had for Marge with $900 in crisp fifties. Willie prided himself on not taking advantage of either of his young ladies: Fran, the one with her elegantly Israeli-formed, sculptured facial features; and Marge, the Irish-Hungarian-Arab immigrant who had "accompanied" him in '47.

He didn't stop to pick up a late paper. Commissioner W.T. O'Brien would have at least a dozen employee-witnesses picking out only his picture after thirty-seven months of heretofore sought anonymity. The Actor's handiwork—no one hurt, smooth, slick, every detail planned—would be headlines.

Not bad for a small, thin, invisible blacksmith's son, who had only become visible after a false arrest on a charge of murder at the age of nineteen.

There was never enough evidence to really convict him, and with Felice Mazziotta's help, the charges were dropped and Willie was set free. Later, Felice handled the sale of jewelry Willie had "acquired" and their relationship continued to develop. He could still hear Felice's voice speaking of "helping this *fragilita* Ireesh-boy-from-aw-the-neighborhood."

Eventually, he had met Felice's son, Johnny, who had helped to spring him from Holmesburg. Now Willie loved the Dunsky son Johnny as much as he did Felice.

Johnny Squint. Perennial cop-fighter; dapper dresser. He provided the all important Triple P's: political, police, protection. Willie paused on the darkened sidewalk, thinking of his good friend Johnny in knots over raven-haired Eve Vale.

Her life seemed to have *stopped* around the time she had given birth to her good lookin' son Dannie. Willie felt that gutsy John could ménd his long overdue trio, notwithstanding Eve's hubby, Roscoe Valencia.

Or should he say, Willie quickly reflected, mend that long overdue foursome. Willie's mind flickered to Eve's sister, the ever-wild Miss Eleanor Cross. She'd changed it from Crosscavale to the shorter version Cross. Willie had no qualms with that, he himself having, in his forty-eight year span, as many names as a small town telephone directory. He agilely stepped over to a pay phone, dialing for taxicab service.

Back on the Farm. William Francis Sutton had come out of the proverbial closet today. He was nationally visible again. The limelight sparked the flames for his future "accomplishments." But now he lay on his desolate bunk with only John Hersey's new book, *The Wall,* for company. It suited the janitor for the Farm Colony hospital, Edward Lynch—his latest identity. It was limbo, but better than prison, where his bowel movements would be monitored, his "talents" smothered to death.

But who would try to send him back? he mused for the moment. The teetering J.D. Venuta? The Non-Citizen Margaret "Marge" Moore? Or was he overthinking with all the protection he had now? Willie got up from the dreary bunk and sat down at his burnished desk, pen and paper in hand, a dim lamp on his right, *he knew he wasn't going back—period*!

He glued his eyes to the empty pages before him. They would soon be filled with drawings and sketches. Details of yet another "Money Store."

Laurels were for other people. He would be content to roll up the sleeves of his blue silk shirt and enter the world of future *plans.*

1951

*M*ama's Boy!

In mid-December, Dannie Vale was taunted by those two, true words from his classmates at Pershing J.H.S. on Ninth Avenue in Borough Park, Brooklyn.

He had just turned fifteen, but knew in his gut that the boys and girls in his school had a right to sneak notes to him, whisper it, giggle it while passing him in the school yard: MAMA'S BOY. His mother walked him from his apartment house on Ninth and 39th to Pershing J.H. on Ninth and 49th every weekday.

Three times a week she had lunch with him in the school's lunchroom, the swell of her skirted thighs too close to his, heated as if by a burning passion. He'd eat his food in gulps.

She picked him up from Junior High every afternoon. The fervent lip-kisses she gave him in front of the student body on these numerous occasions filled his own body with an ugly fervor, and, in particular, plagued his own stomach with nausea, from public, social shame.

One day, he played hooky, sneaking out of his apartment building early in the morning. He made his way down 39th Street *in corduroy knickers.*

On Eighth Avenue, by Tollgate's Bar, he spied two of Johnny Squint's "numbers controllers"—steamroller-shouldered Little Mike, and patchy-skin faced Al Rispone.

"You still alive, kid?" Al Rispone chuckled, greeting Dannie.

"Al-burt's-gonna-get-ya," mean-eyed Mike sing-song chanted, rubbing his stubby pointer fingers together.

Dannie took a deep breath and warily walked around them.

He hustled down the street. Maybe he should buzz Johnny about those two "big-shot's" puzzling remarks?

No, Dannie decided. Johnny Squint had problems of his own. He had been hauled in last week for decking two uniformed patrolmen. The same week, the same day in fact, Dannie's wacky Aunt Eleanor had set out to give her sheltered nephew "kissing lessons." Dannie's gut rebelled, as he slithered to Seventh Avenue and 39th Street's dead end, and threw up yesterday evening's lentil soup supper.

With stinging-wet eyes he made it down to Fifth Avenue, veering into South Brooklyn. He'd walk slow to the Fifth Avenue Playhouse, where he'd quietly view *The Asphalt Jungle*. Besides Sterling Hayden and Sam Jaffe being in the movie, there was a new doll in it by the name of Marilyn Monroe, and at least he'd be well out of his own neighborhood. But his mind couldn't get far enough away from startling, bedbug Eleanor telling him last week that she was out to teach him how to kiss, so he wouldn't be shamed inside and out when the time came for the real thing.

The bewitching nut-job could confuse the hell out of him with her hot and cold moods.

"But that's all I'm going to teach you," she had said.

Dannie could see her now, looking sexy on the foot-high block of cement adjacent to the fortress-like Ninth Avenue above-ground subway station, the windy weather not disturbing her convertible permanent. It was a different hairstyle from her usual long, free-falling hair, but the perm had given her a softer, natural effect, with slight curls around the hanging ends accentuating her blue eyes, making them seem bigger, more appetizing. She'd sat next to him, hands and arms folded snugly around the underside of her tight black skirt, bare knees drawn together, her black flats tilted, V-toe shaped.

Out of the clear blue sky she had mentioned kissing lessons. His face had burned with blushing vexation. Could she be for real? He looked askew at her. She was a beautiful, crazy woman who had come over to his house that late afternoon loaded with new, expensive school sweaters, scarves, and shirts for him. Then she had asked him to walk her across the street. To the station for her short, evening ride home.

"What the hell are *you* afraid of?" she had baited him.

"Not of you!" he had defiantly answered. She was out of her skull.

But she had goaded him, saying he'd look like a fool. She had taunted, speaking through compressed lips, mimicking his last goodnight kiss to her. "Kissing like a damned baby. Do you want someday to shame this whole family with your naiveté?"

"Fuck you," he had blurted out, standing there half open-mouthed, realizing it was the first time in his life he had said that four-letter slang word out loud to anyone.

"Curse it. But you couldn't do it." She was cooler than Jack Frost nipping at your nose.

Egg her on. Get back at her for that, he had fumed. But he was so flustered, nothing had come out.

"If your mind is in the gutter at what I'm suggesting, then you'll never know the meaning of love. Never!" she had continued torment-ing, her stockingless legs brushing with indecent closeness around his thigh. Suddenly he came up with an idea on how to flush her out.

"Piss Alley!" was what he had said, dared. It was a smelly, four-foot wide, forty-foot long, private urinating and "petting" grounds behind the big, brick subway station. That's where he had said she could give him the "lessons."

And it had stunk as he waited.

Let's see if *her* mind's in the gutter, he waited. The stench of the alley had created more chaos in his dinner stomach. Nervously, he had peered below at the Culver and West End line's tracks, the freight yards, where "Pop" the watchman combed the debris for hidden treasure.

After several minutes of the dank wait, he thought he had won. She wouldn't come back here, he had figured, as he eased ten feet to his left and walked out of the alley.

She was still sitting where she had been, with her back to him.

But he saw her rise, brushing off her skirt. She had then held his handkerchief, the one she had made him place unfolded on the cement so she could sit in warmth, cleanliness, and comfort.

Then, his Aunt Eleanor had walked suggestively toward him by the side of the station.

He should have known better—from hectic days gone by—than to think he had "won" so quickly. She handed him his handkerchief, saying, "For your filthy mouth, Daniel. Wipe it."

He had let it drift to the concrete ground.

"Dogs go back there also," she had her hands akimbo on her inviting hips. "And feel-up artists. They grovel back there. Make love like it's so much dung. Is that where you spend your nights when you're out so late?"

She had made him feel so guilty with that damn sermon of hers. Dannie had rested his head against the side of the brick wall, and she had begun teaching him how to kiss.

"If I happen to feel you hard. . .as you were in my apartment . . .sleeping over in my bed. . .years ago. . .twisting and turning in your sleep by me," she was pressing her fragrant sweet body against him, "we'll both know that you're the one with the 'alley mind.'" She had become a complete study in torturous, meaty desire for him, beginning with the "Screen Kiss," two lips kissing his top one, two lips his bottom, nipping cool, biting untamed, crushing. He had received more different kisses than he could count—than he knew existed. He was hard, so damn hard—he had panted to himself while pressing deliriously into the tight bay of her skirt.

"This is all you will do with a girl someday," she had whispered, her bulging scarlet sweater front moving soft and hard on his wind-breaker-jacketed chest. "If you do anything else—if you do the worst," he had all to do from holding her near-pumping buttocks. "I'll know from the lie in your eyes. And the lie in hers. And a minute after I find out," her long fingernails had been running wild through his hair, "I'll bury to the hilt a blade in your back. Between your shoulder blades. Do you think I wouldn't? Test me!" She had pushed him away as fast as she had come on.

He had thrown up in Piss Alley after she had left him, knowing that he had loved those "lessons." But knowing, also, that he had to stay far, far away from maniac her. He tried to fling off that week-old memory and thoughts of why he had such a weak stomach as he entered the movie theater.

He squinted from the balcony at Marilyn Monroe on the screen. She was appealing, seemingly untouchable, unattainable.

He turned in his seat, and spotted two girls, sitting, smiling, making believe they were paying attention to the flick.

He turned back again. Louis Calhern's mistress, Miss Monroe, worried about her "Daddy." But the popcorn in the hands of the two girls behind him crackled as it hit the mark. Right in his hair, brittle, loose popcorn.

Before he could turn once more, a remark from one of them froze him in his seat: "He's a living doll!"

His cheeks reddened, *hoping* to God in heaven that it was the girl with the short fluffy brown hair that had said it.

He sat rigid through the movie, waiting for them to strike again. They didn't.

And he didn't budge. Because of the *umiliante* knickers.

They left, and as they did he heard the same lilting voice: "I'd like to have nibbled on his *attrazione sessuale* blue eyes instead of the stale popcorn."

All he could see sideways, as they descended the balcony's steep steps, was that one had an hourglass shape, the other was shorter, wearing a pleated skirt.

Damn it! he missed his chance. He finally left the movie theater by a side exit.

Dejected, punching his right fist into his left palm, he walked down Fifth Avenue past 39th Street, straight on into Bay Ridge, passing Max Shuster's Clothing Store on Fifth, where they tailor-made *long pants*. The kids at Pershing J.H.S. all bought their pants there.

Dannie took a shortcut home through the hilly Sunset Park, the dividing line between Borough Park and Bay Ridge.

On his way, he saw a group—more like forty of them—of sharply dressed North Street boys by the hilltop flagpole. Dannie had suffered enough of a setback today because of his knickerbockers, so he bypassed them, only to be confronted by another dozen of their tough gang just over the next hill. The three leaders, Christie, Dapper, and Sailor, were in front.

They lived right around the corner from Dannie, but he was still invading their territory. His eyes darted about nervously as a green and white prowl car shot up the park's wide concrete walkway.

Dannie held his ground, and the two uniformed policemen in the car waved over the three leaders. None of them budged. They were like granite in a grain field. The two cops shouted a warning to disband, urging them to keep this park free of bloodshed. Then they drove on in resignation, and Dannie received a dozen respectful handshakes, for sticking by them.

Wow! Not one of them had looked down at what he was wearing, just straight into his eyes. The whole scene spurred Dannie on to go back downtown to the movie theater district. To get a better look at the girl with the sincere, sexy voice.

Over the weekend he hit the RKO Albee, Strand, but had no luck. He tried the Fox. Saw *Kim* at the Met on Fulton Street. Errol Flynn in a Kipling tale.

Where could they live? They were around his age. What would they be doing on a weekend? He wandered the crowds of holiday shoppers on Flatbush Avenue.

Losing hope, he legged it to Borough Park, where he saw Johnny Squint standing, glinting by his red rocket Olds on Eighth Avenue by Pete's Radio Store. He looked regal in a mohair overcoat. Reb, Gretti and Augie, his court apparent, were standing by the car.

Johnny was going to Las Vegas, Nevada for the holidays. He handed Dannie fifty dollars to "get your devoted mother a Christmas gift." He kissed Dannie's lips. *Un famiglia fraterno amare bacio.* Augie threw in ten bucks more, rubbing Dannie's thick black hair, "for luck."

Dannie Vale all but flew home. He was going on a shopping spree, no school right before Christmas and New Year's.

"What a day this has been
What a rare mood I'm in
Why it's almost like being . . .

"In love," he sang out loud to the wind, Jerry Lester's theme song on late-night TV. He didn't have a television set, but he'd seen the show on his downstairs neighbors', the Sesqus', little Admiral. Maybe he'd buy his mother one. "I got a smile on my face, for the whole human race," he sang his way to his doorstep.

By the next day, Dannie had decided to go by Johnny's words, and buy not only his mother, but also one for his father, his nutso aunt, and a present for Augie.

And of course a gift for Johnny himself.

The temptation to scoot right down to Schuster's Haberdashery and buy the custom-made long pants had to be smothered until he felt blood popping in his brain. But there'd be a way to get them for the New Year, even if he had to beg delicious Eleanor's brain out to do it.

It was fun shopping downtown, picking out gifts and spending money on those who loved him.

After the spree, he treated himself to a savory orange drink at the Nedicks Hot Dog counter at Pacific and Fourth. He'd subway it home, loaded with the decorative wrapped presents.

He almost died in his tracks! There they were. The two girls from the movie. By the subway's entrance, right on the corner, not fifty feet from him.

The taller one had on a cherry red skirt. He knew his eyesight was nowhere near Superman's, but he now remembered well her banana nose.

The shorter one had the moon-shaped face and black "bedroom eyes."

Well, let's face the music, he decided. Short pants and all, he stepped through the throng, toward the subway and the two girls.

They were perched on the rails of the stairwell, each on either side, looking so at home, as if they owned them.

"Isn't that the skinny one from the popcorn movie?" the tall one with the hourglass shape and oversized nose spoke in a deep, rasping voice.

"The living doll!" said the shorter one. "Short pants and all." The pixie beauty was so cheerful, sexy. It had been her voice—the one he originally hoped it would be—the one in the movie theater with the short, fluffy brown hair. Dannie was breathing heavily as his knickerbockered legs shook. He was flushed as he walked down between them, toward the dismal turnstile.

"He's stuck up," he heard the girl with the raspy voice behind him.

"He's so cute," came from the sexpot brunette, her voice plaintive. He had to turn and smile up at them. Then he headed as far as his short-pants legs could take him, his throbbing lungs and heart racing three times faster than he was!

It took him half the ride home on the subway to rid himself of his childish embarrassment.

On the trolley car, which would take him the rest of the way home, his head was filled with the shorter girl. Slacks this time around. The first time in the theater, she had worn a neat pleated skirt. But her slacks weren't raggedy or baggy. They didn't have a sheen to them as if they were ironed too many times. She wore them so snug and comfortable that he felt he could spend the rest of his life in them. Returning from his fantasy just in time, Dannie exited the trolley on his corner.

As the trolley ground away, Dannie became aware of a Ford Victoria which blocked the crosswalk to his dark building. Two men were in the closed convertible. Dannie narrowed his eyes. Wise guy Tony-boy was the driver, crabby Gretti was the passenger.

"Whatdya do kid? Help rob a bank?" Gretti didn't laugh, as he gestured to Dannie's gift-laden arms.

"Like to shop in South Brooklyn?" Tony-boy leaned, smirk-laughing.

Dannie stood silent. What the hell was on their minds?

"Like to be out in the cold weather, kid?" Gretti, vulture-eyed, pushed. "Like snowstorms back in, say, '47?"

Dannie stood perplexed, annoyed, trying to figure out what they were driving at. Their car suddenly screeched away along the silvery trolley tracks. Tony-boy geared past the corner's red light. Dannie suddenly saw the reason—his mother, appearing a foot beside him, the crevice of her V-cut angora sweater looming before him. "You're out late, spending money." Her green eyes fixed on his package-filled hands. "Driving around town with known hoodlums." He felt himself being pulled by her to their apartment house.

"I should slap your face good," his mother went wild in the tiny living room, "for making me worry." She had her right hand upright and set.

"I'll kill you if you do," Dannie angrily spat out, challenging her.

If a bolt of lightning had hit Eve Vale she couldn't have been more struck. Her right hand remained suspended in midair as if Zeus himself were holding it. The fire in her eyes sizzled and slowly died, replaced by an eye-glazed, green icing.

He was sorry he'd said it. His own eyes instantly filled with tears, but he didn't want to completely burst out crying in front of her. He hustled into the bathroom, off from the small kitchen, catch-locking the door behind him, his mother still unable to react.

About half an hour later he was cried out. He knew his father was out working the nightshift on the piers. The apartment was deathly still to him from behind the door.

He took the eye from the hook, unlocking it. His flannel pajamas were in his parent's bedroom, and his mother was behind that door. He reached for the knob, but then decided against it. He'd apologize tomorrow.

Dannie undressed down to his T-shirt and shorts and laid down under the sheet and chenille bedspread of his living room couchmade-bed. His Philco radio was on. He wasn't listening much. Just thinking. Of the horror of what he had threatened his mother with. He recoiled, disgusted. It was his Mom, the one he had loved and depended upon.

He turned his thoughts to earlier today. Threats from Little Mike and Al Rispone. Later from Tony-boy and Gretti. Maybe he should finally tell Johnny when he returned from Las Vegas by the New Year, or even tell John's partner, Hugo Duce, now.

His thoughts lazily wandered back to the young girl in the packed, black slacks. What a pretty bundle. Maybe he'd corner Johnny after all and get some advice. The newscaster from the radio was saying we were winning in Korea after first losing. Dannie wished he could somehow forge his birth certificate and get *long pants* in the Army; the broadcaster was talking about a name familiar to Dannie: Arnold Rothstein, who was often mentioned at Pete's, Fiola's, Walt's.

A man named James Meehan had been shot by a policeman. He was the man who in 1928 had set up the famous gambler Arnold

Rothstein. That dirty stinker, gabby Reb would have cried out. Serves Meehan right, Royal Flush Rothstein was everybody's hero. Dannie's mother lowered the radio's volume dial.

Midnight, Dannie guessed. He hadn't seen his mother lower the radio. He yawned, eyes closed, and tossed when he caught the fresh wintry scent of his mother on her knees by the couch. He opened his eyes and saw her in the lamplit room.

He was going to say something—apologize—but the sight of her left him speechless.

She wore an ebony La Trique. The contours of it weren't needed. Now maybe he fully knew what his father was going, grumbling through. Or *wasn't* going through.

She was a fantastic, beauteous mess of black hair.

"You would . . . kill me," she said, wanting to, but not touching him.

Don't cry, he told himself. Hold on, he tried not to shake on the couch, but did.

And the battle raged silently, his mother breaking the barrier.

"You've grown overnight. Money, gifts, I won't mention now. But I'll never raise my hands to you again." She didn't state, but pleaded it.

"If I told you it was my way of mothering you, you'd laugh in my face. Please don't. Because it was more than that, Daniel. It was part of my way of *loving* you. Because I have no one else to love. In that way."

What way? Dannie tried to swallow but couldn't

"You can kill me in more ways than saying you would," she stammered, suddenly falling apart by the couch. Her wails were like lit explosives that Dannie prayed would not go off altogether. He kissed the top of her ambrosial hair, knowing he had won, but feeling as if he had lost. Her lips burned with her biting against his earlobe.

Suddenly, he was muddled, his mother's half-moaning, sleeping position nearly suffocating him. He had to find, search for that pixie girl.

As it was to turn out, those last words of his could well have been etched into Eve Vale's mind, for they would be a stepping stone to his will. A will to prepare him for *the FIRST global hunt across the five civilized continents for the most wanted man in history.*

1952

January

Dannie Vale had a plan. He would follow Johnny Squint's advice tonight, and as soon as he got out of Max Schuster's Clothing Store, he'd go back to South Brooklyn to search for that girl.

That pixie brunette beauty. And maybe, just maybe, he'd get lucky enough to really *get* his very first girl.

"You look great, sharp," Arnold Schuster was saying. "Dannie, right? Trust me, you'll knock 'em dead." Arnold was reassuring his customer. "I'd peg you for a lot older than fifteen in them."

Dannie was pleased. He liked Arnold Schuster. And he was crazy about the new custom-made gray flannel pants. He gave them a last look, liking what he saw in the mirror. He looked older than fifteen in them. Like a man. They fit him to perfection.

Eleanor Cross was pleased too. She was smiling, glad that she had devilishly decided to buy Dannie the long pants. She took twenty dollars out of her purse. Enough to pay for another pair.

"Make them up for him in navy blue," she told Arnold.

"You're a lucky guy, Dannie. Some aunt you have," Arnold smiled, shyly.

Dannie's look was between a scowl and a blush. Some aunt was right.

"Please put the old ones in a bag, Arnold, I'll wear these." Dannie planned on flinging the outdated knickers over the "Cuts" wall. "You really think navy?"

"For a tall, slim guy like you? You reek navy," Arnold told him. "My own Coast Guard memories," he added.

"You got a deal."

"You're good to me, Aunt Eleanor," Dannie admitted when they left the Bay Ridge clothing store. "Sometimes I don't know how to thank you or even why you spend so much money on me."

Eleanor scanned her nephew head to toe and liked what she saw. Six feet, maybe closer to five-foot-ten. Eyes as blue as her own. A true Crosscavale. Full lips.

"Just don't ever hurt your mother or me," she said softly, rubbing her head against his shoulder. She squeezed his arm.

"Come home with me. I'll make us dinner."

The familiar discomfort irked him. He drew away.

"I can't."

"Why not? Don't tell me you have someplace more important to go?"

"Just around."

She gave him a quick look, as if she had just made a decision. A languid smile crossed her face. "Kiss me good-bye, then."

"I'm too old for that." He tried to say it lightly but he knew it sounded awkward.

Her smile vanished as fast as it had appeared.

"Just so you don't start acting too big for your new britches," she snapped, and before he saw it coming, she had cuffed his face right in front of the store.

The humiliation and rage overwhelmed him. Every nerve of his body strained to hit back. He wanted to pull at his aunt's silky black hair with clenched fingers till she bent backward to the ground in agony. Every time she hit him, however lightly, he relived those endless, sudden, inexplicable whacks across the face. She vacillated between hysteria, love, and worry all through his childhood. He hated it, and now found himself hating her.

She saw his reaction and relented. "Go, then, do what you want," she said. "But at least stay away from that *cattivo*, that *chazzer* Johnny Squint. Violence, a user in the flesh. Stay away from him."

"I'm not going to Johnny's."

"Well, Mr. Important In Your New Clothes. I won't pry about

where you are going. Just don't stay out till midnight. You'll kill your mother with worry if you do." She was digging her long fingernails into her lavish, orange-shaded, skirted thighs.

"I'll be home at ten," he said.

"Eight-thirty. You'll have time for homework. You're in High School this term, big shot. Remember?"

"Nine-thirty," he was squinting at the silver lined Fifth Avenue trolley tracks. "At Fort Hamilton High you get time to do part of your homework in homeroom. Would you remember that?"

Eleanor shrugged and gave him a quick mocking kiss on the cheek. She just as quickly took the bag from his hand. "I may keep these," she teased. "Old clothes memories." She turned around, starting to sashay home, her hams wriggling in tight orange.

He watched her go, thinking *facino carnale*. Her hips would handily win an anatomy award if there ever was such a thing.

Still, he was relieved. It was a match with her he had won.

He zipped up his navy blue and gold reversible side of his windbreaker and embarked on his quest for the pure, "real thing." He wished he had the money on him to take the train over to South Brooklyn. It felt stupid to walk, especially since it was cold and getting dark fast. Walking all the way over to that brunette girl's neighborhood reminded him of all the times last December, last year, last month, since two days after his fifteenth birthday, that he had made the treks.

He had travelled to downtown movie theaters, to Pacific and Fourth by BMT Subway train, by bus, by trolley, and at least six times on foot. Maybe he was a fool.

Did she even remember him? It was only two quick looks, after all. But what looks. They had stuck in his mind: looks straight from a tantalize factory, created by "Tingling Inc." Love-ly!

Johnny was right. He had to keep on looking for her because by this time FINDING her was more important than finding *her*.

"Prove you can finish what you start and you've got yourself a heck of a start in life, Dannie V.," Johnny had said.

Still, Dannie had complained that it would be obvious to the girl that he had been looking for her.

Johnny enjoyed playing adviser. "So let her figure you planned it, Dannie. But don't tell her you did, and she'll never know for sure in her little *diavolo* heart." A man had to learn how to handle women, and Johnny was confident that Dannie would learn.

Dannie was getting to know the section he was scouting by heart—the looming Williamsburg Savings Bank and nearby, the

Sarah J. Hale Girls High School. On the corner by Flatbush Avenue stood the appetizing All Beef Hot Dog Nedicks refreshment oasis. Further down Fourth Avenue, away from the Dean Street Boarding House district, was the Atlantic Avenue Hock Shop where men went in carrying anything from radios to rifles. And, of course, the Long Island Railroad Terminal where he had killed many an hour.

The heels of his Thom McAn shoes were worn down pitifully on one side, but he knew Johnny admired him for not giving up, and he wanted to prove that he had the staying power of men like Johnny, Uncle Frank, and the clan that hung out at Pete's Radio Store—the gambling "Front"—men like Augie, Gretti, and Hugo Duce.

He reached Garfield and Fourth and saw a gang of kids clustered together under the lamppost. She wasn't there, and passing them made him more aware of how alone he felt. And cold.

He didn't feel so cool in his new pants after all.

He stepped to the intersection of President and Fourth, taking the Ace comb out of his pocket, just to refresh his rakish Tony Curtis look. As he put it back he spotted her. *Ringizare, iddio!*

He couldn't believe it.

It was really her.

She was up the street, surrounded by some guys and girls. Walk through them, by them, past them, he told himself. Don't let her see you. Too many kids around. Later. I'll double back, catch her on the way home.

"*Avemmaria.* Hey," he heard her call out. "Isn't that the living doll?"

He wanted to die. He felt dizzy, like he had as a kid when Johnny would take him by the wrist and ankle, and spin him in the air, the ground going hurdy-gurdy underneath him. The excitement wouldn't stop itself. He kept walking.

"A three-to-one shot," he heard. "They opened the outta town track and it brings me money in my pockets tonight," one of the boys was bragging. The guy who was talking was an older fellow with deep-set, magnetic blue eyes. Under the light of the lamppost his facial skin seemed drawn tight, like a skull.

The guy saw Dannie turn around. "Hey, where'd you come from?"

From my mother, Dannie wanted to say, but he held his peace.

"You from around here?" the older guy queried crisply.

Dannie shook his head. The guy strode up to him.

"You usually stop and listen to people?"

"Leave him alone, Joey."

It was The Girl's girlfriend, the one she had been with, twice. "Get off his back, big shot."

Dannie was amazed. The guy called Joey backed off, as if, small as she was, she had plenty of clout.

Joey gave him a mean smile, turning it into a meaner laugh.

"Regrets to your uncle, Miss Beak," he said, sauntering back into the midst of the lamppost's group.

Dannie had watched him go, half-expecting him to look back.

The girl who had interfered strode up to him. "He thinks his shit doesn't stink, that one. He's a far cry from his two brothers."

Dannie didn't know which was getting him the most—seeing the Girl here, the brazenness of her girlfriend (who was her uncle? he wondered), the way she seemed to take his arrival on the scene for granted, or that oversized banana-shaped nose on the girlfriend's face.

She was still in a huff. "And I'll give his regrets to my uncle. No, I'll give him way more than that, that BADGE-wanting bastard."

Dannie couldn't look at her. He looked at her shoes. Suede wedge pets. Diamond-cut vamps. She went on like a vamp till the Girl, whose name he still didn't know, came up, pulling her away.

This is the dumbest situation I've ever been in, he thought. Having dinner with Eleanor would be better than this. What was he supposed to do now?

She was wearing the same sexy slacks he had seen her in the second time and was as cute as he remembered her. Her lips pouted as she glanced at him, her round doe-black eyes dancing to a tune of their own.

"You coming?" she said, waiting for him with her girlfriend at the curb.

Coming? Was she crazy? He had been waiting to hear those words for countless aching nights.

"What's your name, anyway?"

"Dannie. Vale."

"Antoinette . . . Annette. Narghelle. Take your pick," she offered.

"Josephine," her friend chimed in.

Antoinette, Annette. He loved the sounds of both her first names.

She lit an Old Gold and started chattering between drags just as if they had all know each other for years.

"That was 'Joe the Blond,' " Antoinette was saying. "He swears he's a twenty-three-year-old Richard Widmark in *The Kiss of Death.*"

Josephine was still angry. "A textbook mind, that wise-aleck. My uncle will give him the *bacio*, the kiss, someday," she rambled. "Joey and his two brothers. The Gallos. Heard of them where you come from? Diplomatic Larry and charming 'Al the Blast.' So what about you?"

"What about me?"

It felt like a comfortable threesome. He liked it.

"You passing by just by coincidence? Or do you have the hots for Antoinette the way she has for you?"

Dannie glanced at Antoinette. She wasn't blushing.

Josephine went on as the three of them reached Pacific and Fourth. "What neighborhood are you from? Just how old are you?"

"I'm from Borough Park," Dannie answered. "And I'm fifteen." He skipped the other question.

"When's your sixteenth birthday?"

"December ninth."

She turned to her girlfriend. "See, Antoinette? He's just right for you. Dreams do come true."

Then she hesitated. "But he comes from a cheap bookie section," her tone was changing, "where Gretti and Mazziotta think they rule. Huumph! Johnny Squint and Company, rule? They've got another thing coming from what I pick up on."

Josephine touched the sleeve of her girlfriend's bulky royal blue blouse and suddenly started walking quickly away from them. She was leggy, seemed built soft under the white lambskin jacket and cherry red skirt she wore. But he couldn't get her nose off his mind, aside from the chip she had on her shoulder.

"What is it with Anna Banana?"

"Don't call her that," Antoinette said quickly. "She despises it. And she likes *you*."

"She what?"

"You surprised? It was *her* idea to come back to this corner after we saw you that first day in the movie playhouse. You know why she liked you and now acts like she can't stand you?"

He didn't know what to say.

"Well, I'll tell you, quiet man." She lit another cigarette. "They call her 'Anna Banana' in South Brooklyn. Never to her face—but because of her face. Her awful nose.

"And she's never been kissed."

Antoinette paused, looking Dannie over. Go ahead, go ahead, he wanted to say.

"It's really simple as pie. You're not from around here, and so you wouldn't know who her uncle is. That means you're free, you wouldn't be afraid to do to her what she wants done. *E intesto?*"

He understood—but he wished he had the nerve to ask who this uncle of hers was. Instinct made him hold back. He knew enough from Johnny to know that if you asked too many questions, it was your fault if you didn't grow old enough to get the answers. But he liked being liked.

He was dying to take *sesso* laden Ant . . . Annette down the subway steps, kiss her, plunge into her "bedroom eyes." *Hold her.* Chain-smoker and all.

She felt it too. He was sure. She peeked up at the lit clock near the top of the gigantic Williamsburg Savings Bank, her dark lashes fluttering.

"I have to be home in fifteen minutes or my older brother will kill me," she said. "But I'll stay."

And she laughed. "The preliminaries are over."

He grabbed her right wrist. "Laugh downstairs underground for fifteen minutes. And we'll see how funny it is."

"We'll see."

She was up against him like a sanctified hussy, leading him down the steep subway steps. She stood against the tile wall of the deserted subway station.

And he kissed her. He had a two-way thrill going for him. The furnace-glow inside him could have lit a church candle to her. She was cuddly, willing to pet. Her *avemmaria* upon seeing him tonight matched what he had breathed to himself upon seeing her, both being hotter than hell for each other.

He kept kissing her. Her lips. Her long lashes. Her cheeks, getting sweaty in the subway draft. And her lips again. He ran his fingers through her hair, kissing the strands.

"If I were your mother, I'd eat you up," she giggled, pressing her body against his, he was pressing her even tighter, against the graffiti-caked tiles.

She excited him so that he couldn't speak, his tongue tied in his brain. He went crazy trying to unbutton the front of her blouse. She was biting her lip, waiting.

"I'd tie you up in the house so you'd never leave," she teased him and made him fumble even more. Finally, without meaning to, he tore the second button from the front of her royal blue blouse. She grabbed the back of his hair, urgently whispering in his ear, "The hell with it." And then he was squeezing her breasts—bigger than he had ever imagined. She arched her back so her breasts filled his hands, reaching out to mess his hair and whispering . . . touch . . . love . . . MINE . . . YOURS . . . all at the same time. He felt one of her hands touching his tailor-made cross-looped waistband, down by his side slash-pocket—

"Antoinette!" Anna Banana's voice came tumbling down the dark subway steps. "Get moving! Your brother's out roaming the streets with a switchblade knife threatening to kill you. You're over an hour late getting home!"

Antoinette rushed to neaten her torn blouse. Anna grabbed her when she and Dannie got to the sidewalk.

"Don't worry," Anna said. "I'll say you were over my house the whole time. He'll believe me. He knows my uncle doesn't allow liars in the family. Dannie, take the subway home," she ended imperiously.

Dannie was so surprised at all the night's happenings and Anna Banana's rescue operation that he was left speechless. He gave her a quick thank-you kiss on the lips.

They were all scrambling and Dannie yelled out, "I'll see you at seven p.m. next Tuesday! I'll take you to a movie." Antoinette was running down the street, but she gestured to him that she heard.

And then he was alone.

No, not alone. He had *two* girlfriends. Annette and Antoinette. A tender cozy bundle with two names. He had two of the same her!

He could hardly move another step. He felt just like lying down on the sidewalk, exhausted and happy. Numb. They predicted snow. So what, he thought, let the snow come. Heaven. He was in heaven now. And he started singing to himself the way Fred sang to Ginger in the dance movie:

"And the cares that hung around me through the week
"Seemed to vanish like a gambler's lucky streak . . ."

Let the sidewalk ruin his new pants, he didn't care. Let the snow come and freeze him. He'd like to run all the way to Max Schuster's Fifth Avenue clothing store and plant a kiss on the plate glass window for the new tailor-made pants.

He calmed down a little, starting to walk briskly home, counting the parked and passing cars along the way. A '42 Nash, a '37 Hudson Sedan, and one Kaiser Fraiser. He could trot the Fifth Avenue route. It was brighter, busier there, but he knew it wouldn't do. He didn't want to run into that Joe the Blond again who might have cruised by now to the Fifth Avenue bookmaking action.

So he stayed on Fourth.

Suddenly, a man was approaching him from the other corner.

Dannie tensed, squinting. The man was small; there was no chance of trouble.

The man walked quickly past the lamppost. Dannie noticed his pale face, thin mustache, slicked-back hair. He was wearing bedroom slippers.

I know him, he thought. I know I've seen him before.

Yes, right. At Johnny's. And that far away blizzard trip?

That's Lynch. "The Master of the precision hold-up," Johnny had dubbed him. "The most cunning of them all."

I'm sure of it.

He'd better remember to mention it to Johnny.

JOHNNY SQUINT "CHAPPY" MAZZIOTTA OWNED A little corner of the world. He didn't have the title or the deed to it, it wasn't listed in the City Hall of Records, and no real estate transaction, signed and stamped, had made it his.

Johnny Squint took possession of his corner of the world when Frank Costello declared him *Fatto*, "Made." Bestowing the official "Good Fellow" Badge on him.

The corner came with Johnny's Badge.

Johnny Mazziotta's corner was actually all the corners extending from Brooklyn's 39th Street, along Eighth Avenue, up to 60th Street. And take with that Sixth, Seventh, Ninth, Tenth, and Eleventh Avenues along the same street boundaries.

When a horse bet was made, a dice game played, a penny pitched in Borough Park, Johnny got a piece of it. Johnny and his amiable—now also formally initiated into the Costello Group —bucktoothed partner, Hugo Duce, collected the ante-ups from every one of the professional gamblers in the area. They, in turn, distributed it up the line till Frank Costello got his.

Dues.

Well worth it.

Because, in return, Frank Costello (a.k.a. "The Ambassador" and "President Maker") could and did distribute back favors, protection, help and *influence* right down that same line.

One hand washes the other, one hand greases the other, and all the hands join to become a solid, disciplined body of men. *Per Nostri Personale*, "For Our Crew."

A body with a head: Uncle Frank, and an arm: Vito "Don Vitone" Genovese. They also had a skilled fiscal wizard, liaison extraordinaire: Meyer Lansky. A *consiglio*, the gracious Mr. Mike Miranda. The rest of the body was made up of four dozen *capitanos*, coast to coast, and two thousand "guns"—stand-up, well-muscled Badge men.

And Johnny Squint was among them! He was Made. "A Man of Respect."

A *friend* in the Luciano-Costello isolated Friendship.

If you were slated to be killed in Johnny's little corner of the world . . . if swag goods were being cut-rated in it . . . if "hardware" were sold . . . cars stolen . . . cops paid off . . . arson the order of the day . . . nightclubs or bars moved in on . . . if anything at all was going on or coming off in Johnny's corner, he had to know about it. Give the nod for it. Be in on it.

And if he failed in any of these responsibilities . . . if he couldn't hold rein to them . . . his slice of a section would never become a stepping stone to the plenary rule of the Borough one day, within his own set of "Good Fellows."

It would turn into his burial plot instead.

It was a simple rule. You were given your allotment of territory along with the people in it to control. You produced the power and the money to support the body you belonged to from your territory. If you failed to produce, if you failed to hold your own against other Crews' encroachment, you became a cancer in the body.

And you'd be cut out, chopped off, so as not to impair the healthy functioning of the entire living assemblage. For the body as a whole was more sacred than a mere limb, a fingernail, a toe.

Once you entered the life of the body, you were on sentry duty for the rest of your life, Johnny knew. You had to be on guard. There was the constant danger of too much notoriety, of putting the body as a whole in the limelight. Exposure of that sort could —and did—cut your earning power. Or send you to prison. And then you were no use to yourself and even less than no use to the organism you had sworn to keep alive, no matter what the cost.

Being on guard meant keeping your finger on the pulse of every activity going on in your domain. If you missed a pulse-beat on even the least important of them, it could lead either to your upgrade or your downfall, depending on how you played it—or whether it was worth playing at all. And any decision you made had to be okayed from "Above." This was to protect you. Give you backing. Your move, your effort, was on the record.

Sure, Johnny also knew, if you chose to undertake a matter on your own, you had the right. Though if you flopped in it, you'd be a sorry soul. But if you won the day, your discretion and your ambition could be seen as that of a come-upper, a man to be reckoned with. The higher-ups in your group, the button men from other outfits, the law, the affiliates, the associates, would spread your winning success in a whispered word to help catapult you to an office of greater power.

Maybe as far as the madhatter Albert Anastasia himself.

Before 1947, Johnny Mazziotta had had no such leeway to act on his own. He had stepped briskly through the bookmaker world and led a knock-around life. True, he had a temper, fought cops, and hospitalized many a beat-artist. But all this was to his credit in the eyes of the already established.

Even the added epithet "Chappy," given to him by Bush Terminal longshoremen because of his persuasive yet "Gentlemanly" behavior while collecting gambling and shylock debts, helped show that he also had polish, finesse, that smooth touch needed nowadays since the brutal '20s, purging '30s, and early, transient '40s.

But since January 1947, after the year-long country tour, with grooming introductions from Manhattan to Pedro of the Costello Group in Miami, a visit to the temperamental Frank De Simone and clan in California, a talk with "Sally Burns," iron-fisting Uncle Frank's Cuban casinos, a meet with Lansky's sidekick "Shadows" in Vegas, all extensions of Uncle Frank's brainy business operations, the opening had come from the superior Forces—with the natural aid of his Dunsky father Felice—Johnny was "in." Knowing of the loose confederacy of friendships between other Crews, outfits; knowing most of all that charity begins at home—you were loyal to your own group first and foremost.

He had carved his own niche. He was noticed, contended with, "recognized." Johnny's "button," like all the men's buttons, was invisible to the naked eye, but it was heard about, gossiped over—sometimes propagandized for the psychological effect that fear of it would create, which could earn you esteem and cash without so much as pulling a trigger. At other times it was hushed up, and at all times dealt with by insiders as well as out in a fashion befitting a man of his station.

The button meant more reverent "hellos." It meant settling policy racket disputes, social insults, unwarranted deaths, where the Crews were attentive not only to him but also to what he now represented: two thousand bones that would fracture your skull if you dared disrespect the least of them.

And now, as a Button-Man, Johnny had a hawk-eye glued in three directions.

One was toward everyday business, the gambling that earned him his living and supplied his people with the financial support that kept them alive and growing.

The second was toward South Brooklyn, the neighborhood southwest of Borough Park, and the man who ran that neighborhood. Mr. Albert "The Octopus" Anastasia. Mr. Murder Incorporated in the flesh. And a couple of his loyal lieutenants, like Pisano, who had sewed up the policy-numbers game in Miami Beach; and "The Mortician" from East New York who buried Albert's array of bodies, some of them *alive*, in his string of legitimate funeral parlors. Then there was always the furtive-eyed Carlo Gambino, who Albert was saving from deportation and using for genteel arbitration. Johnny knew that the rest of the Anastasia Crew wanted their kill-crazy, tyrannical boss deader than a thousand doomsdays, but they held their peace so they could hold their lives!

As for the third eye of Johnny's, it was toward that lone apartment on the corner of 39th and Ninth. Toward the woman whose eyes burned through him. The woman who seemed to arouse him to a life and death battle with a look alone.

The woman who was a curse upon his days.

The kid's mother.

EVE.

Johnny let the January wind whip at his cheeks, his sturdy jaw, as he made his way from his apartment on 39th Street towards Pete's Radio Store. He kept his hands in his vicuna overcoat pockets.

As for Albert, who was he? A man with fat hands and a pudgy *schnozola* who happened to live in South Brooklyn? Who happened to have a place like a palace in the Jersey Palisades? He was a man who sent out "hitters," then had the hit man killed so there'd be nary a trace to him. Squeaky clean.

Who gave a fuck about Albert? So he's the iron-fisted "supremo" of his own set of people, Johnny thought. That was that. Three-Finger Brown had his own set of soldiers up in Harlem. And that was that, too.

The hell it was, the voice of reason shouted at him.

The neighborhood kids didn't call him "the toughest man alive" for nothing. He wasn't bowed to by Joe Bananas—whose fellowship was over 900 strong—for nothing either. And he didn't humble crank Profachi and his 600 made men—most of them good hitters—

for nothing. For Albert Anastasia wasn't just a Dock Boss who put his brother "Tough-Tony" up front to run the Brooklyn Waterfront. Albert Anastasia was an executioner. Mr. *Kill-Him*. The self-appointed switchthrower in every mob from here to Kalamazoo and back. The founder of Murder Incorporated!

Anastasia held kangaroo courts in his mind. And if your name happened to show up, you might as well sign your will.

So okay, Johnny shrugged. True is true. Sometimes the guy Albert hit had it coming. A weakling. An informer.

But only sometimes. Johnny walked slowly. Other times Albert arranged for your grave because, just maybe, you were the one who might someday stand in the way of his ambition. You were the one who would stop him from rising to the top. Maybe it was you who was blocking his way from becoming the Boss of Bosses, the *Dio*, the *Padrino*, of them all.

Johnny didn't fool himself for a minute that he was a threat to Albert's *Führer* ambitions. He didn't fool himself that he had the makings of a *Padrino*. But he kept a wary vigil on South Brooklyn because he was a Badge-Man in Frank Costello's army and if an attack fell upon Uncle Frank, the enemy troops would tear up Borough Park too. Johnny paused completely now on the sidewalk, thinking deeply, his eyes narrowing into the "squint" he was known for.

1947. Willie Sutton's "escape" from the East Pen, the Alcatraz of Pennsylvania. Uncle Frank, through Hugo Duce, had bribed all the guards involved except one. The one who had refused the five grand had done so saying he would not betray his job, turn his back on his duty, but he'd forget he'd ever heard of the "offer," and no hard feelings. *No hard feelings my-ah-COCK!* Albert had hissed, getting wind of the refusal through Uncle Frank.

Albert had sent The Mortician to "reason" with the duty-bound guard. "Five G's for your relatives. You'd look good in your prison uniform *covered in bronze.*" The guard had known it meant a casket, but hadn't relented. That is, until The Mortician gave the guard a day to ponder it and get in touch with Ange Bruno, the Pennsylvania kingpin, who was an extension of Albert Anastasia's long arm!

The guard played along, the five thousand still being held in abeyance for any sudden funeral, that "link" to Albert suspended in no-man's land.

But Albert had found out about another "link," weak as it may be. The kid, Dannie, who was used as a decoy while Marge drove

Willie to New York that snowy night. If any association between Sutton's infamous escape and Albert's part in it became known, the heat on Albert would certainly come down.

Johnny shook it all off. He had spoken with Albert and Uncle Frank. What could a freezing, groggy-through-and-through ten year old recall? Johnny picked up his pace a little, fully remembering his Group's bywords:

Look with a hundred eyes at the men that pass by you, his people always said. *One of them may blind you till all you see is the inside lid of your coffin.* Charlie "Lucky" Luciano, the deported founder of the Group, had repeated this saying often.

So Johnny kept at least fifty eyes at the back of his head directed straight at Albert Anastasia's camp.

And forty of the others on Eve!

What was it with her? he stopped in his tracks. A curse on his days, that's what. He now quickened his pace as he crossed the street.

Mermaid material, her eyes drowning him daily, her dewy, sea-creature breasts protruding naked again in his mind's eye, nodding, dancing, bouncing beneath her sheer bras, spring blouses.

That woman, she obstructs the odds on every horse.

He'd be on the corner of Pete's and catch a glimpse of her wiggling down the streets, and he'd land up screwed in his thinking, locked, entrenched in the throes of inexorable, insatiable passion for her.

He'd be toying with Betty, his mistress, some night, when he'd imagine Eve's hips and he was no use.

That's what bugged him. Those five words. *What was it with her?* She wasn't like she used to be. She and that *pazzo* sister Eleanor had been *strano* for years. The two of them frozen stiff like popsicles. Mother of Mary and Jesus, he wished he knew what had happened.

He remembered the first time he saw her.

She was statuesque, around sixteen, maybe a few months from being seventeen, walking with her kid sister, Eleanor. One year younger. Fantasy-fucking "jail bait." They were both ring-ass wriggling up Ninth Avenue.

Johnny had done a double-take. They looked like twins. Both dressed in delectable Cara Mia rose ensembles. Both having heads of raven hair so silken-thick and long they could go stark naked like Lady Godiva and a Peepin' Tom would never see the parts he was peepin' for.

But from the first, Eve looked gentler. There was something soft about her, pure as the day she was born, making you wonder about any body warmth under her deluxe clothes. She was prim and proper enough to make you want to attack a *saero anima*.

He found out about them. Eve and Eleanor Crosscavale. They lived on 38th Street, where the sister Eleanor still lived. A rookie cop, Hunt, was hanging around them. Johnny figured right away that he'd be a monkey's uncle if he couldn't beat a cop's time.

He had no love for cops even in those early days. Why should he? With three policy pinches and a stretch in Elmira already under his belt.

Yeah, things were rough in those days. The Depression was at its tail end, but still in, and more people than you could count were out of money. But Johnny had money in his pocket from the ponies, drove a rumble seat car, and was a dapper dresser.

He wangled himself an introduction.

"You girls new in this neighborhood? I missed the night you fell from the sky, landing here," Johnny tried to have a flair, a charm about him.

So what if he was a little on the squat side? You'd never call him bad-looking.

He asked Eve if she and her sister would go with him to the movies. They could even bring that cop Hunt along for protection.

"Why?" Eve hadn't smiled, her blue-green eyes a sexual, fathomless hazard.

"Why what?"

Then he realized that all she meant was why he wanted to take her to the movies.

"Because I want to follow your face wherever it goes," he found himself saying. He wasn't the cleverest guy in the world, but he could be direct. Both sisters had laughed, and he felt pleased and warm within himself.

They went to the movies and heard Jolson sing. The girls again wore identical clothes. During the movie, both sisters went for refreshments. Toward the movie's end, Johnny had naturally stretched his right arm across the top of Eve's theater seat, touching for a minute her silky hair, daring to run his fingers through it. When the picture show ended and the houselights went up, he had to do a triple blink to see that it was Eleanor sitting beside him. The two sisters had jokingly switched seats after returning from the refreshment stand. Between Johnny's red face and the sisters' laughter, the movie-goers standing around them all wound up enjoying that scene as much as Al Jolson up on the screen.

Now, for fifteen years, Eve's lit-up eyes had been an ice-green polar region, frozen solid. But back in the early days they were blue-green, like a warm sea. No matter how deep they took you, you'd never touch bottom with those eyes.

Johnny had longed to dive in and be with her—with only her, and he finally got her to go out with him alone.

He dated her for five months. Hand holding, window shopping, long, fancy-free car rides.

Double-features. Her head nestled on his shoulder, her hair tickling his cheek, neck, sometimes even blocking his view. But Bugs Bunny could have been Clark Gable for all they cared.

Once, the fellow behind the box-office window couldn't change a fifty dollar bill, the smallest Johnny had on him. Eve, who worked in a French boutique part time, paid their entrance. Johnny was on the verge of blowing his top at the stout fellow behind the glass. Eve, calm as ever, hooked her arm through his and, smiling, said, "Now you owe me sixteen cents, hon. Do I get my money's worth during or after the show?"

Johnny had burst out laughing. He paid Eve's tuition to fashion design school, her boss "agreeing"—for an extra fifty—that Eve would be told that the string of stores was sponsoring her.

At night there were sparse kisses by her downstairs doorway on 38th Street. Other times, by her upstairs apartment door, there were clinging embraces that said *she'd be his house of fire for their lifetimes.*

So, he hadn't really reached "first base." That was fine with him. It brought the marriage question quicker to his lips.

Jesus, he could remember that night just as if it were yesterday. He had gone to pick her up, ready to ask her that night. Eleanor was there, in the apartment, tearing at her hair like a madwoman who just witnessed someone being burned at the stake. Johnny had had to slap her, to squeeze his thumbs into her temples, before she calmed down.

The words came out slow. Eve was . . . in Brooklyn Doctors' Hospital . . . Sixteenth Avenue . . . a coma . . .

Johnny had stumbled down three flights of stairs with her and driven non-stop to that son-of-a-bitch hospital.

He ran to her room.

She was declared dead before he even got there.

That goddamn Hunt was, at first, standing in the hall. In the room, a nurse was covering up the body.

A doctor came up to him, touched his shoulder, suggested that he leave.

Johnny flipped. He spun around, throwing a wild punch in the doctor's direction, but landing a solid haymaker right on Hunt's jaw instead. He could hear the snuffed crack! in his ears, the sound of that bastard falling, the fussing over him by the doctor.

The nurse scooted out of the room like she was afraid she'd be next.

Eleanor was standing by the bed. Johnny didn't have to throw her out of the room. He led her out by the elbow. She was like the walking dead.

He spent twenty minutes alone with Eve's body before half the cops of Borough Park storm-trooped in, guns drawn.

For one of those rare times in his young criminal life, Johnny Mazziotta wasn't arrested. Instead, the cops "escorted" him to his car. They didn't book him for assaulting an officer. He was just led outside.

The sergeant told him that the rookie Hunt "understood." And then he told him to drive the hell away as fast as he could before they changed their minds.

Johnny drove. He didn't know how, but he did. He drove all night till he found himself by Hugo Duce's house. Gretti was there, too. Glum. Hugo took him into the bedroom and fed him a four-fifths quart of Schenley rye.

"You can't go wrong with this," Hugo said, pouring, drinking along with him. He touched Johnny's shoulder. "You'll see her again . . . someday," he said. He didn't believe that "someday" shit but said it anyway, until Johnny cried himself out and drank himself to sleep.

To this day, Johnny didn't know why he hadn't turned into a full-blown alcoholic after that.

Because he did see Eve again. The very next day.

Enough with history, Johnny thought, as he kept walking. It's a New Year. 1952. Eve has a son, good lookin' as the devil in disguise. And a husband. A night watchman older than the hills.

How the hell did Roscoe Valencia—Vale—ever win Eve? How'd a guy like that get the prize of a lifetime?

Yeah, but Roscoe wasn't that bad, Johnny reflected. He had "covered" and taken that five hundred for the loan of that sleepy, great kid, Dannie. *Eve's only son.* And Roscoe got a waterfront job out of it, too, in '47.

And what about me? Yeah, Johnny frowned. I have a wife, one that swills the booze too much, in public to boot. A wife who squirms into dresses too slovenly, bawdy, too tight for the human eye.

It would be legal good riddance of Rosa soon.

I'll miss the three kids, he decided, but he accepted the loss philosophically. He rubbed his hands together for warmth, thinking he'd found the halfway mark to the woman who turned him on every day as much as she did over sixteen years ago. The break-out. He was pleased with himself. At least he had an ace in this hole called life. Eve would come around.

Johnny finally reached Pete's, the miniature Las Vegas casino, radio repair store. Augie, Reb, and Hugo Duce were shooting the breeze around the poker table. Gretti, Little Mike, Tony-boy, a gaunt Al Rispone and wiry-haired Pete were hot in some confab by the craps table which was cluttered with radio tubes and chassis until game time. Johnny walked by the group which was too busy for even a *buon giono*, and pulled a folding chair next to Hugo. He was irritable, too many things on his mind, overthinking.

Johnny's nine-screws-loose-in-the-head brother-in-law, Benny Napanack, came into Pete's. Benny was carrying a large pizza box. Stale pizza inside. A gimmick, there were over four hundred policy slips under the crust. Benny dumped the paper slips on the UNDER AND OVER dice felt-table, and gave a long look at the hardened, dried pizza—Fuck it, he decided, and pulled up his left trouser leg, extracting a pointy butcher knife rubber-banded around his calf. He then carved up the pizza, and began devouring it.

Reb wasn't paying any attention to nutty Benny. He was dealing, gossiping. The same old gossip. With Hugo Duce. Charity gambling parties, bazaar gambling, some floating crap game. They were pissed at the politicos for having to move them again.

"At least that comic readin' La Guardia made his position clear. Right, Johnny?" Reb asked, his tumorous neck like a balloon filling up with air when he got excited. "With him you knew where you stood. No play. No pay. Period. End of report."

"Yeah, but that son-of-a-bitch forgot somewhere along the way that he was Italiano," Johnny pointed out.

"Sure as shit," Reb flared. "And that other S.O.B.'s lookin' to cut in on our Bush Terminal loan sharking. Al-burt. That would-be supreme supremo. Albert Anastasia. His fuckin' initials shouldn't be A.A."

Gretti coughed and spit out some yellow phlegm into his handkerchief. "So whaddiya have in mind?"

"To change the fucker's real name to 'K.H.'" Reb said. "For 'Kill Him.' That's all he knows. Right, Hugo?"

"Albert?" Benny Napanack chimed in, wiping his sticky hands on his pants legs. "The guy who points his finger and bullets come out of it? Fuck him! I'm gonna put my butcher knife up his lard-ass I get the O.K. from Johnny or Uncle Frank, right, Hugo? 'Don Vitone' can give me the go-ahead. Am I right?" Benny was foaming toward the door, he had to pick up some more eatable policy-pizzas.

Hugo nodded to Benny on the "wild-man's" way out.

Pete was shaking his head. "By the way, that kid was here looking for you, John. You're his hero, his idol." Pete was smiling, good-naturedly. "He'll be back soon."

Johnny took it in, but said nothing. Reb was sailing on. "I'm tellin' you, that mayor bastard and that new Police Commish are both hungrier than starving bears. You pay for police protection and you wind up payin' through the nose. While we're out tryin' to make a livin' off the gamblers, the politicos are makin' a livin' off of us.

"My fuckin' father, God rest his soul, should have raised me to be an honest crook."

Bull-built Little Mike gave a glance at the door.

"John, you got a visitor," he gestured. "Your shadow's here."

Johnny's gloom vanished when he saw Dannie come through to the back of Pete's. He had a special feeling for this kid. It couldn't be helped.

And the kid looked great.

Treats me like I'm his father.

"Hi, John." Dannie glowed down at his own new pants, barrel-kneed, 14-inch pegs.

Johnny got up to give the kid a hug. "Hi yourself, Dannie V. New clothes I see. Custom-made. They from that Schuster store?"

"Yes, Schuster's. And a new girl. THE girl, Johnny. The one I told you about."

"*Congratulazioni*, Dannie! May you take off your new pants for as good a reason as you put them on. For a better reason," Johnny beamed. "I'm proud of you, kid. You stuck with it and she fell for you, right? How can she miss? You got a kisser like your mother and I say that with respect." Johnny roughly held the back of Dannie's neck. "Her and I go back a long time. So she gave you the come-on, this girl?" Johnny turned to the men.

"You all know Dannie, don't you, fellows? Eve's son. Gonna be a spotter for me come next spring."

Little Mike gave Johnny a solemn nod from under his gray fedora. "Sure I know Dannie, Johnny, we all seen him around here a lot. Wouldn't mind knowing his sultry mother better, either," Mike mumbled audibly to the guys at the table. "Although it's a fuckin' wonder a cold fish like her ever screwed long enough to have a kid, the iceberg she . . ."

Johnny Mazziotta's face glazed over with hatred. Before the words were out of Mike's mouth, Johnny landed a whizzing power punch straight to his jaw. The men shot up out of their chairs. The chairs and tables fell back while radio parts and poker chips went flying all across the floor.

Mike sunk to his knees like a bull struck by a sledgehammer.

Johnny kept kicking the fallen Mike until Gretti, Tony-boy and fungi Al Rispone tried to pull the bleeding man away.

"Take your fuckin' hands off him!" Johnny yelled, elbow-cracking Gretti into the side, plate-glass-wood door of Pete's and left-hook decking Al Rispone.

Johnny was a maniac of temper-strength. He threw a right cross, knocking Tony-boy out cold on the now angled, creaking craps table. Reb was backing away, telling Johnny he was only trying to quiet things before a cop car passed.

Bastards! Dannie didn't know what to do; he was seething about what he had heard about his mother. He kicked at Mike. *Dirty pidocchi*! He felt two arms tighten around his chest as he was heaved off his feet.

Augie was holding Dannie back. "*Facile, facile*, son," Augie had him up in the air. "I'm on your side. *Se la prenda comoda*!" Dannie felt something steel-hard indenting his back. He realized in the mayhem that Augie Tenuto was wearing a gun.

From the floor, Gretti, slats of plate-glass sticking into his char-coal-gray suit jacket, stared up at Johnny with a look of such cold fury that the whole room seemed to ice over. Gretti knew he was powerless, that every goddamn one of them, excepting Hugo Duce, was powerless. Johnny Squint had a Badge, and if you touched him you were a dead man. Gretti passed out.

Augie's rust sports jacket was open. "We finish it, John? Fuck 'em where they breathe," he said. "Here and *now*. In Philly we say put an enemy on his back forever rather than have him at your back for a day."

Hugo nodded, agreed.

Johnny Mazziotta's face was a maze of hate, his eyes glinting down at bloodied Little Mike, at Gretti. His eyes drifted to Dannie standing by, and he softened.

"They're all Albert-prone anyway," Augie insisted.

Benny Napanack—named "Napanack" after the upstate nut-house he was in and out of—returned, wild-eyed, butcher knife in hand, wanting to actually scalp Al Rispone. "All these turncoat cuntlappers, right, Johnny? Right, Hugo?" He was cutting at the roots of Al Rispone's thinning hairline.

"Benny, cut that shit out! Augie, hide your gun. Ditch it. The *polizia* may be on the way. Don't want nothin' to happen to you. Let's clean up this mess." Johnny had his eyes narrowed at the flattened Tony-boy, Al.

Pete and Reb dragged Little Mike to his car. Hugo Duce and muttering Benny got phlegm-chested Gretti, full inside, from out of the doorway. They revived Tony-boy, and eased Al Rispone to his feet.

And the *polizia* did pass. Two minutes later. But Reb went over to the green-white squad car, leaned in the passenger window, and the cops pulled away, fifty bucks richer, apiece.

Dannie stood amidst the blackjack tables and numerous telephones, watching Augie and Johnny's every movement. And he noticed, furrowing his forehead, squinting hard at them, the striking resemblance the two men bore to one another. The same brown eyes, rough good looks. The same brown hair, square jaws. Johnny was maybe twenty pounds heavier and didn't have Augie's Philly accent. But except for the scar over Augie's right eye, they were spitting images.

They seemed for the moment to have forgotten him, but he couldn't forget them, not even for a *second*. Johnny coming to such a furious defense of his mother. Augie holding him back. Watching out for him.

Dannie stood his ground, piles of unopened decks of cards, boxes of green, red dice being put back in place. Reb, Pete, and Hugo Duce were gabbing. Dannie got a kick out of the language they used, the special way they said and phrased things, their shop talk. But he heard no further mention of Tony-boy, Al, Gretti, and Mike!

Johnny cast a glance over to Dannie. He wiped his brow. He shouldn't have blown his temper like that. Little Mike, Al Rispone, Tony-boy, Gretti—they'll bury those beatings in the back of their minds. Augie was right. Sooner or later, or maybe just sooner, there was going to be a fuckin' *budella*!

Johnny had the badge, but he hadn't shown responsibility.

The hell with it, he decided. He roughed up Dannie's hair good-naturedly and gave him an unembarrassed kiss on the lips.

"You're learning brother-love, kid."

Dannie let Johnny kiss him. A strange sensation. Like he was Johnny's son, and he'd arrived.

Johnny acted as if the fracas had never happened.

"C'mon, kid, let's go over to Fiola's Restaurant. Have a Coke. Relax. I could use a beer." Johnny felt the closeness, too. Maybe being a father figure to the kid was the closest he'd get to the mother. Maybe.

The two of them went across the street. The other men stayed behind to clean up.

"So tell me what you came to tell me before all hell broke loose," Johnny said when they were sitting in the brown-leathered booth.

"I found that girl," Dannie told him. "She was by that corner with her girlfriend, hanging around near some guy they call 'Joe the Blond.' You know him, Johnny?"

"'Joe the Blond'? You talkin' about *pazzo*, Joey Gallo?"

"Cocky. Short, thin?"

"That's him. Jesus, what's Brooklyn doin' to you? It's my fault. You shouldn't be allowed to see half of what you see or hear three quarters of the time. Just how the hell did you happen to run into Gallo?"

"Like I said, Johnny, he was hanging out by the corner when I found that girl on . . ."

"Where was that?"

"South Brooklyn." Johnny took a deep breath. Then his eyes narrowed. "Listen good, Dannie. South Brooklyn is no place for you. You gotta stay away from there. You want a girl? Take out my niece, Kathleen. She's a good girl. You two could be a number. Trust me. But you gotta listen good to what I'm tellin' you. South Brooklyn belongs to Mr. Umberto Anastasio." Johnny pronounced the name slowly, allowing every syllable to sink through Dannie's head. "He has . . ." Johnny tried to measure his words, ". . . twenty-one hundred *fratellos*. Their savage-switches get turned on pronto if Albert has an inkling . . . sees someone alone, unprotected, that has some kind of connection to him. Dannie . . ." Johnny peered across the booth's table. His eyes had a faltering look about them which was slowly spreading across his tawny face. But he caught himself, intensifying his voice again, "The guys call him 'Mr. Kill Him.' And not for nothin', Dannie! Albert Anastasia is a dangerous man. And that Gallo's a cuckoo clock. A kid who's out to prove."

Dannie was mumbling. "One of the girls called him . . . a 'badge-wanting bastard.' "

"Yeah, he wants a badge all right. He'll maybe get one from Olive Oil King Profachi someday. Or from Madhatter Albert. If he doesn't get a bullet between his eyes first," Johnny finished the beer in the frosted mug. "There I go now, tellin' you things you shouldn't ."

Dannie cut in, puzzled, he had to. "I made a date with that girl. My first date."

"Break it."

Dannie felt like one of those four guys Johnny had knocked out must have felt! "She's . . . got . . . this short, fluffy brown hair," sweat, a cold, hapless sweat pervading him, "dark eyes . . . out of sight. A shape . . . and we held . . ." Dannie was choking on his own words.

Johnny felt crummy, seeing, hearing Dannie's disappointment. He felt so much for this boy. Then he thought of Eve. Thought of their first date. He understood what the kid was going through, but the kid didn't see or understand the overall messy, intricate picture.

"Dannie, you'll *like* Kathleen."

Dannie, dejected, as if a judge had pronounced sentence, tried to sit straight up, stifling a sob. "I ran into someone else there too, Johnny."

"So who's that?"

"A guy I used to see around here," Dannie was holding his head up. "That guy who wears bedroom slippers. Didn't I go . . . did I ever go . . . camping with him years ago, in a snowstorm? I think his name's Lynch."

"You saw Lynch? In South Brooklyn? Are you sure?" Johnny's eyes were slats, he let the obscure "camping" recall go.

"I passed him on the way home. I'm almost sure."

Rosary-like beads of sweat broke out on John's forehead. He got up.

"Kid, you better get home. Your mother will throw a fit wonderin' where you are."

The expression on Johnny's face unnerved Dannie more than the abrupt words. He stood up.

Then Johnny took hold of him by both shoulders. "Look, kid. I want you to be a spotter for me. We talked long enough about it. You got yourself a job. But you gotta make me a coupla promises. Number one: you stay away from South Brooklyn. Absolute. You stay the hell away. And number two: you don't tell a living soul that you saw Lynch."

Dannie's heart beat faster than a race horse edging to the finish.

"Fifteen bucks a day, Dannie. And I don't want you to have to leg it. You're Johnny Mazziotta's spotter. You'll get a new Tru-Test bike."

"You don't have to do that."

"I want to do it, Dannie. You're like a son to me."

Dannie would have cried if crying wouldn't have embarrassed him. He gave Johnny a warm hug.

Johnny smiled. "Now get your ass home before your mother makes both of our lives hell on earth. *Andare!*" he ordered, impatiently.

Dannie touched Johnny's arm, hesitated, then scooted down the sawdust-scattered aisle.

All the way home it was Johnny's special words that kept ringing in Dannie's ears. *I want to do it, Dannie. You're like a son to me.*

He felt more like Johnny's son than Roscoe's. Maybe it was terrible to think, but it was true.

Johnny watched the kid shoot out of Fiola's, then he turned heavily, putting thoughts of Dannie aside.

He used Fiola's "bug-checked" phone to call Uncle Frank and broke the news about Lynch. Uncle Frank listened hard and asked a few questions. Johnny answered.

Uncle Frank sighed deeply. And put in a call to "Mr. Kill Him."

EVE VALE KNEW IT WAS HIGH TIME SHE CALLED ON John Mazziotta. She walked along forlorn 39th Street, her black hair glistening under the January, wintry sun, her almond-shaped green eyes teary from the wind, yet her mind on fire at the piercing, agonizing thought of her son being corrupted by a two-bit neighborhood gangster. Her skimpy high heels clicked toward Eighth Avenue.

John saw her on 39th and Eighth, his back to the door of Fiola's. He couldn't help but notice the heave and sway of her provocative frame, proportioned to the hilt. She was coming his way, and he knew why. So, he ducked into Fiola's. He'd see her inside his turf, on his terms. He settled back in the restaurant's snug brown-leathered booth, and waited.

Beaver-toothed Hugo Duce, straddling a folding chair by the half-curtained window outside of Fiola's Bar entrance, saw her coming too. He alighted deftly from the chair, and gave Mush, the stocky bartender who was club-soda ragging the top of the bar, the thumbs-down signal.

The bar entrance was locked from the inside. Mush placed the burnished .45 automatic on the bar, under the soggy rag, and sat back on a stool behind the bar, opening to the comic section of the

New York Daily Mirror.

No bar patrons legally allowed to swig the rye until twelve noon today—Sunday. Mush wouldn't let one in until twelve fuckin' midnight, or at least not until Hugo, Johnny's *fratello*-partner gave the thumbs-up sign. It was Johnny Squint's joint, and if Johnny wanted privacy in the restaurant section, then that's the way it would be.

Johnny, sitting in the booth, secluded by the partition of the horseshoe-shaped restaurant and bar, smoothed out the sleeves of his pearl gray, vested suit. He heard old brillo-haired Patsy the waiter behind him, his shuffling, hand apron wiping finally coming to a dead silence down the sawdust aisle to the part-glass restaurant door stenciled LADIES INVITED. Eve's voluptuous outline in burgundy coat appeared behind it. He swallowed, waiting for her to enter to talk about *her son.*

It was no use, she wasn't coming in. Heavily he got up, walking pensively, nearly shaking, toward her.

It hit him with the winter wind when he opened the door. The musk-sweet scent, the natural fragrance of her. She stood barely outside, hugging her burgundy upturned collar to her throat. She was in a paroxysm of shudders, breathing a stifled scream in her lungs.

He was lost. Her usually gentle green eyes were aflame, but held the same sexual dare. She was trembling for one reason, he for another.

"It's your influence," she began, the fingers of her left hand tight to her shortie coat. "I'm his mother, but it's you that has more control over him. Do you know what you deserve for keeping Dannie out late nights?" She backhanded Johnny's right cheek, weakly. "You introduce him to cheap hoods from all parts of this city!" Her right hand rose again and smacked Johnny full on the left cheek. Blood-blotches began appearing from beneath the cold skin layers.

He didn't wince, didn't budge, his eyes a steady but distant brown at her.

"You use him . . . to get me. It's through him you . . . want to satisfy some lecherous blood urge of yours." She beat her fist into his chest. "Well you did get to me. Remember that once!" Eve was near-convulsive. "*Remember it*! Well, I don't . . ." She leaned her forehead against the wood mold of the doorway, shivering. "God damn you forever for it." She was a word . . . a memory away from collapse.

Johnny had that weary look on his swarthy face as if he had heard all this time and time again. He wanted to ease Eve into his arms. In her broken state she just might let him cradle her. He wanted to hold the deep down goodness of her, that had always, in the past, brought out the best in him.

But she turned, full-facing him, her eyes a cold yet fiery green. His light brown eyes held her fierce gaze. The eye-clash lasted only a moment before she reached for the brass door knob, her arm brushing his suit jacket, and slammed the door shut in his face.

She stormed from the doorway of the "filthy hood's headquarters," hearing the cracking of glass behind her.

Johnny stood outside the restaurant, by the LADIES INVITED stenciled dining room exit door.

He spied Eve, through the jagged, cracked glass of it, as she crossed toward 39th Street. Tried. He should have tried to hold her in the moment of break down, she may have just fallen into his arms. A gusty wind blew the door's broken glass onto his gray suede shoes, and brought him back to reality.

A worn look crossed his face. Dannie hadn't just taken to him, he had made it his complete business that the kid . . . his thoughts drifted as he watched Eve's diamond-rear swing in that burgundy skirt. Surveying the shattered remains of the door, he thought of the recent melee at Pete's and decided it wasn't his weekend for glass.

EVE GLARED OVER AT DANNIE SLEEPING ON HIS pull-out sofa bed in the living room. Her eyes were furious, frightened little tears in them. The shoulder-strap of her plunging emerald green camisole had fallen down and she tottered on the helpless verge of screaming. "Dannie," she prodded him. "Wake up. I found money in your pants pocket." Her left hand held a roll of crisp bills. "Where did you get so much money? What have you been doing? Did that monster, that animal give it to you?" Her green eyes were glowing now as if ready to spring to the attack.

Dannie's eyelids were heavy, but seeing his mother kneeling by his bed was enough to rouse him from his sleep. A spectacular, beauteous mess of ebony hair cascading down her face . . . her naked shoulders . . . even early in the morning he couldn't bear to look at her. He looked down at the living room floor instead, saying nothing, not even angered that she had gone through his pockets.

"Your Aunt Eleanor, she gave it to you." Eve let the bills float to the floor. "You wouldn't take money from that . . . would-be big shot Johnny Mazziotta. It was Eleanor. She always gives you money. She loves you so."

"I know, Mom," he said. What could he tell her? I'm working for Johnny? She was *pazza* on that subject. He even bought me a new bike for being his main spotter? He said I'm like a son to him, Ma . . . *I wish he was my father?*

But Dannie held his peace. She'd flip out knowing he was earning ninety bucks a week. She was now holding his gaze, pleading with him to stay away from the *inhuman attacker*. Dannie was wondering, longing to ask her just how far back she and Johnny went. He touched her creamy shoulder and in doing so had a vision, a memory of when he was seven years old . . . his aunt and his mother sleeping in sheer, lavender half-slips, elastic up to their bare cleavages. Curvy-fleshy thighs angelic carved, curled on his aunt's queen size bed. Twin images . . . his aunt Eleanor, or was it his mother, had languidly suggested for him to come and sleep between them. He had scooted to his aunt's couch in her living room that long ago night. The memory fading now, he tuned in close beside him, to his mother's pleadings.

". . . would you challenge me, Dannie?" she asked, her hair waterfalling uncombed onto his bare neck. "Stay away from him. Do you want me tortured every night by my dreams?"

Dannie suddenly thought of the time last year when he had threatened to kill her if she slapped his face again. He cringed now as he had done then, picturing her alluring eyes as dried hollow sockets—his curvaceous mother a brittle skeleton. He let her kiss his eyes, but moved abruptly into the sofa's upholstered back, as she went for his right cheek.

Eve stood up, slightly unnerved. "All I wanted . . . was a kiss." She was rambling. "That's all. Just a little loving. Nothing impossible."

He lay gasping, his mother a trifle top-heavy in emerald dressing jacket, heaving deep breaths. He wished she wasn't so . . . strange. But that was like wishing he had another mother and that would *never* do. He smiled, trying to solace her. Her catlike green eyes tear bubbled. "No matter what you may hear about me," she intoned. "Remember that I would die for you."

She then gaily went about making her handsome boy waffles for breakfast, while he ate slowly, knowing how much he *needed* Antoinette, *pronto*. All he could think about were the last two words she had rambled: "Nothing impossible."

DANNIE HUSTLED DOWN NIPPY 39TH STREET ON HIS way to perform his lookout duties. He had already messed it up once and hoped nobody would remind him, but walking into Pete's Radio Store, to unchain his bicycle, he got hit by glares from Al Rispone and Gretti.

"Hey, kid," Benny Napanack was munching wildly on a hot calzone, "jeepers-creepers, you gonna get those peepers before you get us all canned for fuckin' gambling without a license!" Benny's left leg was propped up on an adjacent folding chair, the bulge of his carving knife ominous beneath his trouser leg.

"Mistaking an ambulance medallion for a cop car," Hugo Duce grinned from under his wide, brim-down fedora. "Get eyeglasses, Dannie. You broke up the sweetest of crap games with that boo-boo."

"You're half blind, kid, admit it," Tony-boy threw in from his seat at a six-man poker table.

Augie gave Dannie a fraternal glance; Johnny squinted over at Tony-boy, the latter's head going down, facing his jacks. He stood pat and stayed mute.

Dannie gulped. He hated the thought of wearing eyeglasses. Vanity. The mama's boy look. He had his bike ready to push out the side door, but first he had to check on the four other sub-spotters under his command. Augie gave him a good luck wink with his scarred right eye, and Johnny halted him for a moment with a right hand palm up. "Son, go for the eye test. I'll foot the bill."

"SON . . ." Dannie left Pete's on the wings of the January breeze, pedaling his new Tru-Test bike with gusto.

But he should have gotten glasses—a good strong pair. He thought he saw an official Department of Sanitation vehicle. He realized his mistake two minutes later. Two minutes too late.

Black Marias from both the borough Park 66th Precinct, and Bay Ridge's 68th Stationhouse converged on the corner of Eighth and 40th.

Hordes of cops invaded Pete's. Johnny came out swinging, decking cop after cop on Eighth Avenue's sidewalk, while Augie had made it through the preplanned basement trap door. If Augie were caught, identified by some honest dick, the roof'd nearly blow off the city. Dannie made his way into the street fracas, receiving a kick in his rear from a flatfoot for his efforts while the policemen's vehicles hauled Johnny and his men away.

Dannie stood nursing his rear end, his pride beyond repair at having failed again.

Sans job.

He'd leave the bike chained in Pete's.
He didn't deserve it.

FOR TWO SOLID DAYS DANNIE WALKED DISHEARTENED.
He roamed after short stints at Fort Hamilton High thinking of his
father, Roscoe. How he loved him. He thought of his father buying
him his first three-wheeler, bushy-squirrel's tail attached to the rear
of the seat, a pair of miniature boxing gloves—which his mother
promptly hid forever.

Dannie trod on, dejected, thinking of Johnny . . . being so absolute about his not seeing Antoinette any more. He couldn't keep
that Tuesday movie date with her. What the hell does he care about
the "Madhatter" Anastasia, regardless of what the neighborhood
bookmakers buzzed about "Murder Incorporated's" money con-
tract killings? A man iced in a movie theater in Pittsburgh, a come-
dy actor stabbed in the stomach repeatedly after his stand-up rou-
tine in a Catskill mountain resort. What did these gory stories mean
to him? What does Albert Anastasia have to do with him trying to
make it with Antoinette? It was just a damn date.

He had never tried to get in touch with her, explain why he had
never showed for their date.

He didn't deserve her either.

He trekked along cold Ninth Avenue and stood by 45th Street,
peering up the residential street. Wally Schuster, nearly his age,
lived there with an older brother, Arnold, the sharp young custom
tailor. At least Wally had a big brother to talk to. Dannie had seen
Wally around the old Pershing Junior High. He now spotted pushy
Rogie, a *braggocio*, and his sidekick George Haist, the Finn who
audaciously wore a Count Dracula-style cape, sauntering his way.
Both were numbers runners in their early twenties, and both were
favorites of Hugo Duce. They passed him by with nary a blink.

The last thing he remembered seeing after the raid on Pete's was
George's cape stomped on the sidewalk. He knew they were all out
on bail, Division blaming Boro, Boro blaming plainclothesmen for
the double-crossing raid on Johnny's headquarters.

Dannie headed for the Ninth Avenue "Cuts" in the hope of seeing wizened-eyed Pop, the city watchman, hoarding strewn treasures from frozen cats to rusted bottle caps. He'd chat with the old
man by the shack where he lived and stored the loot. From atop the
Ninth Avenue trestle Dannie viewed the freight yards, the open

subway platforms, tracks and rails below.

He squinted under the glaring sun, his right hand on his forehead, shading his eyes, scanning, searching for overall-clad, crafty Pop.

No luck.

Dannie walked, trying to think of a way to make it all up to Johnny. He wandered down the barren, Bay Ridge side of Sunset Park, damning his own impaired eyesight.

Leafless trees, brownish dirt-grass, the two city swimming pools, gaps of cold tile—the park looked as bare as he felt.

And he still felt he should have been the one that punched bull-neck Little Mike for the way he had talked about his mother. He made it past hunched-up lovers on benches and kids braving the winds, tossing a football. The more he walked, the less of a man and more of a boy he felt.

A *true* Mama's boy, he gulped it down, nearing the Fifth Avenue side of the park, suddenly realizing that he had never even picked up the navy blue pants from Schuster's. He had no use for them now, anyway. Who the hell was left for him to impress with them? He abruptly stopped walking, and his self pity, too, seeing . . . trouble straight ahead.

A *zaftig* blonde in kelly green slacks, a regal black, fur-collared coat draped over her. She had an older lady beside her.

And circling around both of them, on a hill sloping down to Fifth Avenue, were five Scandinavian and Puerto Rican boys his age. The young girl and her older companion were being accosted.

Steer clear, he warned himself. For all he knew, with his luck, the girl would turn out to be gravel-voiced "Uncle" Frank Costello's long-lost relative and he'd wind up being accused of being in league with the five boys.

He hated Brooklyn.

But the blonde was on the dirt kicking upwards like a Mad Russian. Three of the boys stalking her, one trying like all hell to hold her down. The older companion was being held around the neck by the fifth boy.

Rape, in broad daylight? Dannie couldn't swallow, his saliva stuck halfway inside his parched throat. That's too outlandish even for Brooklyn, he decided. Maybe just a family affair, a recalcitrant sister of one of the boys. They were just attempting to get her home for some personal reason. He could hear the older companion's wails from where he stood, and he saw two of the boys ripping at the prone blonde's expensive heavy green sweater. Johnny would interfere, he thought, remembering well Johnny's knock out punches in Pete's. Dannie tossed his reluctance aside and hustled over to . . . trouble—damn it, he knew it!

They had been robbing her, that's all! He sat, nimble, in the spacious upstairs room of Bay Ridge's 68th Precinct Stationhouse, "acting nimble in a swindle," Huge Duce's bywords.

The tall blonde was claiming she was a "visiting Russian princess"; her companion was her governess, both spouting in unmistakable accents.

The five would-be attackers were not contrite. Leo, Ponce, Buddy. The other two names he didn't catch. But he caught all five of their glares at him.

Where do cops come from? From out of the woodwork? Reb's comical lament now stinging Dannie's ears. He figured some good citizen had run from the park, flagged a squad car down. But their arrival might have saved him a shellacking from the hand of the five boys who weren't taking too kindly to his kind, polite way of saying, leave the two women alone and go and pick on five guys your size.

The parents came, an Embassy in Manhattan called . . . Plainclothesmen, revolvers hip-holstered, scampering about. Paper work, more phones ringing, and more relatives arriving.

Dannie had to give a parent's name, a telephone number. He hadn't done a damn thing but forget the golden rule: mind your own business! And he hadn't said a damn word to these cops when he was corralled and pulled in along with the rest of the park participants. Reluctantly he gave his aunt's telephone number. God forbid he give his mother's name. She'd get a seizure on the street, Lord help him and her.

The visiting seventeen-year-old blonde gave him a grateful wink, sitting on the upstairs precinct floor, stretching seductive in her slacks, flirting with him. She slipped Dannie a gift—a ring. "It's real," she hushed, her accent flourishing. "It's my father's," she kept whispering. "It's as good as a passport if you get as far as the border."

He received another reward, the governess bussing his cheek in a clandestine thank-you for coming to their aid. She had been the last one to want to press charges against anyone. Her job was to get the girl, her ward, and the valuable jewelry back to the safety of wherever they came from.

All involved were finally let go. The parents must have "chipped in" to the Policemen's Benevolent Association, or else Russia didn't want a confrontation with America, or something along that diplomatic line.

Dannie stood on Fourth Avenue's sidewalk in front of the 68th

Precinct with a gold-red ruby ring in his jacket pocket, and a witchy, gorgeous aunt beside him.

Dear Aunt Eleanor had waited outside the precinct for him. She wanted to give him a *potch*. Her blue eyes were glaring, intensified by the blue velvet of her trim, shortie coat.

He told her that none of the day's events were his fault. He wanted to tell her that two foreign ladies even considered him a hero, and to prove it he could have shown her the ring that the Russian girl had furtively passed him—her father's name—Aleksandr—engraved on the inside of the band.

Better not do that, he reasoned. She'd scorn it; think it was stolen.

In the taxi-cab she promised not to breathe a word of today to her sister. He'd stay with her.

Blackmail—great. He leaned forward, handing the cabbie a ten dollar bill by his aunt's apartment building on 38th Street.

He walked up to the third floor with her. His aunt spoke of having plans to move near to McDonald and Church Avenues, close by. "A better neighborhood," she was haughty, keying open her locked door. "This one is getting so a decent woman can't walk down the street without hearing at least three indecent propositions a day."

She should take one of them, he nearly snickered. She might do her uptight self some good.

He'd sleep over on the couch. It was as saggy as the one at home. He was dying to get a better look at the ring, so he went into his aunt's bathroom.

He viewed it under the bright bathroom lights. Gold, thick, and a red ruby in the middle. He blinked, cleared his vision, making out the engraved name—Aleksandr. The name became a blur. Whew, Hugo Duce was right, he did need eyeglasses.

But a picture, a poster in the Bay Ridge Police Station, that he had seen now suddenly became clearer to him. It resembled the slender guy with the wisp of a mustache that he had spotted in South Brooklyn, the one Johnny had gotten so tense about. Dannie dismissed his own impaired vision, he could hardly count on it.

The ring was two sizes too big to fit any of his fingers. Why not use it as an attempted peace offering to Johnny? He was delighted with that thought. It could make amends for his faltering eyesight. At least he'd give it a try.

"Where have you been getting your money lately?" Eleanor broke his reverie. She had slipped out of her coat. "Are you stealing? Is that what you've stooped to?"

He shrugged in the living room—her usual harangues.

"A big tipper. You pay for taxis with *dirty money*," her voice picking up that familiar nasty tone, it rang hailstones in his head.

"Mind your own business, Eleanor!" He had been itching to blast her for so long.

She had been egging him on, waiting for this. Before he knew what was happening, her hands were two fierce windmills hurricane-slapping his face. He felt like she was scrambling his brains.

She was going to smack him blind. He flinched, trying to protect his head from the deluge of blows. There was only one way he was going to stop her constant onslaughts.

This time, he fought back. But Eleanor Cross was one hell of a fighter. She clawed, kneed his groin, scratched and bit him as they rolled on the living room floor.

Her temper was reaching its apex. He fought at first to restrain her, but she was fighting to win! She wouldn't ease up for one split-second. His windbreaker jacket was all but off, hanging from his left wrist. She had ripped his beige Manhattan shirt from off his back, her long fingernails clawed into his shredded V-neck T-shirt, his skin. She emanated animal growls, and had the strength of a sun-struck woman.

He didn't want to do it, had tried through the bout not to, but he wound up punching her, in of all places, the *stomaco*, the blow that knocks the wind out of anybody's sails.

He thought he killed her. He had to breathe into her mouth to help her get back her breath which she had lost from the low blow. She looked like she was turning blue, and Dannie was in a state of near hysteria, rubbing, pressing her stomach for some breaths to come up past her chest to her mouth. He tried to loosen the back of her bra through her torn blouse so as to give her breathing room, but the damn catches were stuck. He squeezed her cheeks, breathing like a bastard into her mouth, yelping to himself to let her breathe, let her breathe. Was she going to die? He heard it, feeling it ever so slightly against his own mouth, her breath coming slowly. He was drenched with chilled sweat. She breathed more normally now, and he watched her as if she had come back from the dead.

Water—he ran to the kitchen sink.

"Drink slowly," he touched the glass to her lips, propping her in a half-sitting position.

He knelt by her, wanting to tell her how sorry he was. But "sorry" wasn't good enough for the disgust he felt.

He didn't want to hit her face. To mar her exquisite face, to him, would be as bad as killing her. He couldn't look at her now. She had tried, in her own way, to be so good to him all these years, and look what he did in return. He was a feather away from breaking out crying.

"Mind my own business?" she sipped from the half a glass of water. "You'd have to murder me . . . someday to . . . stop me from making you my . . . complete business." There was a strange sadness in her voice as she placed the glass down on the red carpet. With effort she undid the back of her pale blue brassiere, slipping it out from under blouse. Breathing more freely, her stockingless legs now wound partly under her buttocks, her eyes, her words bottomless.

It was crazy. He knew it was crazy. He suddenly had the notion to ask her if she was his real mother. He shuddered and tears came.

"I deserved what you did," her mood shifted, as it often did. "I push you around. I do more . . . than that. I push you too far with my antagonism. My life is barren, Dannie. Empty. I try to make you as I am. Please don't leave. I won't bother you. I've done enough damage."

There was nothing for him to say. No way he could put it.

"Don't cry," she touched his tears. "It's not your fault. Don't cry on my account," she was crying. "I'm not worth one of anybody's tears." Her tight, royal blue skirt slits revealed lusty thighs.

Was it pathos, lust, some kind of love that made him feel so barren? He slipped his reversible jacket from his left wrist, placing it over her shoulders, it didn't cover her lavish, bare bust which protruded from the remains of her blouse.

"Aunt Eleanor, are you a virgin?" he tried.

"I'm a woman," she answered, her voice like a flame in the evening living room. She began kissing, licking the fine scrapes and deep scratches she had inflicted on his chest.

He found himself reaching out for her, the raw cuts on his body seeming to drive him on, the luxury of her legs twining around his. He felt himself careening into . . . an abyss, yet the beauty so pure in her mist-blue eyes . . . NO, he had to stop himself.

"I can't do it, Eleanor."

She let go of him. "You will, Dannie. Someday you will," she said wistfully. And for the first time since she had picked him up by the precinct, she smiled.

DANNIE OFFERED JOHNNY SQUINT THE GOLD-RED ruby ring as a peace offering January 22, 1952. Just before that offering he had something to live with. Live with or live down, he couldn't tell the difference any longer. He only knew that besides his gut going queasy on him, he felt—from previous Sunday School teachings—that heaven's gates were clanging closed to him for the shameful way he had embraced his flesh and blood, his aunt, for that abandoned moment in her living room. The only thing saving him from retching minute-to-minute, or slicing his own throat, was the clinging, hopeful thought that Eleanor Cross *was not* his aunt, but some siren of a woman who had come out of the past and only claimed that title for some unfathomable GOD-tricking reason that he'd tenaciously find out someday. He hoped to keep himself sane. What else could he do, he rationalized.

Johnny accepted the ring by a booth in Fiola's—a peace offering. Across the table sat Hugo and Augie, Dannie standing head down by all three men, his eyes fixed on Johnny's Brito brown shoes. He shifted to the side, making way for Patsy, the apron-soiled waiter, who put down a silver tray, a steaming red-white bubbly pizza on it.

"Join us," Johnny Squint moved his solid, squat frame over, making room. He had taken off the diamond pinky ring from his left hand, trying on the gold-red ruby one. "Kinda loose, but it'll do. Is it real?"

Dannie told him how he had gotten it, smiling. "It's as good as a passport."

"Tell you what, *figlio*," Johnny was munching the savory pizza slice. "Take our advice and wear tinted or dark glasses from here on out. Prescription ones. Feel comfortable, job or no job. Until then you'll own the ring, but I'll wear it. Bargain?" John wiped his hands on a white linen napkin, stuck out his right one.

Dannie shook it, smiling broadly, and was told to eat, *mangiare*. Dannie's right hand held the folded, pointed, piping hot slice of pie to his mouth, Augie's eye-scar flaring from the grin, Hugo genuinely laughing buck-toothed, at the two being friends again. The word *figlio* was a figure of speech, but Dannie glowed anyway at hearing it.

"And remember," Johnny chewed, "call on Kathleen. You seen her a hundred times in the neighborhood while the two of you were growin' up. And remember also that she's a *buona ragazza*. Treat her accordingly."

Dannie's lips inched forward in degrees, trying to attune themselves to the overheated hot sauce, John's words concerning his niece—a *buona ragazza*—ringing in his ears. Dannie knew it was a *warning*!

ABOUT KATHLEEN, JOHNNY WAS RIGHT. SHE WAS A
buona ragazza—A good girl.

Dannie remembered Kathleen, sporadically, through his adolescent neighborhood years as living religion, not just studying it as he
had on Sundays.

Dannie knew that Kathleen was nothing like Antoinette. He
"dated" her most of that week, and wound up, most of the time,
looking down at her shoes—black mellow polished calf with shoe-
less bows. Old ladies' shoes.

But he enjoyed her, despite the fact that she was so serious, sickly
and kind of quiet. Most of all, the daughter of Jamesie Mazziotta,
Johnny Squint's brother. She still was an escape from the tense little
universe that hemmed him in, and she had the demure innocence of
a parochial school girl. A far cry from juicy Eleanor!

She liked to be pushed on the swings of the kiddie park on New
Uthrect Avenue. She was a little heavy set, chunky, but Dannie
pushed her high and fast with ease.

He wanted to take her to the Ritz theater on Eighth Avenue to
see a movie, but she declined in favor of reading him her special
poem, "In Imitation."

The poem reflected Christ's teachings on fighting violence. Even
when struck a blow from another . . .

Turning to Christ my silent cheek
In Imitation . . .

Such a saint she is, Dannie felt. But by her doorway on 40th
Street, he, true to his mode, checked out again her shoes. It was
hard for him to look her in the eye. She was so sincere, and holy
that somehow he couldn't.

"What do you think of the poem, the message of it?" she asked,
rolling up her woolen brimless cap from around her ears.

"I . . . recently stopped turning the other cheek," he said, shamefully, the punch to his aunt's midriff causing havoc in his own midsection.

"Did the poem make you not want to fight anymore?" she had a
smile that lacked physical enthusiasm, as though it was an effort for
her to do so. Even when she walked, she pushed herself onward,
grinding during a stroll with fatigue like an overloaded truck low-
gearing up the steepest of Bronx hills. He realized she was more
sickly from her diabetes and heart murmur than people said.

"The poem," he held the paper it was written on, "distracted me
from fighting. It made me want to kiss a saint."

She was surprised, her dull brown eyes lighting, showing it. "Do you know any?"

"My mother," his throat was near-clogged. "And you."

"We're not saints." Her eyes were pleased, as she completely removed her wool cap, her reddish-brown hair satiny under the sidewalk's lamppost amber glow. "All the saints are dead. But they enter heaven a minute apart."

He wondered how that could be, but didn't tune into the subject, her shoulder length hair, unencumbered now, delighting him.

"If you want to kiss me, will you kiss me like you kissed that girl Antoinette that my uncle Johnny told me about?" Kathleen did not blush.

Dannie, taken aback, swallowed hurriedly. He remained stark still.

So did she.

"Bedbug" Rocco Bruzzese saved the situation, the admonishment of Johnny Squint—"No Funny Business." Brooding Rocco curbed Dannie's ever active libido. Dannie stared at Rocco who stood by the isolated elm tree, moonlit, adjacent to Kathleen's cement stoop.

"What's your problem?" Dannie blurted out to Rocco.

Kathleen gently touched Dannie's left arm. "He's my girlfriend Gloria's brother. He lurks, stares, but means no harm."

Dannie couldn't buy that as Rocco skulked up 40th Street toward Ninth Avenue.

No kisses were forthcoming between the two on the stoop, Kathleen disappointed, Dannie relieved. But they made a date for the following evening. He'd treat her to ravioli at Fiola's.

And Dannie that next night received a treat himself. Not a sinless *bacio* from Kathleen, but a stomach straining lesson in what happens when you're forced to "turn the other cheek"—In Imitation.

They strawed their glasses of cold, foamy sasparilla soda in Fiola's. Johnny, when there, Dannie knew, would pick up the check.

Johnny came in, Patsy the waiter helping him out of his mohair overcoat. He merely nodded to Dannie and Kathleen and hurried down the sawdust-scattered aisle to the last lone booth.

Dannie turned, feeling as apprehensive as Johnny looked, and then saw through the neon-lit window a powerhouse of a man wearing dark glasses. Dannie swore to himself that he recognized that rock-like man from somewhere. He turned forking his cheese ravioli, buttering his hot Italian bread *Naplidon* style, trying—not like the Sunset Park fiasco—to absolutely mind his own business!

Kathleen ate insipidly as she faced the reddish neon-lit restaurant window. "That's Albert Anastasia outside." She chewed the red-gravy soaked ravioli.

That really rocked Dannie. How did she know something like that? He cautiously turned again. Sure, it was none of his business, but Johnny was his business.

The rhinoceros of a man stood outside the restaurant like he owned it and the strange men around him were his vassals, relegated to him by a feudal God. Dannie, unassumingly, watched three of the strange men enter Fiola's. They weren't your usual bruisers.

They greeted Johnny by the lone booth. One wore an expensive sharkskin suit with baggy pants. Pisano. Real short, energetic, he checked out both restrooms, while the second man, an impeccable dresser, velvet lapel collared topcoat, The Mortician, walked nonchalantly into the kitchen. The third fellow, jutting nose, furtive spheres for eyes, Carlo, sat like he was at home, across from John.

Four more entered the restaurant. Three giants and the fedora'd man with dark glasses—the Madhatter known nationwide as Albert Anastasia.

Within ten tense minutes Dannie saw that wisp of a man, the one he had seen that night in South Brooklyn, hurriedly pass him up the aisle, heading straight for John's crowded booth.

And within three minutes of that Dannie's insides rebelled. The man in the dark glasses, Mr. K.H., slapped the slim man with the wispy mustache.

But it hadn't been only that that had made his gut chaotic. It was the scene half a minute later. The embrace, the kiss, bestowed upon Mr. Lynch by thick browed Anastasia, the same bull who slapped him.

"You break-ah the rule," Anastasia had said. "*Lei Far tu stesso, mi, Franchesk, da apparie dove lei no appartenere,*" the Madhatter had solemnized like a lecturing father.

Dannie stumbled from Fiola's bowing his head by the grated sewer on 40th Street, tearful rage in his eyes.

Why is it that people can slap you, embrace and kiss you all in the space of a few seconds? He heard Kathleen stir beside him.

"It's my fault," he said to her.

She looked puzzled, My God didn't she see the cringing slap? No, Dannie realized, her back was to the rear booth. The nausea was still rising in Dannie's gut. It was he alone who had told John of spotting the slender Lynch in South Brooklyn, but why had Anastasia called Lynch Willie? Dannie wondered, as he felt the loss of the feeling of manhood he had had just three and a half short weeks ago when he walked out of Max Schuster's Haberdashery.

Guilt now pervaded him—he was responsible. Dannie suddenly spied hulking Rocco Bruzzese again, this time by Felix's corner grocery store, four doors from Fiola's. Rocco slithered past Felix's entrance, after gawking at Kathleen.

"What the hell does he want?" Dannie raged.

"I befriended him," Kathleen soothed Dannie. "He's God's child, besides being Gloria's only brother. Please settle down, Dannie," she gently stroked his perspiring forehead, his pale, sweaty cheeks. "As for what happened inside the restaurant," she began leading him up 40th to her two-family brick house, "my uncle John said you did not harm that slender man. You helped him. What he received was a love-tap. Everyone's friends now."

Dannie stood by her house, amazed. The things she must hear and see through her family, he squeezed her hands, and then watched as she labored up the steps to her door. He wandered toward home, knowing in his heart that Kathleen was not sold on that love-tap crap.

Suddenly, Dannie's heart missed a beat. He saw Antoinette—in the compact-slacked flesh—and her girlfriend, Anna Banana, standing on the sidewalk by the corner of his house.

He clasped hands with Antoinette wanting to forget his missed date. But Anna had her oversized nose stuck nearly in his face. "You like to hit and run, don't you pretty boy," she shouted. "You stood-up my girlfriend like she was just a piece of shit to you!"

"No," Dannie was stunned at her verbal attack, though he knew she was partly right.

"No my pretty ass, you pretty-faced bastard!" Anna had the vixen in her like Eleanor, but not the beauty. He cringed at the word "bastard."

"Listen, Anna . . . " he tried, but she maddeningly cut him off, "*My name isn't Anna!*"

"Josephine," Antoinette clung to Dannie. "You promised . . ."

"Shut up!" Anna Banana was beyond the white-heat of anger. "You kiss and run, don't you!" she turned on Dannie. "You kissed my lips and then pulled a disappearing act."

"Oh, no," Antoinette yelped.

"Well here's your payback!" She hauled off in a fury, belting Dannie's upper lip. He stood jolted a second, IN IMITATION. Then the thought of being a human punching bag revolted him, and he freed his right hand from Antoinette's, short-right jabbing Anna's jutting jaw. She buckled to the ground.

"Scap!" she shrieked, commanded. "Do you think we came

alone?" She crazily guffawed pure hate at Dannie. "Bang-Bang! Allie! Joey!" she was screaming. "Scap!"

Three older fellows came charging from a parked car close by. In no time they were on Dannie, swinging and kicking. He went tumbling onto the cold sidewalk, Antoinette crying to "Joey!" in the car to "stop it!" She was in the midst of the three older boys working Dannie over. They were punching his head, trying to place-kick his balls with pointed-toe shoes. Antoinette scrambled, scratching at them, clenched-teeth screeching that they were only out "trying to impress Mr. Al-bert Anastasia," Josephine's uncle, the flunkies that they were, trying to make a name for themselves. Dannie thought he saw Gretti? snake-eyed and complacent by the curb. The kicks to his head more like stomps, he felt the blackout coming. He had his face covered with his hands, his mind flashing the ugliness of his hitting a girl, a woman, both in one week. A blow to the back of his head knocked him so that he no longer felt the beating he was getting. He suddenly felt he was alone, crawling . . .

The blackout came.

WILL COURTNEY. A FALSE ARREST FOR MURDER. LATER dismissed for lack of evidence. But it had gotten frail William noticed. As Courtney. An invented last name, straight out of the white pages of Ma Bell's New York Telephone directory.

Billy Bowles. Over twenty-one. Onto more sought after notoriety. The Broadway Manhattan jewel heist. Near to a million dollars worth but not really worth it when "fenced" for twenty percent of its value. No percentage in jewelry. Period. Especially when the take was divided, split five ways among his then amateur gang.

Jimmy Clayton. Confuse the hell out of the cops. And on to where the cash was stored. Banks. Hence his coining of the term "The Money Store." Lucrative. In Bay Ridge, Brooklyn, on Fifth Avenue, a downfall leading to Sing Sing Prison—the Castle on the Hudson, Ossining, New York, where you excreted in a bucket and dumped it in a ditch every morning.

Escape. Perfecting the art of disguise. Creating a dummy of himself on his cot, scaling the high, thick cement wall.

Lou Holland. Casing Money Stores in Chicago, Los Angeles, Dallas. Robbing them with finesse. Fast becoming the Dillinger of his day. Being dubbed "the Actor" for changing his face—through make-up—as often as the feds changed their pants. All without violence. Nevertheless, prison again. In Pennsylvania. And again, escape.

Mr. Gordon . . . Mr. Mahoney. Freedom short-lived, before being returned to another Pennsylvania Pen where Johnny Squint and Company bought him freedom.

And now, late January 1952, *Lynch. Mr. Ed Lynch,* alias of William Francis "The Actor" Sutton, the Jesse James of the Twentieth Century, stood on the Staten Island Ferry with his compadre Augie/Angel Tenuto, feeling fifty-two years weary—one third of those years spent in jail. His mind traced over the names he had gone by over the course of his "career." They all seemed better than the one he was stuck with now.

Lynch. A New Springville, Staten Island hospital orderly at Willowbrook Farm Colony. Sutton was afloat, adrift, hiding, being slapped in the face by a fat, killer pig named Anastasia!

Augie/Angel stood beside the Field Marshal of Crime, his savior—Willie The Actor.

Augie fermented with anger. It was just like he felt that bastard's debasing slap in Willie's face himself. The *vergogna* of it. The shame of it. Augie Tenuto crouched by the ferry's rail, a dynamite keg of rage. If only he had been there, that evening, instead of burrowed in an upstairs Borough Park mole-hole. He related to his *fratello* Irishman Willie of the one *ufficiale* hope there was—Don Vitone Genovese—through Johnny Squint!

Johnny and Augie had discussed the coffin-eyed Madhatter, Albert, the mad motherfucker who had contracted for *gelt* a thousand and one *hits*, the two of them had been standing by the edge of the 40th Street, Brooklyn waterfront.

What do you do with a low-life leech who has one pleasure in life? That of taking it. *Living* for that!

You kill him.

And after that you "bang out" a couple of his well-chosen, loyal CAPTAINS to insure against coordinated reprisals.

And for more insurance, just in case, you clip a couple of more BADGE men of his. This way you can really rest easy knowing that these few faithful LIEUTENANTS won't be around to even the score for their dead GENERALE someday.

Sounds simple enough. One problem though: After it's all over, you become the Madhatter, and where would that lead? Johnny had walked with Augie from the Bush Terminal Pier to the Rocket Olds.

The decision was reached. Augie had to tell The Actor that he'd have to live with the slap he had gotten from Al-Bert *for now.* At least until Johnny went to see Don Vito Genovese, the treacherous

Underboss of the Costello Group, in Greenwich Village. He had recently returned from hiding in Italy following the Borough Park homicide case that Johnny had straightened out, for it was only a matter of time before Vito, the true tough power, told Frank, the genteel businessman, to shove over.

Willie Sutton absorbed the condensed version of the meeting between his "rabbi," Johnny Squint, and his ex-cellmate, right-hand Angel Tenuto.

Can't step foot in South Brooklyn, the section of the borough I was born in, Willie drummed a tattoo with his fingertips on the ferry's chilled rail. Couldn't visit his mother there, or sit and kill some idle time with Marge, Willie pondered.

He bit his lips. He didn't quite understand the inner workings of the hierarchical structures that "protected" him.

"Vin Mangano is the Boss of Al-bert and Friends. Al-bert the *sottocapo*. Yet, despite this, Al-bert pushes Uncle Frank around and goes around marauding as if he's the Boss of Everything! And *I* go around," Willie thrust his hands forward, over the iron rail of the main deck, "with invisible manacles on. I'm a ferry rider. From Staten Island to Brooklyn. And not even that anymore! Angel, I feel like Hale's character Nolan in *The Man Without a Country.* What am I going to be? This megalomaniac's whipping boy?" He pushed his free hands deep in the pockets of his blue serge pants. "We escape jail together," his voice a wisp of breath into the wind of the night harbor, "and get confined. You to an upstairs flat in Borough Park. Me to the main deck of a ferry. Both with a warden by the name of Anastasia. How do you figure it?"

Augie had tried to tell Willie how it all figured. But all he himself had wanted this afternoon was a "go ahead" from Johnny Squint. A nod. An O.K. to shoot Anastasia in the fuckin' head.

But, of course, what he had gotten was the practical truth. That John didn't have the power yet to give official sanction to kill that big. "For now!" Augie clung tenaciously to the rail. He tried again to run down the long why of it all to gentle, encyclopedic-minded, Willie. But he himself had trouble unravelling the five tangled groups which ran the city's underworld—and their lives. Yet he damned well knew where it left both of them—in the hands of hay-wire-head Albert and Viper-Vito, who, between the two of them, killed as many men for sport as a small war.

Augie hated the idea of admitting it, but he knew he had no true gripe other than the humiliating, socially belittling slap to his partner. He recoiled in his thoughts, as if he now felt that slap himself, the disgusting shame of it that could drive you to dig your head in the ground for the rest of your pride-self-respecting life. He nearly cried with anger as he kissed the man beside him who had saved him from a lifetime inside a prison.

Mr. Lyle Sesqu, Dannie's downstairs neighbor, had revived Dannie the night of the ferocious beating.

Mr. Sesqu, bringing home a late night pint, had found Dannie on the ground and slowly revived him with the Kinsey blended whiskey.

Dannie had awoken to Lyle Sesqu's crinkled, alcoholic face over him. It was a nice old, reddened face as it came into clearer focus in Dannie's black and blue, puffy eyes.

Lyle Sesqu had kept on asking what happened! What should he do? Who could he call?

Dannie had gained his footing, holding onto the neighborly arm, bloody mouth begging Mr. Sesqu not to alert his mother upstairs. She'd kill herself if she saw him like this. He scrambled, zigzagging down 39th, close to swearing he'd kill that Anna if he ever saw her again.

Pete's Radio Store had been hazy before him, and he brushed aside his baby-tears as he stumbled into the side door.

The pain from the beating had been coming on stronger to all parts of his body. He had hoped to find Johnny Squint, but instead was greeted by Hugo Duce, who pulled Dannie inside, ordering Reb to grab a beefsteak, raw, from Fiola's kitchen.

Johnny was downtown, on the west side of Manhattan. In his absence, Hugo tried to patch the kid up. He told Pete to get the kid's bike unchained and run it over with the car. Mangle it, make the mother think it was an accident.

"SO YOU'RE GOING TO FIGHT?" ELEANOR'S WITCH-craft-blue eyes fastened on her nephew like meat hooks as she sat across from him at the Vale breakfast table.

Dannie chewed with caution into his syrupy pancake, choking mentally on those two words that were screamed that night— "Josephine's uncle." It was true—he had to fight Scap, the scrappy ringleader of the trio that had jumped him. His damn aunt seemed to know about the upcoming fight. He thought he had his mother fooled, placated last night, bent, broken bicycle and all.

Dannie did not, would not admit to any fight, his jaw crackling on a forkful of pancake. His father, Roscoe, looked sullen at the table, while his shapely mother, so out of place in the drab congo-walled background of the kitchen, served, braless under her mint green housecoat, a look of lioness fear crossing her eyes. "Fight? What fight?"

"Tell us about it, Daniel," Eleanor taunted. "A double suicide, is that what you want? Eve, Eleanor laid out beside you when you're stabbed or shot in a common brawl." She finally irked Roscoe to a point where he roughly pushed away his plate of pancakes.

Roscoe Vale was fed up. "Get off the boy's back, Eleanor. He's big now. He's got broad shoulders of his own. He doesn't need a broad like you on them."

It's about time! Dannie wanted to shout, his father's lashing out at his arrogant sister-in-law years overdue.

"Maybe *he* doesn't need a *broad*!" Eleanor spat out at Roscoe. "But your uncontrolled salivary thoughts speak of two *ladies* that *you* dribble over!" She was a stunning, yet nasty portrait of sensual, sexual torment. "And stay out of this. It's not your affair!"

Roscoe's hawk nose seemed like a strung arrow to Dannie, aimed directly at Eleanor. "This is my house," Roscoe declared. "What goes on in it is *our* affair, *never* yours!"

"Your house!" Eleanor shot back, smirking. "You couldn't even afford Dannie's sofa-bed. *I* paid for it!" She half stood, as if ready to spring over the food-filled table. "You got a steady job years ago. *How*? I'd like to know. Meager but steady." She licked her moist lips as if part of a ritual bedazzling Roscoe. Dannie, eyes narrowed, noticed all.

Roscoe shrunk in his hard-backed kitchen chair. "You've been a trickster since the day we met," he said with passion. "Two for one," he now near-mumbled. "A lie from the beginning." His faint black eyes were weakly glued to her, as he skirted the touchy job reference.

Eve stood behind Dannie, her hands nervously caressing his shoulders. "I saw the bicycle," she spoke up, her hands roaming the rich strands of his black hair. "Twisted, spokes beyond repair. There was no fight." Dannie longed to get the hell up from his chair, but he wanted not only to hear his father and aunt getting into it, but maybe some morsels from the past.

"From the beginning?" Eleanor, almost purring, was now less outwardly belligerent to her brother-in-law. She knew the lust in Roscoe's heart and knew how to control it. "You wanted a peek-a-boo when certain skirts were above the knees." She was sweetly twisting his balls. "When certain *ladies* slowly, deliberately undressed in this dump."

Roscoe Vale sat still, wanting desperately to lash out at his deceptive bitch of a sister-in-law and the teary-eyed eye-carving of a woman, Eve—his *so-called* wife. But he sat quiet, enraged. The boy. Why make the boy hear all this garbage.

Dannie couldn't eat anymore. His stomach was doing somersaults. Where he got his damn delicate belly he didn't know. His mother was all over him, asking him to stay home, rest. Tonight they'd watch T.V. on the Sesqu's set. Little Stevie, Dannie's age, would be there. Dannie was wishing that his father would throw bitchy Eleanor out of the house and tell his wife Eve to go and . . . dress properly! He got up, grabbing for his gold-blue reversible jacket, wanting to be free of them!

Rosco picked up the *Daily News* from beside his half-filled plate. "Tend to the boy," he said to Eve. "You should know every mark, stitch or bruise on his body by now the way you . . ." He stopped for the boy's sake. His day would come. He shrunk with his newspaper into the ice-age of the bedroom.

Dannie slammed the kitchen door behind him.

"I'll track him down," Eleanor quipped merrily, sipping her coffee.

Eve stood and sighed. She was grateful that at least her sister was strong. She didn't know where she would be without Eleanor.

Outside, in the cold, Dannie headed for Pete's where, at least, he'd be in the company of *men*. He didn't feel like a . . . man as the scream of "Josephine's uncle!" engulfed him.

But amiable Pete advised Dannie that he might catch John by Walt's Diner on Ninth Avenue.

Walt's? Guess Pete's was getting "hot." Dannie trudged up residential 40th Street and saw the huge tree with big boughs and branches right across from Kathleen's stoop. He passed it, downcast, and made his way to the Diner.

Eleanor, right on Dannie's heels, arrived by Walt's just as he did.

Foremost among the sidewalk group in front of Walt's stood Johnny Squint, narrow-eyeing Dannie and then Eleanor, her sumptuous figure poised like a rocket.

The other men around him began to slither away, Reb, Al Rispone, and Gretti, hesitant, ogling Eleanor, an untamed shrew in an eye-peeling indigo bolero jacket. Eleanor wasn't for him, Gretti figured, at least not at this stage of the game, but *maybe* an opening would come. His face morose, he backed into Walt's, without so much as a glance at Dannie-boy.

"My sister has a sodden neighbor who saw no bicycle, Mr. Hoodlum," Eleanor sailed into Johnny. "Bad enough you're half a *mensch* who rapes the dead! Now you arrange a disgusting fight for *your* purposes, not caring if my nephew gets maimed!" She took a wild swing at Johnny, his jaw instantly inching back, and missed by a hair.

Dannie listened, watched, in shock, knowing for sure now that his aunt was a bona fide lunatic.

Johnny—all through it—had said nothing. He would never argue with a woman. But he wouldn't put up with her shit either, especially when his men weren't far behind the scene.

"Go with your aunt, Dannie," was all he said. To his surprise, they left.

All Johnny could think about as he sat down with Al, Gretti and Reb were Eleanor's two words. "*My sister.*" Eve, how he *wanted* her still. He envisioned her, a raven-haired hard-on-a-minute heat wave. How was he to solve a mystery whose green eyes said at a glance that they didn't have the slightest idea he was alive, but at a second look there was a possibility of sex inside of them, and at a half a minute study of them they told you *go headlong*?

The trip would be a sexual soul search that would last a never-ending fucking lifetime even if it were for just a minute of Her. Johnny gulped down his soggy BLT, feeling *sure*, although he had no master-plan, that a way would come along to fulfill his everlasting minute of Eve.

Again, through the boy.

THE MASTER HAD A PLAN, A PLOT. ANGEL TENUTO FELT sure that that was why Fran had come to him late last night telling him that Mr. Ed Lynch would be delighted to see him on the Funny Farm.

Augie had his one-sided, "Hiya, honey" intimate conversation with the Statue of Liberty as he did on all the days that he took the ferry trip from Manhattan to Staten Island to see his ostracized partner; the Manhattan ferry more jammed safely with people than the smaller Brooklyn one. He threw a half-wave hand salute to the Lady—until he would return at dusk.

Those who really care, and those who merely swear they care. The Actor went into it with Augie, thinking before he spoke as he walked on the mushy ground with his left arm around the sturdy shoulders of the younger man. He was talking about the thing that meant the most to him—his freedom—and those who might take it from him.

"Here I am. With a mustache on. It's getting gray. Truly brown. But dyed black. It's all part and parcel of what's known as my head. And what's on my Most Wanted head? A hell-of-a-CASH reward. For some hardworking son of a sea cock to collect. But why should any hard working man or gal turn me in? Because they care? Nope. They couldn't care less, bless their souls. It's for the *money*, the money. And I understand that perfectly! *That's* where the swearing and caring comes in. The way you find the difference between the two. The ones that care. And the ones that brag-swear they care. *Money draws the line!*"

Augie was rapt in attention, trying to digest fully Willie's way of precisely covering a subject.

Augie loved to hear "Slick Willie" expound his well-studied, jail-house-formulated philosophies. The two of them walked by the Mental-Farm Colony Hospital. Willie's New Springville lunch hour. They'd go later to the "Lynch upgraded" one-family home nearby in Westerleigh.

Both men couldn't break the prison habit of circle-walking, talk-ing-the-jail-term-away, switching their arms around one another's shoulders. They laughed about it now, as they had done on the tier during the days before the escape from that regimented, urine-infected Philly prison at Holmesburgh. Augie whiffed the potato farm country smell of Staten Island now, and he listened, trying to concentrate, to simmer his near insane rage at the thought of any-one turning in his friend.

The notorious Actor scuffed his black leather shoes, flat-heeled, no back upper-ankle enclosure, as he dragged them through a bit of rotted wood-marsh by the outskirts of the farm. "Angel," he contin-ued, "I never gambled in my life. Did you ever gamble *with* your life? Besides scientific bank robberies, and calculated 'House of Penance' break-outs. Well, we're gambling with our days now. With our benefactor, Frank, who gambles for the challenge, never for the money. Good ol' Mr. Costello, who'll die broke, but'll take what he knows to the grave. Only I feel that John, you, and I see a win with him!" Willie paused and then reflected on two other people who might affect his freedom: the 'twixt-and-between kid, Dannie, and his unaware-of-most-of-the-world mother, Eve.

The kid had caused Willie the confrontation with Al-burt. But the youngster was blameless. "The mother has it for Johnny," Willie commented, "whether she knows it or not. Deep in her loins. But both are Care-ers. Money doesn't even enter the picture. It's a rare portrait, but true." They went on emotions, not dollar signs, and had no need for a false, vicarious "claim to fame" through betrayal, Willie concluded. The kid lives for Johnny, you can read it in his eyes. The mother *living* for the boy—Johnny being the tie-in.

Now for the plot: Augie felt it in his gut while Willie explained it.

Al-burt: No amount of money would satisfy him, or even his flashy habit for gaudy diamonds.

Don Vito Genovese: there aren't enough maneuvers on the globe to appease his love of daily-guile.

"So, we keep Uncle Frank on top and put Johnny . . . elevate him to, for now . . . CAPTAIN. The both of them have no love for 'Pens.' They would solidify their plans by aligning themselves with three powerful Costello Group Skippers.

"Tuzio: Brooklyn. Likes owning bars. Well, he'll get his fill.

"The Sheik: Lower East Side, Manhattan. The strong old-timer adores country-hopping." Willie would fund the trips.

"Sally (G.) Burns: Shot it out as a kid with the opium-piper killer of Dutch Schultz, Charlotuzz. Sally goes for the skirts. He'll have all the dames he can handle."

"What do we get in return?" Willie prompted. "These three feared captains vote to upgrade Johnny Squint. What can Al-burt do? His crew is as far removed from Uncle Frank's as the Sioux Indian Nation is from Norway." Willie and Angel shared a smile.

What move would Don Vito make? Willie's analysis was in high gear. Approve it, for John had saved Mr. G's slippery ass from New York's electric chair.

"And what do we get? Respect!" Angel snarled his agreement as Willie continued.

"Because Johnny, come spring, as a Captain, has more sway within his own set of people, as well as a little more push with greedy Mr. A!"

And now for The Actor's *pièce de résistance*. "How do we do all this?" He took a deep breath for emphasis. "Simple. We do it through the tested genius of a man, who through his late, tough rascal of a partner Bugsie Seigel built Las Vegas." Angel was right with him. "This same Wiz," he went on to explain, "co-founded, along with Luciano and V.G., the Costello Group. The man I refer to? The greatest economist since St. Paul built the Roman Catholic Church: Mr. Meyer Lansky." Willie had contributed generously to help Lansky fund his homeland Israel's *Hagannah*, which had put Sutton on his good side. Angel loved it. Willie planned to collect the necessary nest from the Brinks caper through his friend Oscar up in New England, and a hit in March on Maiden Lane, safe deposit boxes, downtown Manhattan's Wall Street hordes.

With Lansky on their side, Al-burt would be off balance, and Vito appeased.

Augie carried the framework of Willie's plan in his head as he rode the ferry back.

Vito retains his stature as Underboss and keeps the treachery in his blood.

Albert, who the Kentucky Mint couldn't contain, stays steadily on his greedy path.

But John, come spring, goes from street Dunsky to a *Capitano*'s chair. And we go from. . .slaps—Willie had nearly cringed—to respect, which borders on fear, to the premium of keeping our freedom.

A multifarious process to keep Willie Sutton in a "hands off" position insured by the underlying line of life—MONEY! Augie knew that as long as Johnny (whose aged "Made Man" father, Felice, went back over thirty years with Willie) was alive, kicking, and well, then the little world he and Willie hid in would be full of the "those-who-care" types. Augie paused in his thought and suddenly did an impromptu Cha-Cha on the ferry deck, his arm crazily extended across the water to the Green Lady, beckoning her "to join him." Augie's "dance" ended, and he swore, as the ferry bumped its way into the slip, that the minute anyone so much as looked crooked at Johnny Mazziotta, he would pistol-blow their hearts to bits . . . whether it was hankie-snot-filled Gretti and his private clique, or Albert A., the *Kill Him* King himself. Augie gut-carried that vow as the Statue of Liberty receded into the distance.

DANNIE, THAT MORNING, HAD BROKEN AWAY FROM crazed Eleanor once they rounded Ninth Avenue's corner.

He wouldn't even talk to her, he was that humiliated by the irrational way she had behaved at Walt's Diner.

He had sprinted up New Uthrecht Avenue, not stopping until he reached the Borough Park Theater. There had been no trace of "weird-her" behind him, he lingered, his eyes occasionally on the shoes of a passing girl. Crepe rubber soled. Maybe he just couldn't look girls in the eye. Dannie circumvented his aunt's apartment house. Now he stood by the Windsor Movie Theater, where *Race Street* was playing, clocking a Hudson Sedan gearing by.

He didn't have the keys to his own house. He was still "too young."

Dannie felt awkward standing, hanging around the Sixteenth Avenue Movie House. He had seen *Race Street*. With George Raft and William Bendix. "Georgie," as Reb referred to him, played a gambler, and Dannie had his fill today of being degraded in front of professional gamblers. He shuffled along, wondering if he should talk to his father about the fight to come, get some boxing pointers?

But his father, with that Esquire Boot Polish black hair that was now streaking gray, was so pent up nowadays, a victim of two frenzied women. Dannie reached his aunt's 38th Street corner. She was standing there, an overwhelming sight of black textured hair—the sweep and fall of it. He was still furious at her, *frustrated*.

That was it, he told himself. That was the key to Eleanor. Tired, hungry, and cold, he went up to her apartment with her.

"You know what your problem is, Eleanor?" he began. "You hate Johnny. You hate me. You hate my father. You hate all men, that's why you're so frustrated!"

She was unbuttoning her jacket and shaking out her hair, her eyes burning-blue as he spoke. "You're a frustrated woman, Aunt Eleanor. That's why you pick on all of us. You don't go out with men. So you torment them." He was set for a "battle royal."

But before she could go maniacal on him, they both heard Eve's mortuary traumas coming from the bedroom. They rushed to soothe her.

Dannie knew his mother would be there, but hadn't expected to hear her sleeping, tossing, crying out with half-gagged murmurs of her still being alive!

By nightfall, he felt trapped. Where to go? Eleanor's voice filtered from the bedroom . . . about a "Ruby" helping financially so that they could move to a more decent, a cleaner neighborhood. The living room seemed to darken as he thought, daydreamed of Johnny's "unspeakable act" . . . of Kathleen's brim-hipped, pure, white skirts.

He realized he was freezing, the darn cast iron steam radiators mute and the small windows frozen-tight, fit to crack. He got up and searched the stacked refrigerator for some snacks and couldn't wait for his water to boil on the gas range for some Nestlé's Hot Cocoa.

He wolfed down half a cold meat loaf, loads of Silvercup bread, and a small jar of pimento peppers. Bang! A steam-pipe or radiator jolted him. It reminded him of Benny Napanack crying that the joints—jails—were so cold in wintertime that when that Bang! was heard, the cons would yell "that even the rats were bangin' for heat!" Dannie washed the snack down with a quart of tasty Mission Cream Soda, and then sipped his melted marshmallow-topped hot chocolate. The room warmer now, he didn't need the chenille bed-spread he had fished out from the top shelf of his aunt's neat closet.

He lay on the couch, stretched, partially undressed. He must be getting even taller, he noted, his bare feet extended over the couch's edge. He caught the arousing scent of his aunt's perfume and looked up. *Attrazione sessuale!* He lay frozen as before.

Eleanor sat on the couch's nearer edge, moodily contrite, his mother sedated in the bedroom. It had been such an argumentative day, Eleanor's touchiness sometimes leapt out of bounds. But now she was adorned in a camisole of golden hue, matching scalloped, laced half-slip, her bare legs more than subliminal, vivified excite-ment in the still living room.

"What do you want, Eleanor?" he left-handed his gray-green checkered shirt from off the rug, covering his boxer shorts.

"The same thing as you," the gleam in her eyes as if insane. She had shed the light dressing jacket, revealing a double laden white-pink feast of a different kind of "snack."

If he opened his mouth to speak again he might just find her tongue in it. He lay cursing himself, wishing something would hap-pen to stop this!

But they took Antoinette from him. He'd never even touch Kathleen. Why the hell shouldn't he have his beckoning aunt, her insanity seemingly affecting him, too. She was voluptuous, willing enough. What the *hell*!

She was all honeyed-nipples, a rich redolence of thighs, lipstick-less lips, murmuring that he should "hold out from other girls forev-er!" Her breath, honey itself. Her words seething that he was "the only one for her!" She was rolling him over on top and he came inside his boxer shorts. She started stroking the back of his damp hair, and all he could do was wish that "Josephine's uncle" and the older-fello rieder Scap would *mash* in his testicles during the fight to come!

1952

February

Hugo Duce was short of stature but long on loyalty. If his partner Johnny Squint had a special feeling for the kid, Dannie, he was going to be good to him too.

And given that cold trio, the virginal mother, nutsy aunt and sullen father, this kid could use all the help he could get! Hugo, taking a drag on his Philip Morris cigarette, shot a glance at Pete's large, round, black-edged clock. 8:00 a.m. The "square-off" was slated for 10:00 a.m.—a pot-shot at Al-burt. Time to get back at the animal slap. Beating up on the kid. A "show" that Borough Park, *John's Borough Park*, was going to keep, no matter how trivial the incident, RESPECT. Hugo would have burly Mush, the part-time barkeep at Fiola's, do the driving, while two of Johnny's brothers, Jamesie and Pietro M., would come along, it being beneath John himself to be there after subtly arranging it. Hugo hoped that the kid had followed the instructions about squeezing hand grips, rubber balls, shadow-boxing, sparring, or he'd better have a fuckin' prayer-book in his dungaree pocket.

Hugo flicked an ash on a dusty, tagged, repaired radio on Pete's work-bench, the clock above reading 8:20 a.m.

Dannie searched for Kathleen, finding her on her way to Catholic High School. He wanted, needed, heaven's divine intervention in the crucial matter of his much too encroaching aunt and his own sickening, sacreligious flashes that were polluting his heart. He stammered by her bus stop, her hazel-eyed girlfriend Gloria beside her. Finally, he got it out. "Would you pray extra hard for an . . . *intention* of mine?"

"Is your intention to win the fight in Prospect Park this morning?" Kathleen said without being strictly inquisitive, but with sincerity.

"No. Not that fight."

"Then I'll pray extra hard for it, whatever it is. But if it doesn't come true it's because God doesn't want it to come true. He has better reasons in the long run of His reign than we have in the short run of our lives."

The things she said and the way she said them were years beyond her real age, and they gave Dannie an unexplained feeling of absolution.

"Why don't you just kick the crap out of that South Brooklyn creep," Gloria, her brown eyes lively like holiday lights, practically elbowed her way between Kathleen and Dannie by the crowded bus stop. "And I'll light a few candles for you." She was smiling, openly flirting, a radiant, white-outfitted coquette.

Dannie nearly choked on Gloria's language and behavior. Kathleen remained patronizing through it all.

"Do you know Christie?" Kathleen said, holding her stacked textbooks against her emblazoned, white high school sweater. "Or, Dapper?"

He knew who she meant, but felt Gloria so close beside him that he began recoiling, his face flushed. It suddenly dawned on him that *civettare* Gloria was not only Kathleen's girlfriend but the sister of the neighborhood fruitcake, hounding, deranged Rocco Bruzzese. Dannie felt the left side of Gloria's firm bust pressing against his right bicep. But he stood his ground—Rocco had it coming. Kathleen was serene, with no visible trace of jealousy, but she inched closer to Dannie. "Christie, Dapper, Sailor, they went to Catholic Grammar School with me," she said as her bus was pulling to the curb. "Christie would help anyone. He's God-fearing. Dapper would help anyone too. He's crazy-nice. He chided about Our Lord, but he never fooled me. He goes deep." Dannie, carefully holding her right elbow, was helping Kathleen, guiding her up the steps of the bus. He watched as she showed her school pass. Gloria, on tip-toe, quickly kissed him good-luck on his warm lips before the bus doors folded shut, encasing both girls.

God has reasons for what almost happened? Dannie wondered, feeling almost caught in Eleanor's . . . net? Gloria . . . from out-of-the-blue being an answer to . . . but finally, through his confused wonderings, the reality of the *fight* dawned on him, and Dannie got scared, wishing now he had trained for it! He thought of Antoinette. Would she be watching him getting his head beat in again? He hesitantly, at first, then more firmly, made the sign of the cross! It couldn't hurt.

On the drive to Prospect Park along Greenwood Cemetery, with staunch Mush driving, fedora'd Hugo up front in the passenger seat, Dannie sat in the rear, between ruddy-faced, jovial Jamesie Mazziotta—Kathleen's father—and Pietro M., another of John's brothers. Hugo, half turning, advised Dannie: "*Remember* that these wiry, Ox-bastard kids left you for dead. Let it work on you. Let it steam you up as you're squaring off!"

An involuntary cold-shock shudder hit Dannie. He knew, through mostly his father's habitually reading the *New York Daily News* aloud, that teen-age gang wars were flaring, flourishing, and organized street and park warfare was more prevalent in Brooklyn than in any of the other four New York boroughs. Dannie squinted into the sunlight, seeing little Stevie Sesqu, who aspired to be his second, running along the grassy path of the cemetery.

Dannie clenched his fists. *He should have trained with Stevie.* Boxed, feigning punches, jabs, without landing a blow. Looking for openings. Trying to outflank the opponent. Build upwind storage, stamina during the fake bouts.

"Get hopped up, Dannie," Hugo prepped. "Remember also with every punch how your mother took food out of her mouth and clothes off her back to raise you. They could have *killed you!*"

Hugo sat, faced the glaring windshield. He thought of the kid's tie-in to Willie Sutton's 1947 escape. Mr. Kill-Them-All—Albert A.—would love to see this possible "tie-in kid" dead in an everyday, delinquent gang *lotta*. That way there'd be no "Sit" with the Costello-Genovese Group. Hugo chewed on the paper-tipped Philip Morris, not bothering to light it.

"Get their fuckin' respect," cherub-cheeked Jamesie Mazziotta pushed on to Dannie. "Bite this scrapper Scap's fucking ear off 'till you can taste the blood." Mush, driving the tan DeSoto, grunted, the car reaching the park's entrance on Coney Island Avenue. "And here's a gimmick, kid," Hugo half turned again in his seat, handing

Dan a bronze-colored Ronson cigarette lighter. "Palm it," he said. "If you're losing. Whack him with it, closed tight in your fist."

Dannie took the lighter, squeezed it.

"And keep this last thing in your head, Dannie," Pietro M. muttered through a haze of pipe smoke. "You get ganged-up on and do nothing about it, it's like sending out invitations that you don't assert yourself. Sure, you can't join a gang. Your mom'd see that and die from heartbreak. But you sure as hell don't want to advertise that anyone can get away with engraved invitations to strike you silly whenever they want."

Pietro M.'s words drummed inside him. Dannie squeezed the lighter even harder, his right fist going from red to white. He wouldn't forget to use it when he had to. He wasn't going to be anybody's whipping boy.

Now it was waiting time in the DeSoto by the Ninth Street side of the park, close to Walkon Swan Lake.

Close to noon, Joe "The Blond" Gallo, ringleader Scap, and the South Brooklyn Boys arrived at the park en masse. Scap, in the vanguard, looked a little taller than Dannie remembered, and Joe a little meaner—if that was possible.

They were strutting because they knew just where they wanted to be—recruited into one of the City's Crews with their strongholds in South Brooklyn.

There was a 1950 green Buick Dynaflow parked within Dannie's sight with four or five men in it.

"Who's that in the Buick?" Jamesie Mazziotta asked Hugo.

Hugo shrugged, his fine cord Brooks suit showing nary a wrinkle. "Who knows who's in it. Brothers, relatives. Joseph, Tough Tony, Umberto Jr.? These fucking Anastasia relations all look alike. Even the priest."

"Fuck them all," Mush hunched over the wheel, reminding Dannie of a gigantic canon ball that you couldn't budge.

Jamesie slapped Dannie on the thigh. "Okay, kid, go ahead."

"Kill the cocksucker," said pipe-smoking Pietro M.

Dannie gulped twice as he left the car, tight-lipped little Stevie, his downstairs neighbor, huffing and puffing for breath beside him. They sauntered up to the lake, twenty or more boys grouping around Scap in a semi-circle. Scap, slim waist, barrel chest, waited till both kids reached him.

"Brought your skinny girlfriend with ya?" Scap smiled, gesturing to Stevie.

No, Dannie nodded, his fists clenched by his sides. Beware of the sucker punch. The first one. Johnny himself had forewarned, "Don't let that street-fightin' kid goad you into a wild swing, or relax you! Catch *him* off guard and daydreaming!"

Cocky, vicious Joey Gallo stood inches from Dannie. His pale blue eyes magnetic, amused.

"Then where's your gang, pretty boy?" Scap spoke low, huskily. "I hear you got kids with crust in your neighborhood." Scap gestured to a bull-sized, ready-to-go boy, without taking his eyes from Dannie. "That's 'Bang-Bang' over there. He's got an ax-choppin' cousin in your shithead area. A guy named Dapper. Know him?"

Don't let Scap relax you. "Not to talk to."

"The worse for you," Scap said. "It ain't polite fightin' friends of friends. You ever see the leader, Christie, where you live? A sleek killer-diller. Ever talk to him?"

"Never."

Scap laughed. *Beware the sucker punch.* "You don't talk to many people." He was ditty-bopping to the strain of some unheard rhythm when the boys in his gang started closing in. The loud slamming honks from Mush in Hugo's car stopped them.

They backed off.

"What the hell. Christie, Dapper, Sailor, Billy Gee and all them North Brooklyn boys wouldn'a come anyhow if you asked 'em. Word is you're a namby-pamby, a *Madre's ragazzo*."

That did it for Dannie. He wasn't sending out any engraved invitations to get his head bashed in again. He remained outwardly cool. It was three against one last time around. Scap was all heel and toe movements before him, dancing to an imagined musical moondogger rhythm. Dannie had the courage anew to fight this Scap. "The North Street Boys would have come," Dannie was looking for an opening, "but all I need is to wipe you out!" He threw a punch between Scap's eyes, a good right cross, following up with a swift kick to Scap's left shin. Continuing his offensive, he charged into Scap, both of them toppling and tumbling down to the lake.

Scrappin' Scap fought with a wealth of experience on his side. And he was over-confident, as he struggled on the wet ground next to the lake with Dannie, scissor-pinning the kid's long legs with his— he wasn't going to give him another chance to use them for kicking. Scap elbowed Dannie's chest, and the sides of his jawbone hard, all the while gripping both of Dannie's wrists with his hands. He was waiting for the grappling chance to exert his husky-body weight, roll on top of this "Ladies Man" kid, get a clear field, and pound away at a face that was too fuckin' good-lookin' to begin with.

Dannie fought with "never sending out any engraved invitations to smash him around" in mind. He didn't have the liability of having a glory reputation to uphold, so instead of mustering his strength, he was breaking loose from the close-quartered struggle, his sweaty wrists sliding and twisting out of Scap's grip. Finally, Dannie had them free. Scap was concentrating on throwing close-in punches, but his scissor hold around Dannie was relaxing, becoming forgetful to the point where Dannie had wangled out of it and was up on his feet.

Nothing had really happened yet, but the South Brooklyn Boys were gritting, two, three of them cheering with vehemence. The memory of his previous beating kept flashing in Dannie's mind—the kicks in the head he had gotten then. He stood now and aimed a knee-snapping kick with the front of his shoe to Scap's half-bent neck.

But he didn't stop there. He couldn't. It would be suicide if he did. He started the dirty fighting! He stomped Scap on the side of the head twice, before his opponent could get a quick hold on his foot and throw him backwards, off balance.

The decision was made. It would be hit and back away. Kick and spin away. No in-fighting for Dannie. In a wrestling match Scap would be a rib-breaker without a bit of mercy.

Dannie stepped away after the two kicks. His mistake. Scap was up and facing him. But instead of charging headlong, Scap caught the kid's science of staying away, so he boxed him. Jabbing, jabbing with his hammering left. Taunting him with that extended left, then whamming a right hook to Dannie's forehead, backstepping three inches, coming in again with stinging left jabs.

How far could Dannie run from all this? Hugo Duce and Company were watching from the tan DeSoto. But Scap was a determined scrapper. His arms, shoulders, stooped, huddled, he had the in-reach, one that was keeping Dannie, who had the height, from getting in, not too close, but close enough to get a good sock in. He kept fencing, feinting back, breathing through his nose like in his Pershing Junior High School days when he had hit the speed bag. But he was in a pickle, all he could mostly see was Scap's wavy headed hair. He was going to lose this fight. More than that, he was going to get body-pummelled, get the ever living shit kicked out of him so badly once Scap had him on his knees—on his back. Scap kicked his right knee, the pain of it bringing a throat-held excruciating scream that made him twist twice around, faltering two feet backwards, but still blessedly standing painfully on his buckling legs.

He saw Scap coming in for the kill, charging him, head half-down, going for the *stomaco*.

Dannie, bending, right and left, short uppercutted the belly close in front of him. It was working. He felt Scrap resorting again to a wrestle hold, trying to fling him away. But Dannie held on for dear life, both of them scrambling on the ground's slope, rolling, wheeling bumpy into the lake.

The water was dry ice cold, and fish-slimy. Dannie was sliding in two feet of it. His shoes slippery on the moss, slime-smooth rocks. Scap gained his own footing, while grabbing a triangular rock in his hands. The blow caught Dannie's left shoulder, sending him twirling deeper into the water.

It was a shrill scream that he heard before he went full under, Scap poised above him, growling, holding the rock high above his head. A girl's scream! He sunk underwater, the force of the rock nailing the back of his right shoulder through the slight pressure barrier of the water. He surfaced, Scap searching for another rock, his hands under the water.

The scream had to be Antoinette's, Dannie felt. Suddenly he caught sight of the Ronson lighter floating downward. He hadn't forgotten it. He had it tight-palmed, clutched, hauling off a big roundhouse right.

It landed smack into Scap's nose, the blood spurting onto the two of them. Dannie, elbowing Scap away, reached for a smaller, sharper rock a half a foot from the brownish, curb-like shore.

He was going straight for the side of Scap's head with the rock in his hand, when the swarthy hands of a boy called "Allie," the third boy who had originally jumped him, held Dannie's hand, tearing the rock from it.

"It's two against one!" Dannie heard, his head reeling. It was Stevie who had yelled from a teeny slope, as he scrambled down to the lake.

The 1950 Buick honked loudly. It heralded that the fight was over!

Hugo, flipping a lit Philip Morris in the murky lake, actually trotted up to Dannie's side, congratulating him. "You could've killed that chimpanzee Scap. Good work. Got your honor back and scared those greasy bastards."

As Dannie spoke to Hugo, Anna Banana approached him. She was decked in a white shawl, a gold blouse, and a tight, matching gold skirt which came down just above her bare knees. "You kicked the fuck out of Scap, and the four horses he rode in on," she said. "One knock in the brain with that pointy rock ready in your hand and that would've been the beginning of the end.

"I told my Uncle Joseph to call it off."

Dannie turned to her, incredulous, his rocket adrenalin flow far from settling. "Why the heck are you here? Where's Antoinette?"

Hugo, impatient, pulled a cigarette from his crumpled pack. He recognized Josephine as Anastasia's niece and it made him edgy. "Let's go, Dannie-boy. We'll clean you up and break bread with Johnny."

Dannie looked from Hugo to Anna and back again. "It's okay, Hugo. Give Johnny *mi place molto* for arranging this. I'm going to dry off . . . hang around for a while till the welts go down."

Hugo didn't like it, but gave his buck-toothed smile anyway and walked slowly back to the DeSoto.

Dannie thought about stopping him. Should he tell Hugo that it may have been the phlegmy rattle of *Gretti's* voice whispering he heard that night . . . *Gretti* standing like a viper by the curb the night . . . he was *attacked*? Maybe he shouldn't. The last time he mentioned seeing somebody it wound up a *disturbo*, Mr. Lynch getting clobbered in Fiola's.

Dannie watched as the tan DeSoto wheeled away, Pietro M. giving him the thumbs-up signal through the open side window. Dannie smiled, feeling as if his entire swollen face might explode.

Prospect Park, 526 acres, the largest in Brooklyn, became Dannie's refuge. He walked with Anna slowly up a steep, winding hill. Lying down, soaked, drenched through-and-through, he began feeling the throbbing pains in all his muscles. His body, black-and-blue; his face, puffy and welted.

He lay that evening in the low grass, protected from open view by a clump of wooded brush.

He had spread every stitch of his bloody clothing out on the sparse grass, his faded dungarees hanging from a low branch. Even his shoes had been so water-logged that they had squished as Anna led him to the secluded spot.

Anna's white-crocheted, heavy shawl was wrapped around him. He couldn't see if there were any stars above in the freezing sky. There were too many boughs in his way. While his teeth clattered, he smiled warmly to himself, thinking of Stevie.

"Piggie" Sesqu, Pop, the "cuts" watchman named Stevie. The old city "treasure hunter" had often spied Stevie by the freight yards taking girls' temperatures—with popsicle sticks, the playful girls' panties down past their bottoms, the smooth sticks as thermometers inside their rectums. Dannie had seen Stevie do it once with plump Joan Martin, when they were six, right on Ninth Avenue on a Pontiac's running board. Dannie stopped chuckling to himself. Stevie was at least a friend today—the only young one Dannie had. Spunky Stevie had now come through. Anna interrupted Dannie's reverie, pawing at his square-backed, duck's-ass dampened hair, while sitting on the dirt beside him.

He looked directly at her for a few moments. Leggy. Brown, satiny, shoulder-length hair. But as blind as he was, he couldn't miss her nose. The darkness didn't matter. It loomed larger than ever. But she had said before, while walking (him wobbling) up here, that she had done something that she never thought of doing in her entire life. She had swallowed her shitty pride and apologized: for his original unfair beating, for her belting him in the face, for his bicycle being demolished, for her completely nasty attitude ever since she had met him. But at least she hadn't told her uncle about the punch he had given her, and she had made Joe "the Blond," Scap, Antoinette, and the other two boys that night swear they would never utter a single word about it.

How did she know about his bike being crushed? Gretti? . . . Little Mike? Dannie shivered, but not only from the winter weather, he was thinking now . . . *Did she lead me here to be ambushed?*

"I don't really understand you, An—Josephine," popped from his mouth.

"I like you," she was dead-serious. "You're pretty. Nice and touchable. Great black hair," she was teasing, tracing it with her fingertips. "You're streamlined even with your face cut."

"You . . . like me? You sure show it in a strange way." His head ached, pounded from the stinging punches he had taken from Scap, and his right shin felt like it would hurt forever.

"I want you to do to me what you did to Antoinette."

"You're kidding!"

"Let me tell you something," she was lulling. "I ran to my Uncle Joseph in the car and asked him to stop the fight when you were losing."

Dannie softened, eyeing, near to squinting at his powder blue checkered shirt running with colors and his favorite reversible jacket both spread out on the hill's dying grass. He could be in no rush to leave. His thoughts drifted to Antoinette's erotic, slack-packed crotch—the Eighth Wonder of his world. Anna Banana could see "Antoinette" plainly heaven-written all over Dannie's face.

"Antoinette knew nothing about this scheduled fight," Anna pushed frankly. "I made sure no one told her. You can hide your disappointment between my bouncing boobs or broken ass." They both laughed at that, Dannie wondering, *K.H.*'s *Kin*—niece. He was now more aware of his naked chilliness beneath the shawl. Anna sat comfy, *close*, pensive. He welcomed the feel of her body. She kicked off her gold leather Prima Ballets.

"We don't have much time," she lay on her side, sharing the shawl with him. "There's a gang war, a free-for-all set here for tonight. Red Hook and putrid Gowanus are warring Garfield and South Brooklyn. Five against five. A fair fight."

For a lingering moment, Anna looked bitter, almost as if she were world-weary, ready to throw in the towel. "WhadamI saying 'fair fight'? Fair fight my sinless swingin' rear cheeks. You'll read about it tomorrow. Especially empty-headed Scap tryin', I bet, to prove himself again. Begin as a scrap, grow to a tangle, and end up a slugfest with bats, zip guns. A couple of guys dead. You'll see."

Dannie was thrown by her sudden vulnerability. He still wished Anna was long, brown-eyelashed Antoinette. Or maybe better, Kathleen. Clean Kathleen. Or even that chestnut haired Gloria, such a delectable, kissable flirt. Someone to rid him of the resplendent bustline's natural confectionary fragrances of his docile mother and rapturous aunt. He was near choking from inner disgust.

Anna tenderly tended his "battle wounds." She delicately rubbed his shoulders, which were numb from the two rocks Scap had blasted him with. Then, she planted kisses on all his injuries. His hands, deadened from hammering fists, seemingly without circulation. His legs, calves, joints, bones aching like all damn hell.

"Was I really the first one to kiss you?" he asked for want of having anything better to say. He was frazzled at the prospect of what was to come with her—Albert Anastasia's *blood*, causing him a curdling afterthought.

"Who told you that!" She was undressing in the dusk, her golden blouse-front half open, revealing the bounteous curve of her breasts.

"I was just asking." He turned on his side. "I think you have more complexes than me. What are you snapping at?" He tried to figure what was really in her *diavolo* heart.

"How could you have a complex?" She was practically kneeling over him, her blouse off. "You have it made in the shade. You can live high on the hog with your handsome looks. I live like a *porco* in a sty." Her bra slipped past her arms onto the shawl, her caged desire loosened along with the glossy garment.

He was trying to get past her gargantuan beak to kiss her. His hand drifted down to her hip as she side-unzipped her golden skirt, revealing an hourglass shape.

She lay on top of him. Both were quivering, but she was going into a taunting "vision" of her own with an O'Henry candy bar that she slid from the top of her white bloomers. The kisses they were trading—he had found her wide mouth—were savage. She murmured that his depthless blue eyes belied him being all Italian. She flung the caramel coated candy bar into the hilly weeds, savoring the wrapper in her right hand.

She wanted to jerk-off his pecker with the wrapper around it—no mess. Her bloomers, juice-hot, were down to her bare ankles, as she kissed his ear, eyes. In five minutes he would be making love for the First Time. She was sighing, moaning that he's so romantic, he must have relatives in far away France too. She was teasingly stroking him, and he was on the verge of ejaculation, hearing rhythmic cheers mixed with uneven out-cries.

They both heard warpath shouts. The shots Dannie heard were blasts coming from the thunder of the clouds.

"Maybe we'll 'French-fuck,' " Anna was hurrying, the wrapper jerking loose. "Do you know how to do that?"

Know how? He didn't even know what it was.

Suddenly, there was heavy rustling in the grass by them. Must be a scout from Al-bert Anastasia's troops, Dannie thought as he saw the face of his mother before him, shrouded in torment at the way he had been killed. He held Anna even tighter—they'd have to shoot one to get to the other. But the nearby rustling had come from little Stevie Sesqu.

"Dannie! Let's get out of here," Stevie combat-crawled through the brittle woods. "There's a gang war on! They shot one and stabbed another one by the concert mall. They're scattering in all directions. Over a hundred of 'em. Come on!"

"I thought you went home," Dannie wanted to kiss him, Anna still on top of him. The howling down below by the band mall was louder and wilder.

"I never left." Stevie was flat on his stomach. "I got right out of that DeSoto by Park Circle. I didn't trust those jap South Brooklyn boys. I ran back and was behind a big tree and saw you coming up here. I've been hiding, watching you to make sure . . ."

"You've been peeping!" Anna sprung like a leopard, pulling at Stevie's hair. She was scorching-mad, barefoot kicking and side-fist punching him. "You little punk! You've been listening and watching me?"

"Not you," Stevie was trying to save the roots of his hair from being pulled out. He was gagging on the candy bar, the O'Henry half in, half out of his mouth, trying to hold Anna's hands, whimpering from her pulling.

"Let's go!" Dannie was up, had Anna around her midriff. "Your folks'll murder you for being here." He grappled with Anna, his words causing her to let go of Stevie and follow him.

"You're both . . ." Stevie called, choking on the tossed-away candy bar sticking in his throat, ". . . balls-ass naked!" Then he cut the hell out. Dannie froze in his tracks. He grabbed at his clothes on the patchy grass and branches. They were boards, starched-scarecrow frozen. Anna quickly scooped up her own strewn clothes, bundling them two-handed. They ran, slid down the hill opposite the mall's direction, police sirens wailing in the distance.

Quickly, they made it out of the park in the hectic night to Prospect Park West. Both still bare-assed.

SUNDAY IS A DAY THAT MAKES YOU FEEL LIKE YOU already died. It's an empty, casket day waiting for you to fill it. That's how Dannie felt the following morning on his way to St. Agnes High Mass with his mother.

Kathleen was in church. Her face was three quarters covered by her white kerchief. Too timid to say hello, she had her head bowed, unable to acknowledge to Dannie's mother—she was *Johnny's niece*!

But her girlfriend Gloria Bruzzese, on the wide marble steps outside the church, wasn't a bit shy at all. She smiled and kissed Dannie's mouth, giggling, and then touched the bruised, swollen knuckles of both his hands. "That South Brooklyn geep had a *gabordorsk* head." Turning respectfully to Eve, she added, "Good morning, Mrs. Vale. I'll wager God was delighted to see someone as splendid as you decorating His church today."

Dannie laughed, hearing, feeling his jawbone creak, and he eyed Gloria for her gracious compliment to his mother.

But he looked straight at Kathleen, having a sorrowful recollection of her when she had turned up at his twelfth birthday party and was rejected by his mother, his aunt ripping the twenty dollar bill in a card from John. Dannie suddenly felt his mother clasping his left arm, pulling him away, but he turned back to the two girls up on the steps. "See ya later."

"Swell," Gloria was speaking for both of them, her felt shoulder strapped pocketbook bouncing against her right hip as she swayed down the steps of St. Agnes.

On his way home, safe in Borough Park, Dannie wasn't proud of defying his mother by being courteous to the two girls, but it had to be done. He thought he sensed a twinge of *geleso* in his mother's sparkling green eyes. Heading toward the corner of Eighth and 39th, he spotted Johnny by the chromed red Rocket Olds. He and his mother were heading directly toward him.

Dannie listened to the one-sided instant collision, his eyes on Johnny's Brito brown-on-brown shoes.

Eve blamed John for her son's gashes and cuts. "What are you going to be teaching him this time around?" she shouted.

John leaned silent against the passenger window of his car, listening to Eve's tirade.

And he couldn't help but observe. Her checked-white mixed sweater, chain linked on top. A silken bra underneath. She didn't need one at all.

Her skirtline created an excitement in Johnny's head that would make his day a blur. He always did a double take on seeing her. While Eve ranted on, Johnny thought how a woman doesn't rule "wearing the pants"—*she'd rule with them off.* Inflamed, he was that close to kissing her *mouth shut,* except for the presence of the kid. Suddenly she was finished and she gusted away like a Nevada A-Bomb test blast.

Roscoe Vale, at home, read the thick, Sunday newspaper.

One youth dead in Prospect Park. James Fortunato. Eighteen years old, of 436 Seventh Avenue. Shot!

Roscoe leaned back heavy against the kitchen chair, his relaxing, escaping newspaper reading day, filling the gap of Sunday's emptiness. Another youth, Vento, was in fair condition, taken to Methodist Episcopal Hospital after the park teenage gangwar. He breathed a sigh of relief. The boy, Dannie, was alive. *Ringraziare Dio!*

After Eve and Dannie returned home, and they ate a sparse ziti macaroni and gravy dinner, Roscoe continued to flip the paper's pages, the reading seemingly a way now to ease the heart-breaking silence between the trio.

Eve washed the dishes in the tiny kitchen sink, Dannie helping towel them dry.

"This Vento is seventeen," Roscoe read, paraphrasing at intervals. "His assailants escaped."

Dannie was close to wiping the mockingbird designs off of the plates as he listened. "Don't mention such things in front of the boy," his mother admonished.

"Does this mean we're speaking now?" Roscoe Vale turned on his chair.

Eve nodded a slow yes as she sudsed and soaked the utensils.

"Terrific," he rose. "I'll be in the bedroom. Maybe you'll break down further among your sleeping memories in there."

"Don't speak that way in front of Dannie," Eve flared.

At that, Roscoe looked broken, his thin face and hawk nose a portrait of one of the muted birds on a dish Dannie was wiping.

Roscoe had his head a little ways down, but Dannie could see that his father was trying to arrest the flare in his patience-exhausted brown eyes.

Later, Roscoe tried to fend off Eve's inquiries: Why did Daniel arrive home so late last night, runny nose, so beaten. "Is he prone to accidents?"

"You should know all his bumps, have them pinpointed, any cut of the lip," Roscoe had bitterly countered. "You crawl alongside him often enough." He grabbed his shaggy black sport jacket lying on the oversized bed, briskly made it to the kitchen door, and slammed it shut on his *way out*, leaving lovely mother and "child" in the makeshift living room.

DANNIE HEARD THE FULL STORY ON THE STREET, where full stories are bred. The corner of Eighth and 40th.

His mother couldn't face him after what his father had repeated, again, so he had hit the streets.

The police had pugnacious Scap for accidentally shooting Fortunato! Alleged manslaughter.

The District Attorney, McDonald, was making a big thing out of it, saying he was going to crack down on kids with weapons. Bullshit.

Dannie, cold-sniffling, began edging toward Fiola's, but Hugo Duce told him to stay put. Johnny was coming back with a reward for him.

All the boys were hanging out. Reb, Jamesie Mazziotta, Al Rispone, Tony-boy, and the rest of them.

They were talking about the Brinks job up in Boston. It had to be some of The Actor's handiwork.

They also commented on Uncle Frank's U.S. Senate command performance on the TV tube.

Dannie drifted back ten feet up the corner to Felix's grocery store. The younger fellows were still there, and the talk was about the publicized gang war. He saw Kathleen, calm as usual, and hazel-eyed Gloria, who was waving impetuously, across the street. He stayed put, listening.

"Bet Scap gets framed, five to ten or ten to twenty for manslaughter. Any takers?" one kid asked.

"You know who's gonna take South Brooklyn someday? The kids, the N.B. Boys right *here!* They're training to be Pros. They're only fifteen, sixteen years old now. But give 'em time," another offered.

Dannie took in all the trivia until Johnny Squint pulled up in his fire-red Olds, a beautiful Schwinn bicycle lashed to the trunk.

"Hey, winner!" Johnny called to Dannie as he climbed out of the car. "Here's your prize!"

Dannie refused it. He felt bad for Scap. It wasn't right earning a reward on others' lives, others' blood.

"You like re-run Picture Shows?" Johnny, narrow-eyed, held up Dannie's chin. "Take Kathleen to see *The Jackie Robinson Story*. I think it's at the Astor. That might teach you how when you fight from the ground up, you got a reward comin'. I'll stake you the extra five spot. Whaddya say, Champ?"

"I like Jackie Robinson. But Kathleen doesn't like movies."

"Hey, pal," Johnny tried. "You freezin' up on me over a few lumps you got at the park?"

"No."

"I should have known better than to say that." He held Dannie's sore shoulder, turning, gazing across the street. "That frosted blonde now, that Gloria with Kathleen, you wanna see where her come-on interest lays and do the same to her? Cheatin' on my niece?" John laughed, scrutinizing Dannie with his brown, steady eyes. "You didn't take, by any chance, to that Miss Beak of beaks, Al-bert's niece? The one Hugo filled me in on."

"She turned out pretty nice, Johnny. But it isn't that." Dannie skipped the comment on Gloria.

"Kid, *don't dare* get close to that Josephine, or Al-burt'll have your handsome head as a trophy. *With her help!*" He paused and then forged ahead. "Does your not wanting to take the bike have anything to do with your mother wanting to cut my throat today?"

Johnny's last remark hit close to home, but Dannie didn't answer.

"O.K., whatever. I'll see if I'll have a talk with your Mom. Soon. In the meantime I'll stow the bike. I'll put it in Fiola's cellar. Come and claim it anytime you want. You fought the good fight for it."

Tears welled in Dannie's eyes at John's concern. Abruptly he trotted off, stopping a moment on 39th and Eighth to throw a good-bye wave to Kathleen and Gloria, who still stood on the far corner. He wished someone would have a talk with his mother. She'd been giving him the silent treatment over Prospect Park.

Dannie sat outside his apartment on the first step of the stoop, contemplating going up. If his father was out, things would be O.K. If not, his mother would be undressing in the open kitchen. Her face as pure, as lovely as daybreak, or snowfall, her pea-green skirt drifting down in a ring around her ankles. He'd pretend to be busy, swearing that he had to plow through his studies at Ft. Hamilton High. Maybe she wasn't his real mother, he told himself, but the sudden guilt of denial sent a shiver up his spine. He vowed to heaven above he'd sit here till the rest of the world was asleep, and he'd make sure that tonight he'd be sleeping alone! No one, nothing, would sway him from that.

SHORTLY AFTER THE FBI LINKED WILLIE SUTTON TO the Manufacturers Trust robbery, they issued fliers on him to virtually every bank and storekeeper in the U.S.: Most Wanted.

One of the fliers ended up in Max Schuster's clothing store in Brooklyn. Max didn't take much notice of it, but his son Arnold, who worked as a salesman in the store, did. In fact, he was so fascinated by the flier of this "Gentleman" Bank Robber that he tacked it up over his desk in the rear of the store. Over time, Arnold looked at the photograph so often that the image of Willie Sutton became permanently engraved on his mind.

On sunny Monday, February 18, 1952, at 2:00 p.m., Arnold Schuster, curly-haired, good natured tailor, an ex-Coast Guardsman, boarded the BMT West End Line at the De Kalb Avenue, Brooklyn stop. He was tired after a long day of fabric buying in the wholesale houses of midtown Manhattan's garment district.

Arnold planned on expressing it, after transferring from the slow local. Then he would re-transfer at 36th Street, for the Fourth Avenue Line directly to the clothing store.

He sat, shaded in the underground subway train car, content.

Business at his father Mac's Haberdashery Store on Fifth Avenue in Bay Ridge, Brooklyn, was good.

From force of habit, Arnold's eyes began drifting over his fellow passengers. He liked to pass the time on the crowded subway by scrutinizing men's clothes. Picking out the quality wear. Noticing colors.

His eyes paused on the little, wiry man across from him. He'd seen him somewhere before.

In the store? No. They didn't carry his size anyway.

Sutton. Arnold was sure. He recognized him from his flyer—the FBI Most Wanted circular he and Max kept in the back of the store.

Arnold silently gave thanks to the Lord above while his head started ringing like a cash register. There's a $70,000 reward riding the subway right across from me, Arnold's mind raced as he tried to control his quaking silent breaths, hands. The Number One fugitive. With $70,000 in reward money, Arnold Schuster would not only be a real hero, he'd be a rich man!

The little guy in the nice suit stood up, ready to get off at Pacific Street. Arnold Schuster made up his mind. He followed Sutton off the train and up the concrete stairwell to Pacific and Fourth, by Dean Street, then two blocks over to a garage on Third Avenue. This was his chance! When Sutton went into the garage, Arnold flagged down a police car.

Patrolmen Donald F. Shea and Joseph J. McClellan were incredulous. Why is this citizen—this ignorant workman—fucking up their plans? They had been ORDERED to keep their mouths shut and their eyes closed when it came to the roaming Actor, Willie Sutton.

But they told young Arnold that they'd check—had to at least keep up appearances. He insisted that they take his name and telephone number. There's a $70,000 reward, he reminded them. They wished he would shut up, but they acted grateful.

Sutton was spoken to at the garage by the two beknighted policemen. And then they left—without The Actor. Arnold, who was watching from a distance, couldn't believe his own eyes. Again he flagged down their contemptuously cruising police car.

And the top blew off New York.

"This culminates one of the greatest manhunts in the history of the Department," announced New York City Police Commissioner George P. Monaghan. He telephoned J. Edgar Hoover, the director of the Federal Bureau of Investigation in Washington, D.C., and Hoover extended his congratulations.

Willie had been wanted for numerous bank robberies, for three prison escapes, for questioning in the smooth Brinks robbery—a most daring and profitable job registering in crime annals to the tune of one million five hundred thousand dollars in stolen cash.

The Actor had been a fugitive for five years. He had escaped a Philadelphia Maximum Security Penitentiary on February 10, 1947. And he had been living free—for close to two weeks—on a part-time basis as "Mr. Gordon," in a Spanish boarding house at 340 Dean Street, in the heart of South Brooklyn. More precisely, in Albert Anastasia's South Brooklyn.

Commissioner Monaghan proceeded to promote, on the spot, the police officers responsible for the confinement of the most sought after criminal in the United States. He lamented that his officers, Patrolmen Donald F. Shea, Joseph J. McClellan, and detective Louis Weiner — civil servants — were not eligible, in that capacity, to collect the $70,000 cash reward for Sutton's apprehension, but his personal glow, the one beaming from his face was worth, to him, a million dollars. The glow posed for close-up news reporters' photos. The glow was made up for a live television appearance. The glow cast its flab beams throughout the entire country, outshining even the glare of the February day.

"THIS DOESN'T MAKE SENSE, NOT A BIT OF SENSE," Johnny Squint said, back-handing, crack-snapping the *Daily News.* He sat on a wooden chair in the back of Pete's Radio Store, finally flinging the newspaper on the floor.

It was February 19. The stinging, shifting winds and light drizzle outside had driven Johnny, Hugo, dreary Gretti, *attentive* Little Mike, and a handful of their cronies into the shelter of Pete's.

"Whaddya mean?" asked Reb, losing more noticeable weight, his white starched shirt collar of old, a size too big for him now. "That's Willie," he concentrated on the newspaper picture on his lap and not the cancer eating at his lungs, spreading, the tumor growing cantaloupe size. "We saw him a week ago. Thin and scrawny as ever. Two to one he didn't shave since then."

"He could use a straight razor in his hand now," Al Rispone, grinned, the fungus discoloration apparent even under the bare lamp above the green-felt card table. "Cuffed with his hands behind his back. Nah, but that don't cut steel." He was leaning over Reb's shoulder, eyeing the front page of The Actor, captive, between two policemen. "Same Willie. No tie on. The big buckled belt. You can't tell by the black and white photograph, but even money he's got the same blue serge pants on. He may be called The Actor, but he sure as hell don't dress Hollywood."

"How'd they recognize him?" asked Tony-boy, his thin black mustache twitching under his aquiline nose. "The last I heard he had his hair slicked and dyed. And a straw 'stache crayoned daily. Maybe his Hungarian paramour Marge made him whisk it off for a time. Those fuckin' cops are like bloodhounds. They could smell you out. Passing right in South Brooklyn!"

Johnny shot up, bristling, enraged, his face etched with concern. He guided Hugo into the front of the deserted store. "No cop did this," he said, squeezing his eyes down at the front page in Hugo's left hand.

"A doublecross?" Hugo Duce ventured. "Marge? The alien. Shades of Dillinger's Lady in Red?" Hugo wasn't smiling. "Fran? What reason?"

"I don't know," John pondered. "But I do know the one thing we gotta do first. Get Mush. Get him over to Augie's joint fast. Ply him with Golden Wedding. Four Roses, rye him to sleep. Diffuse him! He'll whack those flatfoots on the steps of the stationhouse. Get that Ginger broad he shacks with sometimes. The one from Baltimore. Let her fuck him till he's an invalid."

"Check. Done."

"And, Hugo," John was livid, a quasi-perplexed look on his face. "Benny. Send cockeyed Benny up to Augie's place. Benny can aggravate the shit outta Christ himself, but he'll keep steamin' Augie busy arguing. Tell my brother Pietro M. to also drop in. Be a referee. Augie's had to be half a recluse as it is, drinking, screwin', hagglin'll keep him in till we sort this out!"

Or before Augie makes the mad-move to break Willie *out*! Hugo held the tip of his wide brimmed fedora down, as he crossed the street to Fiola's.

Within four minutes he returned to Pete's. "All arranged, John" he said to his nitro-glycerined standing partner. "What next?"

Johnny was biting hard into his lower lip. "Two cops happening to spot him by his car. With the hood up and a dead battery under it. I ain't no seventy-three-year-old Einstein, but I can't buy that. Al-bert and Uncle Frank both had cops at that Bergen Street headquarters on the pad so this would never happen. So how does anybody figure it?"

"Two cuntlappin' green wise-ass rookies," said the usually amiable Hugo, heated, "who just got lucky? Or an inside tip-off? Judas gets around."

"Hugo," John snapped the index and pointer fingers of his right hand. "Go with Gretti. He knows that neighborhood." Johnny's eyes glinted. "Check with the two garage mechanics where Willie had his Chevy serviced. Lomard and that Jack Peane. You remember. And Sammy's Service Center on Third Avenue. Let me know what you come up with."

"Check." Hugo walked to the expansive back room of Pete's, for Gretti and an overcoat change.

"Be careful on your approach," Johnny held his two partners around their overcoated shoulders, walking them to the side door of Pete's. "This whole area may be crawling with fuzz and Feds too, who are all out tryin' for pay raises, and makin' believe they're doin' their jobs now."

"I know." Hugo paused by the partial-glass, paneled door. "You gonna see Frank, or Albert first?" he hesitated, before pulling the knob to him.

"Neither first right now," John waited, racy blurs of Mr. Murder Inc. behind his eyes, seeing to it that he never squinted again over this mishap which could begin anew an investigation into the '47 escape. What the fuck went wrong? Johnny heard peevish, gruff Gretti in the background complaining about Willie being way out of bounds again, probably moving from Staten Island to be closer to his mom. John was close to flattening his old partner Gret, again. John tried to hold his temper, but as he passed the blackjack table, twenty telephones shrilling in his ear, he pounded the 21 gavel, sending the numbered chips shooting a foot upwards. Tony-boy would drive him to see a certain upgraded detective in Bickford's restaurant on Atlantic Avenue to also see what went wrong, then a trip to the Waldorf's Blue Room in Manhattan and a sit with the Bosses, to see if things could be set right.

DANNIE SAT BY KATHLEEN ON HER 40TH STREET STOOP along with sixteen-year-old Gloria, who he could sense, almost see, wore no armor—no bra—underneath her velveteen jersey. Yet his mind strayed to the slender fellow Ed Lynch. The tale in Borough Park being about a Mr. Gordon really being the famous Willie Sutton.

The Eighth Avenue corner lamppost had been seemingly lit by the sound waves of it: "THE ACTOR" CAUGHT! Pete had said that Johnny had rushed off earlier with Tony-boy. Dannie would spend some time with the two girls. Kill the evening, before going home to his High School textbooks. He shifted under Kathleen's awning to avoid the drizzle.

Gloria was persisting to Kathleen that they play a little game of "This and That." But Dannie was deeply immersed in thought. This was no time for party games. Well, Dannie shrugged, at least it wasn't his fault this time around that the wispy Sutton got in trouble.

Dannie hadn't seen Johnny much during the month. He wondered if John had that "talk" with his Mom. She had been more scarce, more silent than ever.

As for Eleanor, Dannie was avoiding the antagonistic wildcat like the incestuous plague itself. Saint Peter would crucify him at the Gate and send him over to Valhalla, soul-slain by a walking flame-thrower in the fanged-flesh.

Gloria was prodding Dannie to pick either "This" or "That." Kathleen's ashen cheeks had reddened, while Gloria's voice carried a darling urgency in it, kindling in Dannie, visions of Antoinette. Finally, he chose "This."

Gloria won, and after all those years of seeing her, he finally discovered where she lived.

"You live where?" Dannie was astonished.

"At 1480 38th Street. On the fourth floor. Above your aunt's apartment," Gloria relished having Dannie's full attention. "With my lazy brother, Rocco. And my hard-working father, Francisco. My mother was Dutch, you know, from Holland. She passed away."

Dannie mumbled that he was sorry, unable to believe what he was hearing. He stared at Gloria.

"We have a fourteen-inch Pathé table model television." She was fondling her gold-plated compact. "You can come over ..." Dannie's head was struck again by his aunt's perennial edict, as Gloria rambled excitedly, his dazzling aunt's warnings about what would happen if he "went all the way with a young girl at his age"—he would be the *very last one* the Keeper of the Keys let into where everyone whats to go. "You just keep that in mind!" Dannie let those injunctions go, asking Gloria what she had won when he picked "This."

"You," she showed him her open compact: K—"That" ... G—"This" written in lipstick on the mirror. "Do we go here inside under the stairway and kiss, *you* doing the kissing this time? Or do we go to a movie? *The Outlaw* may be at the RKO Prospect. Take your pick ... again," Gloria stood up, Dannie imagining her ringed, erect nipples beneath her jersey, imagining *also* his Aunt Eleanor's face below as he watched TV above. "Dannie V!" the call brought him back to reality. Half-turning, he saw in the dim light of dusk Johnny's newer red Olds alongside the curb, Johnny waving his hand from the driver's side of the car. "Over here. Pronto, slugger!"

Before Dannie could dart over to the car, Kathleen had unclasped her hands, revealing a tiny white cardboard box. She gave it to him. "T.E.H.M.A.," she smiled. He shoved the box in the right pocket of his gray trousers. "We'll all three go out to eat or to that movie," he said, trying his best to be gallant. Gloria, her usual zip sapped, ran her hands through her light chestnut hair, minus the heretofore, dyed, frosted blond streaks, and managed a broad smile.

"Get in!" Johnny gave Dannie time to half circle the car, and climb in the passenger's side, by Hugo Duce. He gunned up one-way 40th and screeched a right turn up Ninth Avenue, hastily throwing a kiss to his sweetest of nieces, Kathleen.

"Why the boy?" Hugo was at a loss to explain Johnny's hectic figuring.

"Why not a kid?" Johnny was speeding, trying not to show his distress. "You want to go in? Should I go in and show my kisser? I want to see if that dick is lyin'. You can't trust them as far as you can throw this car. Dannie!" He shifted his attention. "You know an Arnold Schuster?"

"The tailor? Yes." Dannie's right hand held the edge of the seat tightly, trying to keep his balance, wondering if he was Johnny's mascot, some kind of good luck charm.

"Squint. This is crazy," Hugo's voice interrupted, the sincerity in his voice permeating the car. "First I tell you that the service station workers were bug-eyed, seeing no one but the *polizia*. Then I hear that you haul off in the downtown, public restaurant, and nearly knock a detective's head off. Now you get a kid to find out if what the bull said is true. Johnny, where's the reasoning?"

"Here," Johnny parked the car by Fifth and 56th. "If it was the Bulls who took it upon themselves to do it to Sutton, then I'm off the hook. How ya gonna be responsible for triple crossin' lice who take with one hand and stab you with the other? You can't beat that. But if it's true what they said and it was this Schuster, then I merely take it up, immediately, to Uncle Frank. Dannie, come on." He opened his car door, and Dannie, following him, skirted around it to the sidewalk where Johnny stood.

"Listen," Johnny held him around the shoulders, walking him slowly to the Fifth Avenue corner, shoppers meandering by, out of earshot. "Ask no questions. You kept your mouth shut that time in Sunset Park with that Russian broad and those five kids. I'm proud of you. You fought Scap, beat the piss out of him and was there when another kid got killed. And you held your peace."

Dannie held his peace now, the light rain mantling his cheeks.

"You're like my blood," Johnny said. "Just do what I tell you to do and you'll never regret it. *Fistase*? Understand?"

Dannie nodded.

"You're no longer a baby," John stopped him three feet from the corner. "I go back with your lovely mother a long time. You know that. And we're no strangers, you and I. You're over fifteen and know the score by now. Listen. Around this corner—5507 Fifth Avenue—is that Mac's Clothes Shop. Didn't you tell me you got your first pair of long pants there? That you've been buying them there ever since? Right?"

Dannie remembered well the name of the store, the two tailors, father and son. "My Aunt Eleanor bought me the first pair. I was fitted for a second, navy blue, but I didn't pick them up."

"Perfect," Johnny was relaxing. He dug in his pants pocket, handing Dannie ten ten-dollar bills. "Go inside the store now before they close up. Look for that supposedly bright, nosy salesman. You know him. Arnie. About twenty-four. Curly hair, maybe nice-lookin', kinda long nose. His short, dumpy father, Max, owns the place. Don't pick up your navy blues. You've grown. Order another pair. Two pair if you want. Anything. Take your time. You're no ordinary kid to me, Dannie. I think you know that. You were a spotter for me and no one suspected. So do exactly as I say, and say exactly as I say and you're gonna help a lot of people live a long time. Just make exaggerated conversation with this Arnold Schuster all about this Willie Sutton being captured. It's like the talk of the City. Do it all as he's measuring you. Make it seem like you're a starry-eyed fifteen-year-old. Tell him the cops don't deserve that seventy thousand reward. Talk like you're just talking and talking to the sky, not really him. Have you got it so far?"

Dannie had it all so far, but he was preoccupied with something more important to him.

"Johnny," he stammered. "Do you like . . . love my mother?" The words ricocheted off the back of his mind.

Johnny's eyes were creases. It took him 45 seconds of silence to uncrease them. "I had a quickie divorce," he answered. "My *ahgumada* now, I may marry. And I do like your mother. In fact, I've always loved her. And still do!"

That's all he wanted to hear. Dannie breathed jubilantly, listening to the rest of Johnny's instructions, before he went into the store. He was on his way to finding himself.

ANY GOOD *CAPITANO* KNEW THAT IN THE INTRICATE mesh of battle one must take into due consideration the consequences of first, should it be entered into, second, can it be won, and third, what if one loses?

Johnny Squint took none of these into consideration.

He was a soldier—a *soldato*. One with a right to act on his own local matters, which he did.

When Dannie came out of the clothing store, John knew by the report that it was indeed Arnold Schuster who had led the two police officers to Willie Sutton. The cops were, for a change, not being deviant.

Now what to do? Kill this Schuster to maybe appease Sutton? A Schuster that lived at 941 45th Street, Borough Park, in the midst of Johnny's little corner of the world.

Why kill him? The public didn't know. St. John—Augie—didn't have an inkling. Sutton himself didn't know. Let the deed rest with the cops. Let them get the credit and the blame. The credit from the exultant Commissioner. The blame from Al-bert, Uncle Frank and Company. And it would die there.

But Johnny took an instant precaution, again, that very night. He collared the presiding detective in charge of the Sutton arrest, meeting him at the downtown Brooklyn, Lafayette Hotel. Johnny told him three things: "Stifle the fact that the Actor's arrest had come about through a citizen, keep the glorious credit in the department, and have a 'chat' with the owner of the gas station to ensure that they keep their mouths shut!"

Lou, the detective, understood only too well the ramifications of Johnny's heated talk with him. If it came out that it was a clothing salesman that had been instrumental in Willie's downfall, and not the two police officers, then the members of the Department involved would be accused of a cover-up, causing a major stir with not only the Commissioner, but a public that would wonder why this classic capture stemmed from an overly observant civilian, and not the diligent workings of dedicated civil servants.

The matter was settled. John settled himself behind the wheel of his Oldsmobile, Hugo Duce beside him. The issue would die, and

Sutton would, in time, be told that the police had double-banged everyone concerned. Let Al-bert in his grandiose South Brooklyn take the fuckin' weight in Willie's discerning mind. Well, what could be done? Knock out a squad of cops over it? That's a Dutch Schultz way of thinking, not *ours*. John was sure he had attacked the matter locally and solved it.

But as a "soldier," he was a wing. One that could not fly long on its own. He attended the meeting that night, and spoke with his General—his superior. The only openly known man in the world that he felt he had to answer to. Uncle Frank.

They met hastily in the Blue Room of the Waldorf Astoria Hotel in Manhattan. But Robileto the Mortician, Al-bert's Captain, was there also, as was Carlo Gambino, Al-bert's ski-slope-nosed spokesman. And Vito Genovese—Don Vito—the taskmaster.

Uncle Frank, wearing a soft, felt, pearl gray fedora, presided, speaking as if a feather was eternally lodged in his throat.

Eggs Benedict were ordered all around. No one at the meeting drank any liquor. The meet itself lasted thirty-one long minutes.

Outside the Waldorf, Johnny climbed into the red Olds, Hugo Duce at the wheel.

Johnny related as Hugo drove back to Brooklyn.

Uncle Frank had been as humble, as polite as ever. Carlo Gambino either had a leaky kidney, wasn't interested, or kept leaving the table to phone his Boss Al-bert. Robileto the gentleman, terror-faithful to Mr. K.H., had remained silent. And Don Vito had been a portrait of false placating.

The decision? *Do nothing about Schuster.* Keep it quiet. Bury it. Keep it from Willie. Let the Actor despise the pudgy crumb who slapped him, even more.

As long as wily Willie believed that it was the doings of the flat-foots, Johnny stormed as the car sped along Manhattan's FDR Drive, it was Crime against Law. Willie's usual game-style. The flat-foots took the payoffs and at the same time japped everybody concerned. Par for the course. Al-bert would be happy that his payroll dicks didn't dare double-cross HIM.

"Ahhh, *long* day and fuck it all," Johnny sighed relief as the car passed through South Brooklyn. "I did my part. Willie will do his slippery act on a future break out, and nobody but a handful will ever know that it was a nobody—Schuster—that started all this crap out of nowhere. As my niece, God bless her, Kathleen says, 'the damn Gates swing open and closed a minute apart.' But I probably just bought this nobody clothing salesguy an extra forty years before he gets there."

Hugo pulled up by Fiola's. Dannie was in front of it. Both Kathleen and fetching Gloria on either side of him. Dannie was turned more toward Kathleen, favoring her.

"There's one of your handful." Hugo spoke, gestured. "Is that kid serious with your niece?"

Johnny halted Dannie's run to the car with the outstretched flat of his hand, palm up, extended through the Olds' passenger window.

"Kathleen's sick," he said to Hugo, eyeing the wool cap overlapping her ears. That would have to go. She'd go to a beauty parlor where they'd straighten out her hair, bringing out its luster. Johnny watched Dannie stop, turn back toward the restaurant and the girls. "My niece, along with diabetes, has enlarged heart murmurs thrown in. The witch doctors mumbo-jumbo that it'd be a miracle if she reaches twenty-one."

"The kid know about his father?"

"Does anyone know about anyone?" Johnny slouched back on the red leather seat, near exhaustion. "Does Uncle Frank know his days as a Boss are numbered 'cause he's weak? Do forty mil in the Tri-state area know they've been hoodwinked by bad-apple cops? Does the untouchable Al-bert know his days are numbered too 'cause he's too strong? That his sly-eyed spokesman Carlo G. is playin' footsies with Don Vito lookin' to oust him, *for good*?"

"You got the future down pat, John?"

"No. But I got things in mind for Kathleen and Dannie V." John looked sideways, over at his niece's smudged rain boots, she should be wearing shoes, anklet twists, open-air sandals. That Gloria would be wearing a bikini in her attempts to attract Dannie, Johnny mused, February drizzle and all. "I want to see Dan and Kathleen get that *elusive moment* of happiness. I got plans." He closed his tired eyes a moment. "As for the sit, I think Vito—the Don himself—has his own plans for every big shot mentioned or otherwise in that Blue Room tonight."

"Has Vito any plans for you?" Hugo lit up a Philip Morris, dragged deeply, the smoke swirling up against the car's windshield.

Johnny slouched deeper into the leather upholstery. "I got the almighty button through the commanding first vote of V.G. after my Dad, Felice, initially "proposed" me. A little while later I proposed you. Your first O.K. comin' from V.G. also. Don Vitone's loyal to his own within our Group. So as long as we're loyal he'll look after us. We got all the hope in the world, *mi amica*." Johnny opened his eyes and looked at Dannie on the sidewalk. He had some good plans for that kid. High hopes. Nah, some great scheme-dreams for him, he closed his tired eyes again, but waved *sua affetto una* over to him with his outstretched hand.

ARNOLD SCHUSTER HAD PLANS. MORE THAN THAT. HE had a few great scheme-dreams of his own. And he pressed them for two days after the Number One Most Wanted—Willie Sutton— had been taken into custody.

He had decided to press them even harder after that teenager, Dannie Vale, had come into the clothing store and lauded the bravery of New York City's finest in nabbing The Actor.

Arnold had re-fitted Dannie for his navy blue tailor-made pants then measured him for sixteen-inch pegs for his new powder blue pair, boastfully, impulsively blurting out that it was HE who had led the City's Finest to the famed outlaw, and that it was HE who was entitled to the $70,000 reward.

But for forty-eight hours the police at the Bergen street Headquarters had ignored him as he pressed for his claim, all but shooing him away.

It was HE who was riding the Brooklyn-Manhattan Transit's West End Line at two o'clock in the afternoon of February 18, and, recognizing the criminal, followed him, hailing a squad car, *twice*. But why was he being ignored by the presiding detective at the Bergen Street Headquarters?

Out of die-hard frustration, from being turned away again and again by the Police, Arnold turned to his family attorney, Harold Weiss, pouring out to him that it was his habit to keep FBI circulars in his father's clothing store. He had personally requested that the flyers be sent there. He, alone, had spotted Willie Sutton in the subway car, getting off the train at Pacific Street, and trailing him up to Pacific and Fourth, over to the garage on Third Avenue. He, alone, had notified two officers in their prowl car, TWICE. But why was he being shunned? Wasn't the recognition deservedly his? The reward money rightfully coming to him!

Harold M. Weiss listened dutifully and began making telephone calls: to the Bergen Street Police Station, the Queens County Jail, three of New York's major newspapers, and to the New York City Police Commissioner's office. If the reward were claimed, Arnold had agreed, Weiss would deduct one-third of the seventy thousand dollars for his professional efforts.

The two traveled together, Arnold recounting with fervor how he felt when he had first recognized The Actor. "I looked across the car at him and had to do a double-take. But he put his head down, slightly. I kept saying to myself that it had to be him. The same eyes as in the poster. Short. There was no fooling me with that dyed mustache. After I followed him and notified the two police officers, I saw how right I was now, Mr. Weiss. The two garage mechanics— even at that distance—should remember me even if the police refuse to. I almost started a row the second time around. Still, I know that Willie Sutton himself, if he looks me directly in the eye, will remember the minutes before his arrest and never forget me."

Harold Weiss camped by the Long Island City Jail in Queens demanding to have his client gaze once more upon the face of The Actor.

He stormed into the Bergen Street Station, insisting that his client be allowed to confront the two arresting officers. He flaunted his right not to be blocked from interviewing the nearby garage mechanics and warned that he would be face-to-face with Commissioner Monaghan if he had to live in a tent outside his office.

Weiss pressed, urging the police department to make a public announcement about the heroism of Citizen Schuster. Muckraking, yellow journalism, and national publicity will all be the rage.

There was no need for Harold Weiss to demonstrate any longer. His rantings had prevailed.

The next day proved it. Arnold Schuster's name was in all the papers, the headlines reading: PRAISE FOR THE MAN WHO SPOTTED SUTTON.

Arnold posed in his natty gray sports jacket as his picture was taken shaking hands with the Commissioner of Police.

His fame, along with The Actor's, was scattered in tabloids, in newsreels, on television and radios across the nation. But his efforts, along with those of his untiring attorney, to collect the reward money were thwarted by the banks that put it up, the businessmen that backed it up, and the City that guaranteed it.

It would take the remainder of February, possibly the month of March, to collect their due, Harold M. Weiss assured his client.

WILLIE—MR. GORDON OF 340 DEAN STREET—SUTTON had been calm inside the Bergen Street Headquarters. He had escaped prisons in Philly in 1945, 1947. And made it out of "full proof" Sing Sing in 1932 by gently tying up a guard, scaling the wall, dressed as the guard, a wood-carved, shoe-polish dyed "revolver" saving him a bundle of time.

Now he owed it all back on the original sentences. There was no use living in the wreckage of the future, so he remained calm, but concerned about Angel "St. John" Tenuto becoming too hotheaded about this . . . set back—acting too soon on his own.

He had gone to see Meyer on Delancy Street, Manhattan's Lower East Side. Had seen his Mom. Had set up "shop"—transient, at Dean Street, seeing Marge every other night at 547 Pacific Street. He had even been "casing" the Maiden Lane Manhattan "score." All had been good reasons to be in Brooklyn.

At first he had figured that the authorities had crossed-up the Madhatter, Uncle Frank, even when they approached him at the gas station. His impish blue eyes had remained outwardly calm, belying the torment brewing within him.

But he knew now that a clean-cut, nice looking young fellow, the one who had been staring at him in the subway car, had been the reason for his own capture. The customary twinkle in his pale eyes dimmed.

A fluke.

He was locked in now at the all too secure, dusty as hell, Queens City Jailhouse, facing double life terms as a fourth offender. The correction guards paraded by his cell by the seconds to see if he even stirred a hair.

He had defied the Madman of South Brooklyn, gaining his own self-respect, but losing his freedom. *Again.*

Willie flicked his bleary eyes, the only light, wavering from the outer gallery's bare bulb, streaming ever so slightly into his steel cell. He scanned the book that one of the guards had "swagged" to him. The book was contraband, but the guard had been proud, impressed that he was one of Willie Sutton's overseers.

Willie kept skimming the book's pages, titled: *You Can Change the World,* written by the Reverend James Keller. Fluttering the pages in his hands, he mused, "You can also *buy* the world." His mind roamed, sadly, to Al-bert, who needed the Himalayan mountains to bury his dead; to Don Vito and Meyer Lansky who both needed the Alps to bury their money.

Well, he had touched base with Meyer, perspicacious Meyer absorbing the idea of Johnny Squint's "Promotion." Quids, dollars, kruetzers, and several other entrenched Costello Captains would aid the plot. Willie could have been close to clinching that. Well, Willie sighed, at least he had escaped the wastelands of Staten Island. He wondered how his next escape would come about. He looked intently at the book. He'd read it to pass the time.

It won't be long.

THE CAPTURE OF THE ACTOR AND THE TRAITOR, Arnold Schuster, who turned him in, were the morsels of the month, chewed over inside Walt's Ninth Avenue All-Nite Diner, at Pete's, on Brooklyn stoops, outside of grocery stores, candy stores, and at Fiola's.

Willie Sutton was an escape artist. A convicted gentleman bank robber. A hero who took from insured Money Stores without bullets flying.

With never a drop of blood spilled.

Never!

George Haist, the big Finn who paraded around like Hungarian Bela Lugosi, blustered that he knew more about Willie Sutton than anybody in the whole fuckin' neighborhood.

"He's a rebel angel. He went to church every week. No lie," Haist announced.

"Yeah? What was he doing, robbin' poor boxes?" crazed Benny Napanack retorted with an oversized mouthful of Sicilian sliced pizza slobbering his lips.

"Didn't do a good job," Anthony Nino, card shark supreme, added. "When they found him he was dead broke."

"Bull*shit*! He had over three grand stashed in his boarding room. If Wily Willie lay foot in a church, it was to steal vestment disguises for a new target," muscular Mush's voice was dry.

"Hey," laughed Tony-boy, "did you catch where he said he never 'banked' his money? Man, that's hot stuff." Tony-boy wondered where the millions Willie had, really were.

Little Mike shook his head. "They found a 'heater,' of all things, on him. Inside his belt, underneath his trousers—in the station-house and another one at his pad on Dean Street. For the *pistolas* alone they can give him life and then some, with his record."

"And I say," Georgie Haist swirled his cape like the Count in a horror movie, "that The Actor ain't gonna be in long. He's better than Dillinger when it comes to escapin'."

"Schuster," Lucky the gambler tossed in. "That rat. Made a

mockery of Borough Park—OUR neighborhood!"

"That creep, Arnie," baby-faced Anthony Nino spoke with white-hot hatred. "He puts the 'tag' on Willie and what's done about it? Days and days now, and bullshit so far."

Rogie all but flipped, hunching his shoulders, pulling at his thin sandy hair. "This whole area's gonna get a bad name because of that fuckin' stool pigeon." His head was down, feet half circling the chipped, cracked sidewalk. "Sure, Schuster. Used ta buy the tailor-mades at his old man's place on Fifth. But no more! That place is black balled. That Arnie, always there with that shit eatin' sales grin of his. Carved his niche, the world knows him now, eh? It's dollars to doughnuts if he ever lives to collect that reward. I bet Squint or one of the hitters here on Eighth gets the nod to 'waste' him. It's written in the stars."

It was enough for Dannie. The same chronic topics seemed to cause static in the electric wires overhead which hung from one black telephone pole to the next.

He was killing time, evenings after school. Weekends. Waiting for Johnny to show, but it didn't look like he was going to show anymore this night than he had any night for the past week. Dannie had never gotten any word about a "chat" between John and his Mom. Dannie left the group chatter, desolate.

During the dreary, wall-climbing nights, by March's beginning, Dan had formulated a plan: to cast aside the relics, throw them away and begin again. Why not? There must be some other entrance into life, some other way to belong rather than his old blind-alley existence.

Dannie sat precariously atop the eight-inch ledge of the four-foot concrete wall of the Ninth Avenue overpass-bridge adjacent to the Greenwood Cemetery, the darkened city freight yards 60 feet below.

The night weather seemed arctic, and he zippered up his gold-blue reversible jacket.

Behind him, about 250 yards to his right was his house. Where no one lived. He hadn't seen his father in ten solid days. The last he heard, from big mouth know-it-all Rogie on Eighth Avenue, was that Roscoe Vale was driving around Johnny Squint's '48 stick shift Plymouth convertible, the one he had before he bought the second new, snazzy 98 Rocket Olds.

That hadn't made a bit of sense to Dannie. For some reason he had wanted to swift-kick Rogie between the legs, but that made less sense, it would be dignifying the ridiculous. He kept looking down at the evening tracks gleaming silvery beneath him where his droll, benign neighbor, Pop, the artful city watchman, collected castaways.

His mother had become a night prowler. She wouldn't be home, so that kept him locked out. Too young for keys. He gulped down that simpleton rule, thinking of just why, and what, his mom was prowling for? For his father? For Johnny? For the sake of being out of the house nights?

Dannie had Kathleen's poem, "In Imitation," in his left hand. He read the last stanza under the light shafts emanating from the windowed, fortress-like Ninth Avenue station:

The lies cloaked in messages or said
That brand with fiction false the deadly face
Betrays the paper dark on which they're read
Maligning me—
Whose facts could fell the foul to fair disgrace—
But I am blessed by those who speak
Turning to CHRIST my silent cheek
IN IMITATION

He let go of the crumpled piece of white paper, and it zigzagged in the wind, landing between the tracks. He had far from IMITAT-ED Jesus Christ thus far.

Keys. On a circular tin ring. To the Schwinn bicycle's lock. Let it rot and rust in Fiola's smelly wine-whiskey basement, he decided. Choosing to cast aside another relic he dropped them. The keys plopped downward to the rocky yard below. They'd become so much junk, as the bike would. The relic payoff. A bike for proving his manhood in Prospect Park. Everybody agreeing he had won the match with Scap who was now rotting in jail. So now what? How come Johnny hadn't come through with that "spotter" job again? Dannie suddenly saw creased-skin Pop angled 70 degrees from him, on the inclined "Cuts" slope.

"Careful, Dannie lad." Pop's face was like so much hewn rock, his eyes a watery cold blue. "Over a 60-foot drop from where you're perched," Pop's shrill old laugh pierced the wind gust.

Dannie shook off being startled. Pop was a relic in the flesh. Dannie smiled at motorman-capped Pop. Then turning, looked straight down below. What next? Hurl himself? He heard Pop's eerie laughter.

"Dannie, lad," Pop, still laughing, was wavering down the steep dirt path, "all the junk comes to me in my untroubled domain here," he wailed into the wind. "From headlines, to hats, to three-fingered hands. You've got years before the piles and the heaps getcha." And with that he disappeared into his junk-haven.

Dannie shivered, scared at his own thought of flinging himself below. He might wind up alive and maimed, crippled from the waist down. He felt he was crippled there already, as his head filled with thoughts of sinuating, unspoiled Gloria, when they had watched TV last evening.

Her father had been out in the neighborhood bar drinking off a hard day's work. Her berserk twenty-one-year-old brother, Rocco, who had made her rinse out the blonde frosting from her hair—it was cheap and trampish he had ranted for days—was also out, probably ogling around Kathleen's 40th Street block. They had sat comfy on her living room sofa, one floor above Eleanor Cross.

The evening with mouth watering Gloria was more like a dream in Dannie's brain as the March wind swayed him on the trestle's ledge. She had invited him up to her dismal, four-room apartment, frightened when alone some nights. He had held her heated hand as they talked about Kathleen's new look—her glowing hair, free from thick woolen caps. Gloria had been exceptionally engaging as her fourteen-inch black/white Pathé television set cast its lightning-fast dotted images across her lamplit parlor.

Gloria, in between licking Dannie's neck, had said her brother called her a brat, that they constantly fought like cats and dogs over what TV program they were going to watch when their father was out. Dannie, once in a while, had crushed her with a kiss. She had been either that enticing, clinging, or it pleased him to know his damn—Miss Rheingold—Miss Subways—"superb-candidate" aunt lived, slept, by herself, right downstairs.

Dannie's head was filled with tracers, zooming mental pictures of him and Gloria as he slowly saddled the ledge, the wind picking up with heavy intermittent blasts. Gloria had made him cross his heart, in her girlish way, and hope to die if he had left her alone. She had seductively told him how Rocco had chipped her cheekbone when he had flown off the handle at her not wearing bras, her short skirt-line, all the while, easing upwards with her sidling, shifting movements, while he brooded over his chained desires.

The dim scenes spun inside Dannie's head, out on the ledge, the tip of his nose, his ice-cheeks fit to crack from the bitter cold which bit at his ears . . . he had been dry-humping Gloria, belly laughs coming from the T.V. Her skirt had been way up, but her soft panties were still on . . . she was moaning, trying not to, he had both his hands underneath her, holding, barely, her paradise ass . . . both clothed.

Her lovebox, her spine-tingling words, terms had driven him, his hands to her freakin' thighs. She wanted to go "steady" with him, but had nearly cried that he'd love her more if she remained a virgin. He had lain on top of her, still dry-humping, hoping he'd wear right through her damn panties, their panting, grunting blocking out the T.V. set's sound. He had felt something happening to her body, deep between her legs . . . she all but screamed, writhing, gyrating, saying, close to out of breath that she never knew heaven lived inside of her waiting body before. She had collapsed gossamer-like on her back on the sofa . . . his eager hands groping along her inner thighs, while she held her arms around his neck . . . could he make it "all the way" with her? He had trembled on Eleanor's ceiling as he felt life leave him between his legs.

Stymied. Crippled? He gripped the bronze-colored lighter that Hugo Duce had given him to sock Scap with. It torpedoed down below. Another relic.

Guilt? It came from Kathleen's pure, conscience-attacking teachings combined with an idea that "breaking a girl," taking her "cherry" wasn't right unless you were going to marry her. Maybe he respected outspoken Gloria too much. Dannie fingered the T.E.H.M.A. Medal.

His thoughts shifted again. This time to Stevie Sesqu. The only friend he had that was his age. He had moved with his family to Park Slope, the first of the month, to be nearer to the hat factory where his father Lyle worked. Dannie had no relics or souvenirs to throw down into the freight yards, so he recalled little Stevie's loyalty in Prospect Park and had to let it go at that.

A fat endless row of grape-box bearing cars chugged away beneath him.

Dannie sat, tight-fisting the Medal, the silver chain, the abbreviated Sacred Heard inscription, T.E.H.M.A. *THEY ENTERED HEAVEN A MINUTE APART.* The Good Thief and Jesus Christ. Straight from their crosses.

He had asked Kathleen what it really meant. She said it wasn't her saying. That she was taught that GOD doesn't measure time the way we do. A minute could be forever. And forever could be a minute. But we get our say, there by the Gate. And if what we have to say, and what our lives have said is pleasing to the Lord, is right in HIS eyes, then we enter and stay.

It sounded sensible, somehow. He shut his lips tighter, thinking that it was one thing feeling sorry for yourself, but another to hate—not being able to stand yourself. His body shook on the ledge, shaking not so much from the cold as from memories . . . his mother sleeping close to him so many grown-up nights . . . his aunt, her fifteen-year-old nephew almost making love to her. He wanted to puke. His fist opened and the Medal disappeared down into the freight cuts.

How could he wear it knowing his own thoughts. Had he just cursed himself for a lifetime for letting the Medal—relic—drop? It was much more than the March winds that made him tremor back and forth to the danger point of losing his balance and going head-long onto the top of a box car.

Could he gather clippings now? The *Daily Mirror, Herald Tribune, New York Times*. About Scap facing Elmira Reformatory, about Arnold Schuster now a big hero, and about Willie Sutton earning his Master's Degree in Crime on Brooklyn's back streets.

What would he do with the articles? Fling them down. Let the wind take them onto the shabby weeds, or on the top of freight cars. Would that do away with the mess, the things that happened?

Why not go to Kathleen tonight? Maybe she'd tell him something to keep going. That life is only quick fumbling minutes. That's all.

Why not face the truth as to why he hadn't seen a trace of Johnny for nearly two weeks now? That John must be fed-up with him hanging on his coat tails all the time. Dannie wondered if that were the truth.

Where *was* Johnnie? Ever since this Sutton thing, Johnny had evaporated. He just didn't come around.

The heck with Willie Sutton, the heck with all of them. Dannie sat rigid, dirty trains disappearing into nowhere. The city yards were ancient Pop's territory, foraging through weeds, rocks, for trinkets, rusty treasures, finding starved-cold dead cats at the end of their road.

Dannie felt like he was at a dead end too. Nowhere to go.

Home to his hysterical mother if she were there? Or over to carping, flaming, gangster-despising, Yiddish-speaking Eleanor's to let come wet his pants? He was ready for a woman—a real one, an Antoinette one.

Not his aunt. That mystifying, tight-hipped desirous, yet vomit-inducing crackpot.

Maybe Gloria's house again? No, Kathleen might feel hurt.

Not that hot-cold teaser Anna Banana. His testicles would be cut off if he tried almost-making it with her again—and her nose of noses and all! Nobody touched Albert's niece.

And not Kathleen. She was for talking to, his theologian, riding the swings with, filling him in on the growing, expanding doings of the brash, intense North Brooklyn Boys. Dannie could well imagine them adoring her. The deadly, compassionate leader Christie, also strangely Catholic school God-fearing, listening to her message of peace—for those who take or use a life shall enter heaven a minute apart—God's minute, not man's.

Did Anna tell caring Antoinette about the bout with Scap? About the aborted episode on the sloping hill? Dannie wondered. God, Antoinette's super sensitive torso!

Dannie caught his breath. Why the hell did he have to listen to John and not see her?

Restless, Dannie fidgeted on the bridge's ledge, looking out at the looming open subways, the deserted Cuts. What should he do with himself?

Maybe he should marry Anna Banana, raise a bunch of bananas, and have an uncle-in-law with the power of God.

Why not? And why not just go to Heaven, get his hearing now, and get it over with.

Why not a thousand things, he felt so ashamed. He remembered how dedicated he had been in seeking out Antoinette, and he began to take heart. He could go on. He swung his legs around, jumping to the Ninth Avenue overpass sidewalk. He had amused himself enough, now he'd take a walk.

To where?

Go to Eleanor's. What the hell. She's out of her alluring mind, but she's possessed, willing.

He began walking up 39th Street to Eleanor's. Fuck it! He whirled around, disgusted at himself, and decided to go night prowling instead—after his mother and father.

He found them, along with his aunt, at one o'clock on that early morning of March 7. The three of them seemingly in a football huddle on 39th Street, by Johnny Squint's ex-wife Rosa Mazziotta's apartment house. Johnny's divorce gift to Rosa, the '48 Plymouth convertible, parked by the curb.

"Here's the boy!" Roscoe Vale shrieked. "Why don't you tell him the story? He's old enough to hear it!" Roscoe told the two women that Dannie would know and hear all, here and now, with them present, or he would take the kid he had reared, raised, and loved in private tow and let him know the truths without the benefit of them being able to protest or defend!

Eve Vale and Eleanor Cross were like two haunted-eyed goddesses in silken black garb as they shrunk from that meaningful threat and stood petrified on the wind-shaken corner. Eleanor, her voice as if from the inside of a tunnel, hissed *Er kricht arein in di bayner* at Roscoe.

Dannie stood as *stone* in the midst of them, resistant to the two horror-struck women's pleadings to skulk away.

And in the span of less than one hour he heard most of the story of himself, the three of them throwing words at each other like knives, accusing one another, the voices fireballs of loathing. They shouted, attacked and explained with not only words, but hidden and shown emotions, their verbal breaths fighting the wind, their base hate and concealed, ulcerated feelings coming to heated, painful light under the corrosion-covered, high city lamp glow.

Dannie followed the unleashed saber-slicing words.

Roscoe Valencia—he was sick of the farce of a name change to Vale—was originally from East 187th Street and Arthur Avenue in the Bronx, the "Little Italy" section. During the Depression he had been out of work. His one brother, Lilo, deceased now, had promised he could find him a job. Waterfront work in Bush Terminal—the Brooklyn docks.

He moved, alone, to Brooklyn. He was working two days a week, but managing to eat for seven.

Eleanor. It was as if she had him clocked, sized up to the "T," from the beginning: lonely, nearly twenty years her senior. Her sexual insinuations, lies, gutter-guile, had played a gnawing game with his loneliness, desires!

Eventually, through Eleanor, he had met Eve Crosscavale. She was eighteen years old—and pregnant!

Eve Vale cowered at the words, becoming a standing human ball, her hands and arms squashing her coat front and half covering her face, her right sheer nylon-stockinged knee, hefted, cuddling her left.

Eleanor Cross's arms and hands were threshing at Roscoe, but he held her wrists with the sinewy strength of his own hands. "A clutch with your eyes, but never a touch," Roscoe taunted as he held on. "Even when Daniel was in his crib and you slept over, you'd have me in your psychological grip—by *my balls*! With your fuckin' sweet nothings."

Roscoe was actually telling her things, speaking to her at length, for the first time that Dannie could ever recall.

They were scathing, but hollow sounds, for the man that was speaking them was *not his father*! Dannie's mouth remained half-open, he was frozen to the mortared sidewalk.

"Eleanor, you got too many problems for one human being!" Roscoe was going to have his say, he flung her away from him. She was too sultry, too *sesso Guardi*, a problem most women would give blood for. But she proved, since he met her, that she wasn't even a human being! "You know what your biggest problem is?" Roscoe laid into her. "You never got laid in your life!"

"Two for one, what a stinking LIE!" The bile was coming out, Roscoe, going on and on, was trying with some containment to make up for sixteen years of silence. Hints of sensual nights, stripteasing, all leading nowhere. Roscoe was spilling the story of Eleanor's deceit, fraud. He had been a victim of a dirty, false dream!

Eleanor, rubbing her wrists, didn't know what to do with her hands now. She juxtaposed and juggled them, finally putting them to her mouth in stark repulsion.

Dannie looked down at the bare, square-lined 39th Street sidewalk. He wished he could throw all this away with the rest of his relics.

Sex was out of the question for both of them. "I don't know where the hell Daniel came from? Was he Saint Joseph? Was it a virgin birth?" Roscoe, at last, had the rapt attention of all three, his impassioned words now projecting into the cold darkness of night.

"Not once! Not once in sixteen years that I took you in did we ever actually sleep together. Utter lunacy!" He now directed his ardent fury at his wife. "You look like a siren, but you're not even a cold fish. You're a dead one. Why? I'm not good enough for you? But I was good enough to support you. Feed you. Raise your son. And what did I get in return? An unnatural, spooky life." It was spewing out of him uncontrollably. Eve and Eleanor were both struck dumb, while Dannie stood in shocked amazement. "You slept next to me for years," he continued, "but most times, wouldn't so much as unbutton your houserobe in front of me. Yet you undressed in the kitchen, slept in the living room. I'm sure the boy didn't want it that way. Why? Am I some kind of freak? Why did I take it all these years? Because of your ghoul-dreams? Or in the crazy hope that one day you might love me? Love anyone besides your son? Once you'd think I could have enjoyed that precious body of yours. I'm a sick man."

At that, Dannie blinked his eyes and tried to swallow, finally managing to choke it down his parched throat.

"Sisters!" Roscoe kept the floor, his tones more even now.

"Why didn't I leave years ago? But how could I leave the boy?

How could I leave my tender, virtuous 'wife'? Sisters! One I never slept with. One I never spoke to. Why? Were you raped, Eve? Was that your hang-up? Eleanor," he turned on her now. "What did I ever do to you?" She didn't respond. In fact, she acted as if he wasn't even there—just as she had for years. "Did you think I was degrading your sister in a bed of matrimony . . . of convenience? That I wasn't good and pure enough for her?"

"Dannie," it was his turn now, but Roscoe's tone was different. Dannie was an ally in this knotted trio that had used up his life. "Was I harsh?" he continued. "Was I mean to you? Did I give you the care—the concern that a real father would have given you? When you get older, Dannie, you'll wonder how I put up with this devious beehive I lived in. The . . . stupid perjury . . . the painful loins, agonizing nights . . . in the ignorant . . . hope . . ." his voice going gauzy . . . "borne because of you. So don't hate me now after I've loved you all these years." Roscoe relented in his near life-long wrath at the two sisters and opened his heart to the boy that carried half his name. "They are evil, bewitched, Dannie. Get away from them for your own sake," he implored. "Your mother came here tonight to catch me. With who? With Rosa Mazziotta," he pressed his right hand to Rosa's doorway, seeking support from somewhere. "Do you know why I did what I did, Dannie?"

Dannie could and did imagine, as Roscoe trance-held him.

"I did nothing," Roscoe's treble voice mellowed in the March blustering wind. "Rosa came to me. They say she's a tramp, but each man believes what he wants—what suits him. She came to me to get even with your mother and her ex-husband who quickie-divorced her," Roscoe was convinced in what he was saying. "I took what she gave me, Dannie, for whatever the reasons were. I took it because my age didn't outlive the hunger—my need for it. Why your mother prowled each night to find out if it was true, I will never know. Pride? Fear of your finding out a truth? I don't know. But I know this," Roscoe let go his grip, stood as tall as he could on the sidewalk. "I will tend to Rosa's three children as if they were mine, as I have tended to you as if you belonged to me. I am not your natural father, Dannie. Your mother, in her trauma dreams howls of death, but only she alone knows what it means, and if she doesn't, your bedeviled aunt may know." He paused, as though gathering strength for the final salvo. "All I know is that I've done the best I can by all of you. More. I know I tried beyond human endurance, and I can't go on any longer. And I only know what Rosa tells me . . ." He was going to get it out if it killed him. "That your real father used you. I figured it out with Rosa's help. He used you, on a stormy night, to spring that criminal Willie Sutton and that Augie. You were a rented nephew—a decoy, Dannie. You can't imagine the shame I feel now at just learning the whole of it." Dannie could almost hear the sob Roscoe was choking down. But he couldn't be put off. Not now. "And I know what Rosa claims— that your father is none other than . . ." Roscoe fought from saying it, but found himself wrapped in Rosa's words, " . . . that her ex-husband, the bookmaker king of this section, Johnny Squint is your true father." Roscoe Valencia was immediately sorry he had said it. He had his index finger and thumb of his right hand over his closed eyelids, he couldn't see, but he felt the zap of a lashing cold backhand across his left cheek.

Eleanor Cross would have smashed him again and kept on slapping him if Dannie hadn't stepped in between. He turned to his . . . to Roscoe, wanting to hug him, kiss him for the tenderness he had shown him when he was growing up.

Fifty-year-old Roscoe had had his say. The day was beginning, but over. Roscoe returned Dannie's look and gave him a weak smile. He wanted to say so much more to this boy blessed with good looks that he could never have given him. He stood still a moment longer, not touching, soothing the blotch on his cheek, his brown eyes saying that he was open to Dannie come what may. He turned again, glancing at his wife, Eve, a vacant yet once more yearning glance. Then he turned and shuffled into Rosa Mazziotta's apartment building.

An avalanche of emotions hit Dannie. He was shocked, scared, repelled, and exhilarated all at once. Through the bedlam of his mind came the incisive reality that, of course, Roscoe was not his father! But it's sad, he reflected. He did love his fa . . . Roscoe in his own way.

"We can well do without that *shidukh* slime," Eleanor carped, standing defiant by the corner, alarmed at the impact of the "escape" revelation, her fingernails fangs waiting for Roscoe's sourpuss if he dared show it again! "And don't you believe a word he said." She reached out abruptly for her nephew's hand. "Come home."

"Dannie, come with us," his mother had unraveled herself, fear pervading her green eyes. Her son was "marked!" She nearly lunged for him.

Dannie withdrew his hand from Eleanor's. Like the striking suddenness of a whiplash, he backpedaled away from the two women.

Free; for once in his life he felt free. "I am going home," his words sunken in the wind. "To my father!" He spun on his heels, running. He loved both his mother and aunt, but loved them both in a way that had confounded Roscoe. He ran like all hell was chasing him, finally reaching Pete's Radio Store, where he side-fisted on the curtained-glass paneled door. Reb came to it, peering a moment before opening the door.

"Reb. Is Johnny here?"

"No."

"Can I stay and wait for him?" Dannie asked as he rapidly closed the door behind him.

Reb Sica hunched his frail shoulders thinking a moment. "Guess so," he said. "What is it kid?"

Dannie saw the figures of his mother and aunt outside the closed door. "It's them." He didn't point. "Can I stay here and wait for him? Can I sleep here? In the small back room? The basement?" The banging started. Reb, the curtain pulled partly aside, eyed the two women frantically pounding their hands into the glass of the door. He narrowed his eyes, recognizing them. Dannie's comely mother from Ninth Avenue, and her zany sister. He was about to open the door.

Dannie grabbed for his hand. "Reb, please. Johnny will O.K. it. Don't let them in, Reb. Johnny'll get mad if you do. Please!" Reb looked from the kid to the two women outside. This was way above his head, but he had Johnny's temper in mind—the feelings he had for this kid. He didn't want to rouse his boss's hot head. Finally, he came to a decision as he opened the door an inch, his foot jammed against the bottom wood panel. "Ladies. Go home. It's late. This Borough Park's like a slew of fallin' bombs from a B-57," he tried to be as nice and delicate as he could be.

"You'll bring the cops down on us. There's a few . . . games going on in the back. You'll get me, the kid, all of us in a world of trouble." Enough said, he pushed hard against their pressing weight, shutting the door tight.

WHEN A MAN HAS TO BE MURDERED, THE MAN WHO has to murder him has two primary thoughts. One is how to do it; the other is how to get away with it.

The How entails "setting" the person "up"—isolating him. If it's done properly it leaves that much more room to make sure that you get away cleanly.

The round of meetings that had kept John out of Pete's for two

weeks furnished the Why. In fact, as he sat on a backless stool at
Fiola's bar drinking Three Feathers rye whiskey straight, the WHY
of it was well past that stage of Johnny Squint's thinking.

More like the Why's of it. He sat in his realm, his little corner of
the world, recollecting how in less than three weeks the "outside
forces" had practically dictated the killing be done, and by this
weekend! He sidled off the stool, waving to bovine Mush the bartender to send his refurbished drink along with him, to the distant
booth by the wall of the elongated Dining Room.

"There's a smell in your corner, Mazziotta. And it ain't the season's winds that's bringin' it there," Albert had hissed, in the closed-
to-public meeting at Jimmy Red's Ristorante on the lower East
side, Mulberry street, New York City. Albert was breathing down
Uncle Frank's neck to have "his man" in Borough Park clean the
Schuster mess up, appeasing Willie while simultaneously showing
EVERYBODY that RATS get to hell before anybody else! Johnny
figured that Al-bert had a point. He'd set an open example to make
the next guy think three times about minding other people's business and sending them to a cell in a living, stewing hell!

"You tolerate this one, it could lead to two, three, till all the *cru-
miros* in Brooklyn find a nest in your domain," Uncle Frank had
warned him, while toying with his milk-fed veal parmigiana at Peter
Lugers Steakhouse in the shadows of the Williamsburg Bridge.
John gulped down his warm rye.

It was also important to feed Willie's ego—show him The Boys
cared. Another escape may well take place. Plus, Willie's sidekick,
Mad Dog Kling, in the slammer also, was screamin' for blood,
some*body's* blood!

Johnny sat alone, Old Man Patsy the waiter setting another
Three Feathers shot in front of him.

Could they tie *him* up with the March 8, 1950, robbery of the
Sunnyside Queens branch of the Manufacturer's Trust Company
bank?

Conspiracy to obstruct justice, aiding and abetting a felon before
and after the robberies, harboring a fugitive . . . the list was too long
for Johnny's mind. He nurtured the rye, his mind afire, neck twitching involuntarily. A shadow crossed his face, and Johnny looked up
to see Hugo approaching the booth.

"A little mess in the neighborhood," Hugo said. He set himself
down next to Johnny.

"Don't I know it."

"No," Hugo said. "Not the stool pigeon citizen. Less than six blocks from here. A different mess."

Johnny took a quick, sidelong glance at his partner. What now? He shifted in his seat, leaning his elbows on the booth's table top, and listened.

"The kid, Dannie, came in to Pete's at about two o'clock this morning. Reb let him in. Your ex-wife Rosa came ten this morning. Seems there was a *budella* involving Dannie, his mother and aunt, and his father, Roscoe. In short, John, your ex claims that Dannie's your kid."

Johnny slowly motioned to old Patsy, who was standing by the deserted row of booths, telling him to bring the Three Feathers bottle, an extra glass, and to shut this part of the restaurant-bar up tight for the evening.

"Like old times," Hugo Duce swigged the bitter whiskey, Patsy shuffling away, perennially wiping his hands on his soiled apron. "Like the night you came to me and Gretti," Hugo continued, "and we polished off a bottle of Schenley. You thought Eve was dead that night. And then she rose from the dead—pregnant. The past's come back to haunt you, John. She's outside," he gestured with his chin to the neon sign window, six booths away.

Outside, Johnny's gaze fixed on the large, red-neon glowing window before him and the silhouetted shadows beyond. He saw himself, so long ago, beside one of those silhouettes on a hospital death-bed. He half swallowed.

Why is it a woman can do this to you? He glanced down at his pinky ring, the purple-tinted ruby.

Why on a Friday evening where there HAD to be a killing before the weekend was over? Johnny breathed a long sigh, throwing his head back, resting it along the top of the booth.

He knew Roscoe was seeing Rosa, knew his ex had baited that poor sucker as part of her vendetta to get revenge on Eve, who she blamed for her and Johnny's breakup.

But Rosa couldn't see past the nose on her face. The divorce had nothing to do with Eve. He only wished again it had. It had been his ex-wife's bragging, lushing, and parading around the neighborhood in undersized, glued-on skirts that had caused him, a man of respect, to get away from the garbage that was cluttering his life, in the neighborhood that he OWNED; a neighborhood where people weren't blind, where they could see from behind window shades. Johnny's temper flared. He tried to contain himself, but the Schuster business was diverting, untidying his head. Then, as if he got a bolt from out of the blue, Johnny saw the way to clear two messes in one weekend.

The ruins of his past life: Eve and Dannie. He found a way in his mind to bind Eve to him forever, because that's what he wanted. Craved. Her. Beside him. The tantalizing doom that her gateway green eyes promised, delving so deep, so on top of her! He had to shake his head violently to get his mind back to the business at hand—the other neighborhood mess: Arnold Schuster.

But he became uncomfortable. Too many memories, now. "She wants to see me?" he whispered to Hugo. Hugo nodded.

Johnny tensed and poured himself another drink. "Tell her to come inside. But not with her fucking sister!"

Johnny sat, and old Patsy, as if by clairvoyance, put Jimmy Dorsey's "Green Eyes" on the jukebox. John's taut frame strained, the whiskey loosening it. He poured, drank. Hugo made his way around the horseshoe-shaped partition, the restaurant's entrance door was locked. John waited, closing his eyes, his Adam's apple locked in his throat. When he opened his eyes, Eve Vale stood by his booth.

He blinked. She was a vision, though an ashen-pale one, the March breeze outside failing to add a rosy color to her cheeks.

She was dressed in black as though she had never risen from that coma hospital bed, but had stood waiting for her own prolonged wake these past sixteen years.

But her eyes never changed! Johnny sat breathless, the male crooner speaking for him: *"Those cool and limpid green eyes . . ."* the flammable, haunting green of them a sexual dare whether she meant it or not! Johnny was stirred by her as on the very first day he had spotted her. He rose as she sat across from him.

It was going to be hard, like pulling teeth, Johnny knew. He'd have to say something, make the first move, to get her to open up. He poured her a straight whiskey into the fresh glass that Patsy had brought, the song's lyrics, music coming from behind him, prodding him:

"Your eyes that promise sweet nights —
"Bring to my soul a longing—"

"Go ahead," he said. "It will help you get started. Drink it slowly."

Eve sat immobilized, staring vacantly.

"Come on," he pushed, holding the thick shot glass to her. "Drink and we'll get this on the road. Drink and tell me what you want."

"I want my son," she said, spurning the glass. Her voice sounded jittery, the old glittering fireflame appearing in her almond-shaped eyes.

"Sip the drink," Johnny, his pulse racing, felt that he was going to win this battle before it began. "Sip it, and unwind. And you'll get what you want."

He watched her. She was suspicious at first, her eyes an obsidian alert. Then, taking her drink, she held his eyes while she began to sip. "Don't let him stay in that 'den,' the Radio Store." She drained the glass, seeming almost human without the mind shackles of that Highlander bitch Eleanor around. Johnny held his breath. "He thinks you're Number One in this neighborhood," Eve went on. "He thinks other things about you too. He won't come home to me." She set the glass down on the table, simmering down. John kept plying her with more whiskey.

"You have influence over him. Talk to him. I want my Dannie with me! Order him!"

Johnny heard what she said and heard what she didn't say. He had it all down pat, doing some quick calculations in his mind. Everything was coming together. He had his strategy all worked out. Why it had taken sixteen years, he wouldn't even venture a guess. Eve hadn't said a word about Roscoe. She didn't want a guarantee that her husband would never see Rosa again.

She only wanted Dannie. *Something he could give her*—on one condition. It was long overdue. He refilled their glasses. Tapping his glass into hers, they drank together; Helen O'Connell, the singer, was now wailing from the bubbly-neon jukebox . . .

"*. . . For happiness I fear*
"*That they will ever haunt me . . .*
"*All through my life they'll taunt me . . .*
"*But will they ever want me . . .*
"*Green eyes . . .*"

"You'll get Dannie," Johnny began as the song ended. "In a better neighborhood far away from here. One in which I won't have to live near the stigma of Rosa. I'm married again. But it's one of convenience. My second time around. But like your first, I see now, there's no real love in it. You'll get Dannie, Eve. But where he goes, I go."

Eve stared at him straight in the eye, more like her eyes were becoming glazed, transfixed. "You're propositioning me, John." Her hand, the glass in it, were poised in midair. "You want me for a mistress. You want to attack me like you did . . . in my sleep of death . . ." Her words cut into him like a knife. This was not what he had wanted.

"I never said I attacked you," Johnny stammered, trying to

regain control of the conversation. "And I never said anything about you being a mistress. You'll be my *wife* as it should have been the night I went to ask you that very question."

"You never said you attacked me?" Eve wouldn't listen. She was obsessed, speaking from a distance of sixteen years. "My sister told me! It was worse than rape. It was evil satisfaction! Preying on the dead. You made me into what I am today. You made me run from a man's touch. Run further toward my own son! Now he recoils from me. Dannie, the only one in the world I can trust. That's how much that horrid night in the hospital killed me. And my Dannie *who may recall 1947*!" She was on the verge of tears.

Johnny didn't know whether to blow his top or just to get up, and hold her. He wanted desperately to drive away those sixteen years.

"Believe what you want about the past," he was hard pressed to swallow, as if sand was stuck in his throat. "But believe this about the future. I'm annulling my marriage to Betty. You do the same with your hubby. I'll foot the bill. I made love to Betty with *you* in mind. I shouldn't even say I made love to her. I don't mean to degrade her, but it was just that I had sex with her. With you," he looked up at her, imploring, "it could be both." Johnny had to skate over that *1947* remark. He'd see Rosa posthaste about it.

"As for Dannie, and your misguided feelings . . . that was yesterday. This evening is marriage." He freely poured two more drinks. "You talk about the dead. What have I been since that hospital night? I've been as dead as I swore you were," he swilled the whiskey down.

"You came here to get Dannie back. I'll give him to you. But you're taking what we both need with him. A husband to get to the bottom of your cedar eyes. To get to the bottom of you!"

Eve was taking pleasure in her sixth drink, becoming a full-blown woman again in finishing it, she half rose, slipping out of her black coat.

Johnny was taken aback. Her trim waist, enveloping hips that made his blood itch from the seminal language they spoke, both fitting snugly in her black skirt—all but mermaid material. An infectious shimmer coated her, the sensuality of it breaking down his barriers.

He stood her up, wanting to see, feel the flame-wine that had run in her veins when they used to kiss goodnight by her upstairs apartment door. He kissed her. She tried to pull away, but froze instead. He pressed his lips fully into hers, and she began responding, her lips parting, her hands up, touching, gripping the sides of his hair, embracing, her mouth starved. She slowly pulled back.

But the bargain was sealed.

It was settled, Johnny Squint sat alone in the booth. He'd get what and WHO he wanted.

But for some reason he didn't quite trust the mystery, the temperament of those endless eyes when Eve had left. So he'd take out some insurance against them as he had planned before she came into Fiola's.

He'd send for Dannie in fifteen minutes or so. Make him part of the scheme of things once more, to a point where Eve could never back down; never say no to his proposal once he delivered Dannie to her. A Badge and a boy and he'd have his lush glen in Loch Ness called Eve.

What is it really to kill someone? Johnny asked himself as he savored the whiskey, savoring more lusciously the kiss Eve had eagerly given him, her curvy frame a hint that green eyes could make dreams come true.

He'd have Eve in a house. With him. Where she belonged.

Schuster dead in Brooklyn where HE belonged.

In the end, he'd get it all, with an O.K. to the enraged Angel, or one of the "associates" ready for a Badge-reward for the solid hit. Sour Gret, stolid Mush, frog-necked Little Mike, maybe even the dying Reb. Any of them, upon success, would be sworn into the "club," *Pronto!* Whether or not he'd take part in it himself he hadn't quite decided yet, but he knew that before the end of the weekend he'd be on top of things again, maintaining his feudal spot in his part of the world, and getting all that he should have gotten from the very start.

He half-turned, summoning the statue-like Patsy by the Wurlitzer, telling him to hustle across the street to Pete's to get the boy Dannie over here *rapido*!

1952

That night Dannie stood across the avenue from Max Schuster's Custom Clothing Store.

He shifted his feet on the lamppost-lit Fifth Avenue sidewalk, curling his toes inside his socks and shoes. He turned, shivering, from the wind, and pretended to window-shop the dimly lit stores.

Trying to get warm, he twisted his hands deep in his gray pants pockets and hunched his shoulders under his windbreaker.

The lights in Max's clothing store went out across the street, with only the night burglary protective light staying on. He had been watching the store for an hour. Johnny had warned him that Schuster may have clandestinely been provided police protection and asked him to watch to see if they cruised the store, picked him up, or followed him home. This was key. The neighborhoods were in a fever, filled with whispered warnings that some crank might come along and take a pot-shot at Arnold just for the stupid glory of it.

Dannie caught a whiff of perfume and saw a young, fair blonde passing close by him. He became distracted as she smiled. He smiled in return, then turned away. No distractions. He shut his mind to her.

Within three minutes, he saw Arnie closing up for the night. He looked at his gold, flexible-band Bulova wrist watch that Johnny had supplied him.

8:45 p.m.

Dannie walked along Fifth Avenue, questions he thought Johnny would have asked filling his mind. Would someone pick him up? Were there cops on his tail? Uniformed, plainclothesmen, or undercover D.A.'s squad men? Was that short, tubby figure with the black fedora on who had left earlier, Arnold's father, Max? Dannie shuffled along the Avenue, following Schuster as he walked home.

The distance was about a city mile. The time he arrived at his front door at 941 45th Street was 9:12 p.m.

Dannie, aware that his eyesight wasn't that good, was sure it was Schuster he had followed. The big ears, the somewhat curly hair.

And he didn't know why Schuster had walked. To save the bus fare? To get the brisk night air after all those hours cramped in that store maybe?

He felt fairly certain that no cops had trailed Schuster. He hoped, because of his impaired vision, that he was correct in his observations.

He went back to Pete's Radio Store and reported to Hugo Duce, brooding Gretti, Mush, and moldy-faced Al Rispone. Johnny wasn't around.

Laying down on an old couch at 10:15 p.m. in the rear of Pete's, he realized there were no games at all on tonight.

Chilly, he tossed under his windbreaker and tried to sleep.

But three questions he hadn't asked caused him to stay awake:

One: Are you my father?

Two: Why was he watching Arnold Schuster?

Three: Was *he* there when Willie Sutton and *Augie* escaped from prison?

The suddenness when Johnny had summoned him over to Fiola's through Patsy earlier this evening had stumped him. The revelation that Johnny had been with his mother ten minutes before he got there had thrown him into a dumbfounded state that was now just beginning to wear off. He had sat at the booth with Johnny and listened in rapt attention. He would see his mother no later than Sunday. And that's an order!

Sunday would be a new beginning, one that should have begun

sixteen years ago.

Were his mother and John getting together? Was he the cause of it? Could he live with his thoughts of his mother? Would he be living under a roof that Johnny presided over? The thoughts kept coming in torrents.

Roscoe. Rosa. What of them? His temples beat.

Arnold Schuster. Tonight. What of him?

Finally, his thought-twisted tossing subsided as he fell into the muffled claws of sleep.

1952

March 8

Saturday night. Dannie turned out the gold side of his reversible windbreaker. He was at his post on Fifth Avenue. His Bulova read 9:00 p.m.

Arnold Schuster closed his father's store for the night and began his walk home, Dannie a half a block behind him.

He'd follow Arnold home. Go back to Pete's. Then Sunday would be HIS day.

But he saw the figure ahead of him stop, mid-way home, and talk to . . . Dannie squinted in the dark . . . four guys. He was about to make an about face, but felt it would be too obvious. Maybe they'd notice it. So he walked straight ahead, past the group.

"Hey!" he heard, slowing his pace. "Hey!"

He was about 30 feet from the five of them when he turned inquisitively.

"You," Arnold Schuster shouted from within the circle. "Your two pair of pants. Isn't that you?"

Dannie stood still.

"That's you," Arnold peered in the dark. "It's been a while now.

They're ready. Weren't you the one I spoke to? You left the large deposit."

Dannie, remaining silent, just eased backwards, sitting himself on the closest cement stoop front.

"I'll be right there," Schuster shouted, turning to the young men he was talking to. Their ages, as best as Dannie could estimate at that distance, ranged from eighteen to twenty-three. Dannie waited in the shadow of a two-family brick building.

They were discussing a party at a club—a meeting hall. Dannie could hear their animated voices from where he sat, telling Arnie to get home quick, freshen up, change his clothes, and join them.

Arnold Schuster walked up to Dannie after the group jovially broke up. "That's you," he scrutinized Dannie's face. "The one I spoke to in the store over two weeks ago. Which way are you headed?"

"Ninth Avenue."

"Same here," Schuster said, as he began walking along with Dannie.

Well at least his "spotting" in this affair would be over; he'd been "spotted" himself. He listened to Arnie recounting that it wasn't Shea, or McClellan or Weiner or any other Bergen Street policemen that deserved credit for the capture of the infamous Sutton. "It was me!" he nearly shouted. "Haven't the newspapers proven it! See?" It wasn't the police who were so diligent or brave that day!

Dannie just walked briskly, his hands thrust deeply into the pockets of his gold windbreaker. Arnold was talking about his sixteen-year-old kid brother, Wally, at home. "My brother and you . . . what's your name again? Dannie, right? You'd make a great pair. Wally's out looking for girls. You're a good-lookin' kid. You must be busy fighting them off." They reached the corner of Ninth Avenue and 45th Street, a dead-row of tree-lined two-family, mostly brick homes. The Avenue was deserted. Then, Dannie saw it.

A '52 Lincoln. Capri. Two door. Dark blue.

With Gretti . . . no, Hugo Duce . . . was that him in the passenger seat? Dannie narrowed his eyes as the 160-horsepower car whizzed soundlessly by. Was it Johnny or Augie behind the wheel?

"You shouldn't have did what you did," Dannie blurted out, suddenly afraid.

"What? Point out that gangster?" Arnold was relaxed. Cocky. Too at ease with himself, and his surroundings. "It's done," he said. "And in spite of all the threatening telephone calls and letters from cranks, a bank robber is behind bars where he belongs. And I'll be wealthy enough soon to expand. Buy another store. Maybe start a chain."

Dannie saw the Lincoln maneuver into a parking spot a block away, by 44th Street. Schuster was telling him how he had his phone disconnected. Now these crackpots wouldn't have a chance to threaten him over the wires, from far out of state no less. But it was just as bad in this very neighborhood, what with four nights ago a car full of "wise guys," from Eighth Avenue, he thought . . . young ones in their early twenties, driving up on the sidewalk two blocks from here, while he was on his way home. They may have also been the ones that had broken the store window. They were looking for trouble, circling, screaming in delight that he was a squealer! But he had ignored those cheap taunts . . . empty threats.

"Run home," Dannie touched his arm. "Don't go to that party. Run home!" His eyes were glued to the Lincoln down the block.

"Why?" Arnold looked around, up and down the bleak Avenue.

"Don't ask," Dannie glimpsed up 45th Street, it was grave-dark and still. He glanced down the Avenue at the big Lincoln. "Just *run* home!" Dannie urged desperately.

"Why?" Arnold quizzed again. He followed Dannie's glances, but saw nothing.

"You were the one . . ."

"Get out of here!" Dannie heard the shots again, in his head, resounding in Prospect Park. He pushed Schuster away from him, realizing they were trying to use him this time. Was it worth the price of a father? Arnold Schuster finally caught the intensity of Dannie's warning, backing away from him, turning, and walking hurriedly towards home—twelve doors away on 45th Street.

He reached the driveway of 913 45th.

Thirteen. Never a lucky number, they say, for many. Even less so for Arnold Schuster.

The figure of a man stepped halfway from the driveway.

Dannie heard explosion after explosion on the residential street.

He saw Arnold Schuster's hands jolt to his eyes, folding limp to his groin, his body giving way, falling like a domino on its back!

The slithering figure from the driveway backed away and swiftly disappeared.

Run like a bastard, Dannie's brain told him. Run over to Schuster on the cold sidewalk. Scamper to the Lincoln? He turned, stared, felt impaled on the corner.

A minute ticked by after the death flashes of bursting light and roaring peals came from the gun.

He saw the distant form of a fedora'd man down the avenue, hastily entering the Lincoln. The car with the tremendous overhead valve power, wheeled away, and Dannie chased it. His . . . father may be in it. He raced down Ninth Avenue, chasing the Lincoln Capri out of his sight, until he was on his haunches, breathing for desperate air to fill his laboring lungs.

Go back, he decided. His eyes were wind-bitten tears. Damn savages!

He felt helpless with the Lincoln gone. But he walked back, in a seeming-trance, to 45th and Ninth. He saw a woman walking a dog, the dog licking at Schuster's blood-filled eyes. The woman's screams rose above the dog's yelps. It was as if Arnold's two eyes had volcano-erupted from his sockets. Dannie's belly erupted vomit.

He had the teary sense to turn his reversible jacket inside out, from gold to navy blue. Stepping from his own curbside puke, he mussed his hair, and moved away from the corner lamppost.

The woman had run to the nearest houselight, the one coming from the 4423 Ninth Avenue window sign of S.M. Fialks, M.D.

The police cars swarmed there less than seconds apart, as the Doctor, in his bathrobe, was out on the 45th Street sidewalk, his black leather kit opened in a gesture of futility. He knelt in the night beside the body, and then stood up, head bowed in resignation.

Dannie inched into the crowd that had built up, coming from in front of spare television sets, radio programs, family weekend gatherings; a dense jam of onlookers cramming, shoving to get a look-see.

Dannie stood as if buried among the people. His eyesight may have been bad, but his hearing was good, and he heard the fragmented testament of the doctor to the inquiring, shoving, chalking police. "A youngster, a boy, a gold jacket." Dannie inched his way from the surging crush of humans and walked down Ninth Avenue, expecting with each step to be beamed-in by a police car's spotlight. Finally he reached his apartment house.

He skirted up the stairs and banged on his apartment door until his knuckles were worn, bruised.

He had no key.

And he had no mother at home. No Sesqu's down below with a telephone. He returned to the street.

There was a pay phone in the Ninth Avenue above-ground subway station, and this time he had money on him. A hundred and sixty dollars. What was left over from his earned money as Johnny's gaming "spotter" and the custom pants ordering. He received change of a dollar from the paymaster booth's clerk.

But who should he call? he wondered, closing the folding door of the telephone booth behind him.

Johnny first! He dialed Pete's Radio Store. Wrong number; it was a guy with a gruff, nasty voice.

He could never remember numbers correctly. He dialed information, but Pete's wasn't listed. Next he tried his aunt's number. The one she had transferred to her new apartment on McDonald Avenue. Eleanor answered on the first ring.

She begged him to come home, his mother also getting on the line. He wanted the warmth and safety of his mother and aunt tonight—Roscoe was gone.

But suddenly Dannie had the four guys in mind that Arnold Schuster had met. They might remember him and he'd be traced. No way would he go home. He begged his mother not to call the police or missing persons, because he wouldn't be home for a while. The Doctor's words of a "youngster in a gold jacket" echoed in his head, causing him to plead with his mother to understand, to have patience, to trust him, love him. He'd be home very soon. She said it must have something to do with Johnny, but somehow he managed to get her to agree. Tomorrow was the day, she kept repeating. He kissed the mouthpiece of the telephone before hanging up.

Johnny, Gretti, Mush? Dannie stood mulling in his mind, as if mortared inside the public telephone booth. The killer — the one who re-entered the Lincoln? He had missed one of the silhouette's exiting the Capri on Ninth, going mid-way up 44th Street, furtively through the driveways, backalleys, over a garage yard fence, and lying stealthily, heartless in ambush. All of a sudden he was glad he hadn't been able to reach Pete's.

Hugo Duce, Augie, or Gretti driving that Capri? He felt in a crater of trouble. With people like ruthless lord high executioner Al-bert Anastasia on his mind, he left the train station.

The Capri was parked ten feet to the right of him facing Greenwood Cemetery on the bypass above the freight yards, blue, big, his own blue eyes bulging quarter-size. Was that Johnny's red rocket Olds parked three car lengths down from it? Could it be?

He was afraid to go near it, so he turned, pushed through the station's metal door and turnstiled his fare.

On his left, the West End Line would take him to 36th Street, South Brooklyn. He recoiled from that. They kill you for less than the price of a phone call down there. He slanted to his right, the

West End to Coney Island and the Atlantic Ocean.

The train was a long time coming. He boarded it, sat, and cried for Arnold, his stomach a shell-shocked cavity. He was on his way to an answer, a hunt, a hideaway, or his tomb. He'd call Johnny's new house. The train bounded, screeched, when he reached the Stillwell Avenue, Coney Island Station.

Last stop!

1952

The Beginning of The Quest: Sunday, March 9

For fifteen cents you could get the late Sunday edition of the *New York Times,* on cloudy March 9. And read all about it: MAN WHO SPOTTED SUTTON SLAIN IN BROOKLYN STREET.

If you liked gore, you'd get your money's worth. There was a photo of the young victim, Arnold Schuster, lying sprawled on his back in front of his home, felled by four bullets.

A family portrait in print: mother, father and brother hearing the news flash on television, running out onto the street and seeing Arnold dead on the sidewalk.

If you read between the lines, you'd find out not only that Arnold had been shot with a .38 caliber revolver, but also where he had been shot.

Once in each eye. This was so everyone would have *bad eyesight* in the future.

And twice in the balls. Because the manhood of Arnold Schuster was taken away, as a result of his good eyesight.

New York's judges made their speeches. "This ruthless murder is a direct challenge to law and order. It is the most dastardly act committed by the underworld gunmen who perpetrated this bold killing of an innocent and law abiding citizen of our community who simply did his duty calling the identity of Sutton to the attention of the police."

Judges Goldstein and Leibowitz (Al-bert's former attorney) were confident that, "those responsible will be brought to the bar of justice for this heinous crime."

The liberals lodged protests that the victim had not been protected by either the District Attorney's office or the Police Department. They charged that the law enforcement agencies of New York were in cahoots with the criminal element of the city.

Dannie, one of the readers, shuttled out from his two-dollar-a-day furnished room by the Coney Island Boardwalk, and bought every different paper on the news stand at Stillwell Avenue.

He had called Johnny's Bath Beach home before going back to his room. Tried Pete's again. No answers! A young boy had been spotted by a Doctor's housekeeper on Ninth. He was going slowly mad, trudging to his room, the one the fat Italian landlady had rented him as long as he paid in advance. He had scoured Surf Avenue, the side streets, saw the vacancy sign, and knocked and knocked until the color of his money had obtained him shelter.

He listened to the news obsessively, trying to piece it all together while watching the twelve-inch Admiral television set that the landlady allowed him to view in her apartment, for an additional fifty cents. "Con-Edison are no cousins of mine," she had intoned, making invisible his half dollar somewhere in the flab of her apron-skirt.

WPIX was offering a reward. Rudolph Halley, the City Council President, was making a pitch for public cooperation—the same one Arnold Schuster had first fallen for.

The four young men that Schuster had seen one half hour before he died were being questioned.

At 2:30 in the morning officials had questioned Willie Sutton in the ultra-secure Queens County Jail. Among the authorities were Assistant District Attorney Silver, from Kings County, Brooklyn, two Queens District Attorneys, two inspectors from the New York City Police Department, and the Queens Jail Warden, Milton Klein.

Willie said he knew only what he had heard on the prison broadcast.

"The killing of Arnold Schuster sinks me," he had stated. But he showed no remorse at Schuster's death. Why should he? He didn't even know him.

Yet he sent his true condolences to the Schuster family.

Either way it was the same. Willie already owed 105 years to the states of New York and Pennsylvania in unserved prison terms. And what with the Sullivan law—illegal possession of a pistol for a felon—outstanding against him, and the positive identification of at least several bank tellers, clerks, and one manager, he was also sunk for the 1950 Sunnyside Queens bank hold-up.

But the police had a lead. They were searching for one, Frederick J. Tenuto, alias "Angel," A.K.A. "St. John." He was a psychopath who had escaped a Philadelphia jail with Sutton in 1947 and was reputedly a loyal member of the Sutton gang.

Dannie stared at Augie's picture, full-blown on the *New York Daily News* front page.

Was *he* himself part of that '47 escape, Dannie flinched.

Was it Augie in the Lincoln that night? Augie. So steadfast, ready to back up Johnny with a gun when John had belted Little Mike. Dannie thought of Augie then, so compassionate to him, holding him a foot off the ground, as if also defending his mother. Dannie cringed. Augie, a fugitive all that while!

He went out again to telephone Johnny. Betty, volunteering that she was John's estranged wife, told Dannie that she hadn't heard from him, but she asked him to leave a number where he could be reached. He hung up, and returned to his boarding house.

THE MARCH 10 HEADLINE WAS THAT 150 POLICEMEN were seeking the Schuster slayer. The motive a mystery.

U.S. Attorney Miles Lane labeled the killing a challenge by the underworld to the United States government. "And we will meet this challenge!" he proclaimed.

More of a sideline than a headline was that funeral services for Arnold Schuster were held at Flatbush Memorial Chapel. Burial at Montefiore Cemetery, in Springfield, Queens. Dannie tried to stifle his welling tears. Lord, he was so *damn sorry.*

"A cold-blooded killing," the greedy landlady remarked at the publicity.

More like hot-blooded, Dannie knew, thinking of Johnny's temper, the meanness of men like Al-bert, and the dedicated rage of Angel Tenuto. The rest of the news of the hour was filled with reports that Schuster's demise was tied up in New York crime. The public was horrified by the rackets, and would meet this underworld dare face-to-face. Dannie thought it about time to dare to telephone his mother and aunt.

He did, from a pay phone on nearby Neptune Avenue. He resisted the pleadings to tell them where he was, the renewed promises of his mother to do away with herself, and the threats of his aunt to have Johnny Squint hunted for abduction, for that's what it must be. He asked if anyone had . . . inquired about him. The answer from his aunt that the awful, malaria-faced Al Rispone and the repulsive Little Mike had been asking his whereabouts had made him swallow dry gasps. His mother, retrieving the phone, said she was to blame for trusting Johnny that by Sunday everything would be set right, that they could all start again. She had been wrong in confessing what her *damn* past had been, nearly prodding her to the edge of . . . on the living room couch nights. He got nauseous to the throat—John KNEW that? Leaving the telephone receiver dangling from the coiled black cord, he staggered from the booth, retching on the way to his lonely furnished room. He wasn't too sure now if he wanted to find Johnny after all.

THE REMAINDER OF MARCH IN HIDING WAS ONE which Dannie spent existing on Nathan's famous hot dogs—and throwing them up as soon as he ate.

His dreams were invaded by gunfire and death, his shrieks one night bringing his landlady pounding on the door. How could he control a nightmare?

He was attentive to the news, bombarded by it. New York's Mayor Impelitteri was pledging aid in the hunt for Schuster's killer.

Police Commissioner Monaghan was asking the public for help, vowing them protection.

The two garage mechanics who had figured in the Sutton arrest were being threatened. Two hundred detectives were now on the case. Schuster's kin were under protection. A gang of Eighth Avenue boys were "rounded up" and put on line-ups to see if they had threatened Arnold Schuster before his death, were responsible for breaking Max Schuster's clothing store windows, or were the ones threatening to bomb the *Brooklyn Eagle*'s newspaper delivery trucks with posters asking the public for aid in tracking down the murderers — and to see if any of them resembled a boy who may have figured in the killing of March 8th.

Dannie hardly slept at all now.

1952

April-May

Dannie, devastated as if on a dangerous distant cloud, decided to try to see the man at the center of it all: Willie Sutton.

A hasty impulse, he nevertheless subwayed it to the borough of Queens, New York.

"Up, Willie. Down, Schuster!" was the cry of the throngs of college students outside the Queens County Courtroom.

All through The Actor's speedy trial, the same pulsating screams could be heard on the Queens Courthouse streets as Dannie heard them now, April 1st, "Up, Willie. Down, Schuster!" Willie Sutton's sentencing for conviction of a Queens Bank Robbery, as a fourth offender, and for two counts of the Sullivan Law, was about to be pronounced!

Dannie cautiously mixed with the over-zealous students; he felt reasonably safe since burying his tell-tale gold-blue reversible jacket in the sand by the cresty Atlantic Ocean, under the Brooklyn Coney Island boardwalk.

He needed a pass to get inside the guarded Court building, and an elegant, slender student, Fran, after being crushed up against him, offered to get Dannie in. She was a comely, Israeli exchange student in her mid-twenties. Dannie was grateful to her.

She whispered something to him about the presiding Judge

Farrell while they sat in the packed courtroom, her short, boyish-cut brunette hair tickling his left ear. Dannie was preoccupied, thinking that everyone was looking at *him*, but he was hoping like mad to get the chance to talk to Willie Sutton, to get some inside info on John, that Willie may well have heard through the "grapevine."

Willie Sutton, alert, perceptive, glanced at two books on the defense table before him: *Peace of Mind* and *Peace of Soul.*

Beside him was a wrinkled man wearing tinted eyeglasses. One of his partners in the 1950 bank robbery—Tommy (Mad Dog) Kling. The authorities had apprehended Mad Dog through J.D. Venuta shortly after the capture of The Actor.

Willie was sentenced to two separate consecutive fifteen year to life terms as a fourth felony offender, but he didn't seem too shaken by it.

He was giving quick statements to the media and the public: he abjures violence, he intones. Dannie pushing, inched to the court-room's wood rail along with Fran, to hear Willie spout that: crime doesn't pay.

"Get Augie. The buy-out." Dannie heard, Willie a half a foot from him, his eyes averted.

"Where? How?" Dannie breathed, crushed by reporters and autograph seekers.

"Through Johnny," Willie whispered through a smile as he was led away by four uniformed guards.

Dannie stood muddled, feeling that the brief confab had accomplished nothing. He felt bad for Fran, her eyes tearful as Willie Sutton disappeared from the Court.

"He's buried alive," Fran said outside on the sidewalk. "Past being a three-time loser."

She explained to Dannie that she had recognized him despite his flattened, Brylcreamed hair. She was Willie's "companion" from Staten Island—not a student.

Dannie was puzzled. "Recognized me from where? When?"

"From Fiola's in Borough Park." She related the two occasions she had seen him. He had been standing outside the restaurant in short pants with John Mazziotta and Augie. The other time was when Willie had received a slap in the face from that fat slob of a tyrant. Both times she had been parked across the Avenue sitting behind the wheel of a car that Willie had bought her.

Dannie blushed at the mention of "short pants." His face flushed even more at the recollection of Willie being slapped because he had spotted him in South Brooklyn.

Fran gave him her address and telephone number in Staten Island. She told him to stay in contact. If she heard anything about Johnny Squint, she'd relay it to him. Before leaving, she mentioned that Reb, the short, comical bookie from Pete's Radio Store, was dying of cancer in Coney Island Hospital.

They parted, Dannie promising to get in touch with her. He had the premonition that there was something else on her mind.

That night Dannie weighed the prospect of seeing Reb. Reb had always been a decent guy. His only mean trait came out when talking about the hateful Al-bert, his tumorous neck bulging from the thought of Al-bert encroaching into the gambling boundaries of Borough Park.

A death-bed visit is where they say people tell the truth.

He'd take the chance, telephone the hospital, get the room number, lay in wait, size things up, and make sure no relatives or "friends" were present.

Reb was in critical condition. Open visiting twenty-four hours a day as long as his days lasted. He'd plead with Reb, tell him he was Johnny's son, and wanted to find his father. Dannie slept well that night.

When he made his move that first week in April, the time seemed right, the hour late enough, the tiled hospital corridor deserted. But he found he had made it too late. Reb Sica was dead.

Dannie slowly walked Ocean Parkway toward "home." Heaven had beat him to the punch. If Reb had known where Johnny was, he had taken the secret with him. Dannie sat alone in his room, drawing another blank, filling his mind with the fantasy of having sexual intercourse with Gloria Bruzzese, Antoinette Narghelle, and Eleanor Cross. It was better than recapturing Arnold's eyes being lapped, swallowed by a dog on 45th Street. Dannie hoped he wouldn't have his first wet dream. He only had one pair of underwear that he alternately wore and washed. Eleanor was winning the contest among his mental images, and he was on the verge of giving up and calling her, but he held on.

By mid-April Dannie had only enough money to last him maybe three more weeks. He had scraped, painted the landlady's fire escapes, which had bought him a free week's rent.

He had stopped telephoning Johnny's home. Betty still maintained that she had not heard from her estranged hubby.

Pete's Radio Store number had been changed, Dannie kept attuned to the news.

The gun that was used to do away with Schuster was found five blocks from the slaying after the area had been fine-combed by squadrons of detectives. It didn't make sense. Maybe it was a police set up . . . a plant. The empty lot where the gun was allegedly found was on West Ninth Avenue, the opposite direction from where the Lincoln had been traveling.

Brooklyn longshoremen were being grilled about the gun, because the revolver was found to be among a stolen Army shipment consigned for abroad.

The Schuster killing was seen as deterring possible witnesses in the waterfront probe of Al-bert Anastasia's criminal activities there. Twenty-five of the longshoremen were suspect. The grilling had gone on for over eighty hours straight. Eleven of the dock workers, from three gang shifts, were arraigned as witnesses. The buyer of the guns was apparently described by them, but Dannie couldn't for the life of him find the buyer's description. Why not? He searched page after page, column after column. Were they holding it back? Did they really know?

There were vagrants, nuts, mental cases all over the Tri-State area confessing to Arnold's killing.

At the end of April, Dannie had the desolate urge to call someone. Antoinette or Anna? To contact them would be suicide.

Kathleen? Suicide too, if her father, Johnny's brother, relayed it to Gretti, Al Rispone, Tony-boy, or anyone else.

Sassy Gloria Bruzzese? He'd adore her beside him on his bed, as lousy as it and his room were. Would she come? Would she tell Kathleen? Would it be involving her? He couldn't do that.

So he gave in, deposited the nickel into the pay telephone slot, and called his mother again.

But she was under a doctor's sedation, his aunt raving that he was driving both of them to a madhouse. He felt like saying they didn't have far to go, but he was so desperate for someone to talk to that he let her go on. He would get down on his knees and pray his mother would be all right, he promised, but she had to please keep her promise not to contact the authorities over his disappearance, for it could mean his actual disappearance. His aunt thought him a lunatic, and he could have countered again but instead entreated her to take care of his mother. Then she grew familiar, intimate on the telephone, and he thought she was stalling to put a tracer on his call—she was a Supervisor now at the Telephone Company on Sixteenth Avenue.

"Do you miss me?" she breathed huskily.

He swallowed, sensing a trap.

"Do you need money?" she said.

"No."

"Do you need . . . a woman?" she seemed dead-earnest.

"No!" He wouldn't give her the satisfaction.

"You do," she knew. "You'll be sixteen in December. Come home. Explain this insanity to us. We're on the brink of becoming *chometzdekih Yideneh*! We want to protect you. Is this anything to do with . . ." she lowered her voice to a hush, "what happened in Borough Park in March? Through that *quinto*, vile, despicable Johnny?"

"No!"

"I don't believe you!" she tore into him on the phone. "You're shielding him! Come home! I'll tell you the truth about your father! Come home!"

Another trap, he let her rave.

"Are you there?" she asked, calming down, fluctuating as always between fever-pitch and tenderness.

"I'm here."

"Daniel, come home. You want what you almost took from me once. Twice. You'll find out the reasons why . . ."

He hung up, the hot dog of the day about to come out of him. He was holding it down in the pit of his queasy stomach. She was a *lussuoso* thirty-three-year-old, but why did she have to be his mother's sister!

He rested on the firm, supportive mattress of his furnished room, after completing his set of forty push-ups. No hot stove, no refrigerator, no nothing, but his life! He lay alone, thinking of what his aunt really had on her mind. He tuned her out, tossing sweat-chilly in his hectic, frightened sleep, gunfire resounding inside the walls of his brain.

IN MID-MAY HE FOUND THE WARM LIGHT OF DAY. HE was out on the street with fifteen cents in his pocket.

You could purchase the follow-up newspapers for a nickel. A weekday *New York Times*. There was a world alarm out, from May 2, 1952, for an ex-convict sought in Schuster's killing.

A flashily dressed Borough Park, Brooklyn, bookmaker.

A Bush Terminal Pier representative of Frank Costello's.

He was known as "Chappy" on the waterfront, as "Squinty" in

Borough Park, as "Johnny Squint" Mazziotta to his intimates. Dannie had wondered why it had taken so long for John's name to be reported, when the longshoremen had "described" the buyer of the case of guns in April? Johnny and the gun!

From the moment of Arnold's brutal death, the New York City Police Commissioner had been outraged. The public was steaming after seeing Arnold and the Commissioner on television, nationwide, after the capture of The Actor, shaking hands—a gesture of the police meeting face to face with John Q. Public, demonstrating how the average citizen could help in the capture of notorious public enemies. The T.V. newscast had shown the promise of wealth on Arnold's face.

He had truly made his brief mark on the world. Dannie walked on, grieving, squinting up at the cloud-barrier sun. He blinked the heavenly beam of the sun from his eyes and walked on with Kathleen's credo in his flooded mind: They'll Enter Heaven A Minute Apart, except for those who take or use a life.

Dannie prayed that he wasn't on the wrong side of Kathleen's beliefs, as he zeroed in on the case at hand.

They had found the murder weapon, a .38 revolver, in an empty parking lot on Ninth Avenue, five blocks from Schuster's house.

Can't be, Dannie kept drilling himself as he steered under the West End El Line toward the center of the Bath Beach section.

If it was Johnny in the driveway, Augie, Hugo Duce or even possibly Gretti in the Lincoln Capri waiting by Ninth and 44th, would he have just tossed the gun away only to be found and traced? He would have had to left-hand, backhand fling it while driving, and it would have had to sail halfway across the avenue, over the sidewalk, and well into the lot. Unlikely. They were professionals. It didn't make sense. Did somebody leave it there, later, so it would be found, and John traced? Was it an outright plant? Dannie figured that a more likely place to get rid of the weapon would have been over onto the subway cuts by the Ninth Avenue Station where he had seen the Capri and Johnny's Olds parked. Dannie was pacing himself to Johnny's house. But why dump it so close at all? He neared 259 Bay Nineteenth Street. Maybe it hadn't been Johnny, Augie, or Hugo Duce after all!

He liked that thought, but thought too of March 8th at 9:35 p.m. when he had gone back to 45th and Ninth—the *murder* scene. He stayed clear of Johnny's last known address, directing his steps into Bensonhurst, thinking that John may well be in the gambler's paradise, Las Vegas, where he'd gone that time during the holidays.

The gangs of longshoremen working the period of time the gun was stolen (missing along with other cases of revolvers) were drilled, questioned, brow beaten, exhausted to a point where the name—Johnny "Squinty" Mazziotta—had finally been uttered. The case of guns in question went to *him*! More significant was that the invoices proved that the murder weapon was definitely among them.

The Quest: find Mazziotta and the killer, or killers, would be found, for Mazziotta supplied the gun. Dannie turned onto Bay Parkway, tired, famished for some savory food other than his steady diet of Nathan's Famous hot dogs that were daily ejected from his fastidious gut. He stared at a phone booth on a corner near Alley's Men's Clothing Store.

More important than his squeamish digestive system was that he was broke and in sore need of clothes, he telephoned his mother.

She was erratic, her voice lost in a daze.

She beseeched him to come home, he was fighting himself not to cry, but was crying anyway, asking her to meet him on 18th and McDonald Avenues. He looked at the face of the Bulova wrist watch John had given him. "In one hour, Mom," he instructed. "One hour.

"And please be careful. Walk around and around to make sure no one in a car, truck, or cab . . . or anything is trailing you," he hung the phone up, but the extra instructions had cost him his last nickel.

The alarm had been sent over the police teletype system for Johnny as of May 2. He had become the target of the most extensive manhunt in the history of the world. A quarter of a million Wanted circulars were printed and distributed throughout the Licensed Garda networks from here to hell. Officials vowed they would find him!

A quarter of a million dollar reward was posted by civic groups, newspapers, T.V. stations, businessmen, the City, and community organizations.

Johnny's picture and description would be distributed to law enforcement agencies internationally—an area populated by over two billion people.

A special National Telephone Headquarters line had been set up to receive information.

Radio stations were blasting the description. Thirty-six years old, five-foot-six-inches tall, black hair, brown eyes, squat. Known to frequent racketeer hang-outs. Dannie walked, wondering, WHERE WAS HE? WAS IT HIM THAT NIGHT? He was in hiding. It had to be, but why was HE *used*!

His mother was on the corner he had designated. She wore a coral briefed coat that accentuated her whistle-bait figure.

The area was afternoon-busy with people, and he felt safe, but shook his head, no, as she was about to reach out to him. He veered left onto McDonald Avenue and into Gregnano's restaurant.

She was all over him, kissing him, commenting, as she wiped the tears from her face, on the noticeable weight he had lost. She embraced him so tightly in the tiny vestibule of the restaurant that the mustachioed waiter had to make an obvious show of false throat clearing to get them to unlock and sit at a table, Jo Stafford's "You Belong To Me" emanating from the restaurant's catty-corner speakers.

He sat on a hard-backed chair across from his mother as she nervously held his hand across the table top and asked repeatedly why he had stayed away from her. "Was it because of what Roscoe said the night you ran to Pete's?" she asked. She broke down into spastic tears and shaking as the befuddled waiter took their order.

Dannie chewed the crisp celery like it was manna, the WHY's burning on *his* mind also! *Why* would Johnny leave knowing he had that long overdue special Sunday meeting. Why?

He didn't answer one of his mother's inquiries while he ate the *ansalad*. All he told her was to go to the Ladies' Room, powder up, dry her eyes, and come back looking like green moonbeams.

That had helped snap her out of her fits of tears and depression. But now, he was ready to ask her ONE question.

"Is Johnny my father?"

He saw her eyes go wide into the wilderness of a blank stare, her body begin to coil into the clothing she was wearing.

"Don't withdraw, Mom," he touched her fingertips. "Is he my father?"

"He . . . is . . . your father," she stammered, hollow, afraid, hauntingly beautiful. Her eyes were possessed by the past, and she choked, unable to command another word from the depths of her. But she had said *enough* for now. Dannie sat as if in a tunnel, a trance. He had lost his father before he found him.

His mother hadn't finished the story when she left to get his aunt. She had only ten dollars on her, but it was enough for the *antipasto*, her burgundy wine, his Golden Wedding rye and tip. The waiter hadn't asked him to show proof of age. The news interval, over the speakers, reported that 20,000 had been killed in Korea.

He must either look older than he was, or else the waiter had thought that his mother was his girlfriend. He knocked the whiskey down, ordering another. Damn Reds and Gooks, he flared.

He drank, waiting for his mother's return, going over the facts of the news at hand. Harvey Bistany—AKA "Oscar the Syrian," a robber friend of Sutton—stated he had been in Brooklyn with Willie and Johnny Squint in late January.

Johnny had become the subject of the First Most Wanted Manhunt in human history that spanned the five civilized continents!

As for Willie, he owed 68 years for his escapes, and was, consequently, shipped to Attica State Prison, Attica, New York, where his cell, his movements would be T.V.-monitored directly in the Warden's office. Dannie concurred with Fran's statement that Willie had been "buried alive."

Angel Tenuto had long since been ruled out as a suspect. The fact that he was also wanted and had been a friend of Sutton's had originally led the police to consider Tenuto a prime suspect. But skepticism arose when a State psychiatrist, upon reviewing Tenuto's file, stated that the suspect did not have any psychopathic tendencies that would enable him to commit such a crime. Dannie balked at that. Augie, he had read, had been serving time for murder, killing for the sake of a friend. Dannie wondered if that was a psychopathic tendency.

But it had been further uncovered that Tenuto was not mob affiliated. He was a loner. The search for him was diverted by the newer, more tangible, development of the case: the finding of the gun.

Max Schuster, Arnold's bereaved but irate father, had promptly sued the City for negligence. The first person ever to sue a municipality. His suit charged that his son's plea for protection was denied. He'd lose. It was in the stars. Dannie recalled the old neighborhood saying . . . nobody beats City Hall. He saw his mother and aunt entering the restaurant.

They looked like the Dolly Sisters. Same coral coats, hand-stitched Arnoldton wool suede, jaunty belts in the back that went nowhere.

He noticed the male appreciation they received as they hung their coats by the small vestibule.

His aunt's iris-blue sapphire eyes tore into Dannie's even before she sat down.

She took him in. He looked slovenly, disheveled. What was he?

An admirer of a lowly bookmaker that had been arrested no less than twenty-two times, one involved in a slaying that had shocked the people.

He let her talk, while he drank. She was the one with the money.

"You had money." She was beside him at the table, nudging him, his mother across from him, silent.

"What did you do with it?" There was no stopping her in public. "Throw it away on movies?"

"No," he managed. The evening waitress came over to the table. A young one with auburn hair. She smiled at him. "Can I take your order?"

"Flirting, while I was worried to death," his aunt's long, polished fingernails stung into the back of his right hand, after he had given the order.

"That popinjay Tony-boy, and those other freakish friends of yours, those corner killers were sought for questioning in this horrible *assassinare* affair. And what are *you* doing drinking? What have you become?" He felt like knocking his aunt's brains in as she poured it on. The waitress refreshed his drink, cramping his aunt's style for the moment.

"Clothes. You want your clothes? To wander where? We raise you for so long and you think you're leaving so quickly. You're not! You'll come home with us and explain fully! Your mother sold the meager furniture from your Ninth Avenue apartment. She divided it with that decrepit Roscoe who had to move out of Borough Park. So much for that arranged affair. But now you need money. Without a decent explanation you'll get nothing!" He sat composed as the waitress brought the hot antipasto, baked clams oregano, stuffed green peppers, fan tail shrimp. His aunt shut up as the waitress served.

He ate slowly, trying to pacify his stomach. He asked his mother where his fa—Roscoe was. Then he made both his mother and aunt swear on "his life" that they would never so much as utter a word to vengeful Little Mike or Al Rispone that they had seen him. He ate the main courses lightly, pasta *Fa Gioli*, then his manicotti, and drank his rye straight.

The meal was over, the matter settled. He was going to find Johnny! The authorities had a furious investigation going. The first, most vehement global investigation in the annals of crime had been launched. Find the gangland killers of Arnold Schuster—the public's spirited servant. Otherwise it would be a deterrent to ALL law abiding citizens in the future!

But he had his own reasons for wanting to find the missing man who had become his father through the moment, not of life, but of death itself!

"You're wasting your time. He's not worth it," his aunt commented, snug in her shortie coat under the Culver Line El outside Gregnano's. His mother had returned to 426 McDonald Avenue, ten blocks away, by taxi to fetch a suitcase of clothing for him. She had gone easily when her sister had asked her to do so, the only thing his mother saying to his aunt before she left, was to be easy on the boy. Dannie knew well of his mother's aversion to arguing. But his aunt Eleanor loved to fight! She was on his back again as to how was he going to live, support himself, and go to school. "Are you running from the law for what Johnny may have trapped you into?" his aunt taunted, her sixth sense peaked. She was always trying to outflank him, and he was feeling the seven shots of the sweet tasting Golden Wedding, heady in the night air.

"You love sex so much, Eleanor, and I *know* it!" he countered, to get at her. "So why don't you have it more often?"

"How often have you had it?" She kept her hands in her wide side pockets. "And with who have you attempted it besides me?" She was purring like a cougar.

He wanted to lie to her; tell her a half a dozen girls.

"What did you mean," he changed that sore subject, "when I called you last month, and you said if I came home you would tell me the truth about my father?"

"Come home now, and I'll tell you." Her voice was icy.

She was a screwball, Dannie had decided long ago.

"You're bluffing," he said. "A trick. One that could get us all hurt if I'm caught now in your company. But I'd like to know what's behind your mind, Aunt Eleanor. What makes you *really* tick?"

"If we had consummated the act," she shot back, "done it on those two occasions and I became pregnant what would you have done?"

He never thought of that, but now that he did, he turned on her. "Probably have shot you, then myself."

"You bastard!" She was on him by the overhead Culver Line El's iron girder, her fingernails blazing, set for his face.

He knew that would goad her and was ready. But the word "bastard" goaded him more, he had her arms pinned behind her, her back straining against the girder.

"You know something I don't know?" he barked through gritted teeth as he held her fast, lifting his left knee to protect his scrotum.

She was trying with her right knee to cripple him.

"You are a bastard," she hissed, her face only an inch from his. Eleanor never gave up. "One who wants to kiss me goodbye." She said the word with a different inflection. He caught it. Maybe she had meant it in that sexual way from the start. He was kissing her, her tongue darting sensuous, delicious in his mouth.

"If I didn't think you'd go to jail where I'd never be able to have you, I'd never let you leave!" She had her arms tight now around him on the sidewalk under the El.

He was spinning, his hands under her coat, her breasts firm and warm, plush hills against his palms. He was getting lost in her fierce beauty.A motor was running close to him, and he let her go in time to see a taxi-cab pulling up by the outside of the restaurant.

His mother had his luggage. Three suitcases. He helped her out of the cab and placed his traveling gear on the sidewalk.

A cluster of people exited the restaurant. Dannie stood with his mother and aunt until the revelers had pranced by.

"You kissed your aunt goodbye," his mother faced him. "Now hug me goodnight. Never goodbye." Her squeeze matched perfectly the sensuality of his aunt—a butterscotch bouquet in a coral coat.

"Here," Eleanor held her hand out to him.

It was a rubber-banded roll of money.

"A thousand dollars," she stuck it deep in his pants pocket. "While Willie Sutton was loose I was never one to keep money in banks." She actually smiled, her rich blue eyes aflame.

Why? He stood in the dark. Why did he feel the same way about them as he knew they felt about him?

His head reeled, he heard his mother saying she had served divorce papers on Roscoe, as he wanted, for adultery, not annulment. His new address was in the blue suitcase. She knew Dannie had to go, he must be in dire trouble, but she made him vow he'd call her every single week until his problem was outlived and cleared up.

Then he took leave of the two most beautiful women that heaven had created, a furious year apart.

1952

The Hunt, June-November

Dannie was terrified at the thought of Little Mike or Gretti finding him. He didn't know what their orders were. He was still bewildered by the uncertain figures of March 8.

Recalling Arnold's blood-soaked eyes made him sick to his stomach, his soul. Nevertheless, he began his hunt. He figured that he had an inside track on the Homicide Squad and the hound dogs of 111 nations.

They were hunting to get Johnny Squint. Now he was hunting for him. For him, it was a far different, much better, and more personal reason.

His first effort would be Roscoe Valencia. He was living with Rosa Mazziotta, waiting to marry her, and rearing Johnny's three children—that Johnny might contact. It was mid-June when Dannie made his way to 345 Fountain Avenue, a city co-op project on the outskirts of East New York in Brooklyn.

After six days of spying on the Plymouth convertible parked on the winding Fountain Avenue, Dannie spotted Roscoe at 11:00 p.m., June 17. Roscoe had his black lunch box bunched under his left arm, his right hand fiddling with the keys to the Plymouth's locked door.

When Dannie sneaked up behind him from across the street, it startled Roscoe, causing him to drop his lunch pail which clattered on the dark street. Roscoe had good cause to be wary these days. He hurried Dannie to a project bench that was near-buried in clumps of city-planted trees.

The homicide detectives and members of the Federal Bureau of Investigation went in and out of his fifth floor apartment at will. The Federal Agents, Robert P. Lawton foremost among them, were staking out the corner of 40th and Eighth from the rooftop of Pete's Radio Store in the hope of spotting Johnny, Augie or Hugo Duce directly, or being led to one of them via their cronies.

Little Mike, Al Rispone, and Tony-boy had spoken to Roscoe at the Brooklyn Pier. With the aid of phlegm-congested Gretti, who had not yet surfaced since the cowardly slaughter of Arnold Schuster, they had secured him six steady nights a week. The trio had instructed him to make sure that Rosa told no tales out of school to the authorities. "They also asked about you, Dannie," he mumbled, a frown drawn across his face.

It was a long walk back to the Church Avenue bus, but Dannie took it in stride. He hadn't kept fearful Roscoe on the bench too long, but he had found out enough.

The FBI were of the same mind as him. Watch the movements of Johnny's ex-wife, keep in touch with the whereabouts of John's three children. Yet the government had the manpower and resources to keep tabs on Johnny's family.

Dreary Gretti was still out of sight—out of lawful reach. Dannie waited by the bus stop. It must have been him that night in the Capri. But if he knew that Dannie was Johnny's son, would he try to hurt him, *quiet him* before he ever told anyone about the part he was made to play in the events of that night. Dannie exited the bus at Church and McDonald, one half a block from where his mother and aunt lived. He saw the figure of a short, skeleton-like man crossing Church Avenue, surrounded by an entourage of fedora'd men.

Nervy Joe Gallo. Dannie held his breath as he watched Joe the Blond enter Scarola's restaurant on Church Avenue.

Would it be safe to approach Joey? Dannie stood stone still, his heart beating fast. He couldn't take the chance, he firmly decided. Joe was too entrenched in gangland. He headed into the underground subway, while his thoughts returned to Roscoe.

Roscoe Valencia had been glad to see his . . . son. He would always consider and call him that, he had touched Dannie's hand, asked how Eve was, and told him of Johnny's three children: the two young girls so black-eyed and pretty, the younger boy, in a shell, but respectful, and a fourth he and Rosa were planning to adopt.

Roscoe at first had tried to obtain an annulment from Eve Crosscavale on the grounds that the marriage had never been consummated but had changed his mind. What Family Court Judge would believe it? So he had asked his wife to serve him with divorce papers.

Despite the old neighborhood gossip to the contrary, Roscoe believed that Rosa was a good woman. She made a meal a feast and made his bed a comfort. What more was a man supposed to ask for?

Dannie asked one favor of his fa— of Roscoe before he left. If Johnny ever tried in any way to contact his three children, could he let him know? He gave his aunt's number and address. Roscoe had promised to do so, and then had kissed him before he left for work. Dannie had returned the kiss with fervor.

THROUGH THE SUMMER DANNIE GAINED NO GROUND. There were reports in the *Daily News* that Johnny Squint had been seen in a Detroit Race Track, by Uncle Frank's swank Central Park West apartment, at Vito Genovese's headquarters in Greenwich Village, and once at the Lafayette Hotel in downtown Brooklyn. But the leads never panned out.

Rumors in other newspapers had it that a body had been found buried in the Canarsie section of Brooklyn. The police believed it was Mazziotta. Killed to silence him. But the comparison of dental records showed that it wasn't Johnny Squint.

At the beginning of autumn, Dannie called his mother and aunt. His mother was at the doctor's, her withdrawal symptoms worsening. His aunt called him a son-of-a-bitch for not telling her where he was living. His response: "If I'm a son-of-a-bitch then you must be my mother."

The preliminaries over between them, he asked if she knew a way for him to obtain identification in the name of Daniel Cross.

She did. After all, his true name wasn't Valencia. She would go down to the Department of Health on Flatbush Avenue Extension and get him a birth certificate. A duplicate, but in the name of Cross.

She would also acquire a Social Security card for him. At the Coney Island office. There would be no problem, she assured him.

And as for a coming military draft card in time, not to worry. She would take care of that if it took him that long.

Dannie had four main ideas. He'd check back with Roscoe, in case Roscoe was timid in contacting the "two shrews," as he had once heatedly termed them. He'd drop in to Scarola's restaurant, check it out, and maybe run into Joe the Blond. His third idea was to get a job. The other was to see Kathleen Mazziotta.

AT THE END OF SEPTEMBER, ROSCOE HAD A SURPRISE for Dannie. A letter from Antoinette Narghelle, found "stowed" while packing. Roscoe had been much too nervous at their first clandestine meeting to remember it.

The letter was thick, crumpled. Dannie opened it that early morning in his room and found a silver plated man's I.D. bracelet inside with D A N N I E engraved on it.

Hope! He began reading and saw that it was written right after he was originally jumped and beaten by his Ninth Avenue apartment house.

It was a combination love letter and warning.

She loved his hair and eyes. She wanted him all to herself and would never forget their first night together. Never! He was the first boy to touch her that way, whether he believed it or not!

The warning part came more in story form. A 1948 story about a Tom Collentine. Ambushed in Manhattan and slain in a dock war. Dannie read on, devouring the letter:

He was a murderer himself so it didn't matter much. They gave him a flat tire so he couldn't drive, so please don't feel so terrible (as I do) about your bike. (There are people who stay with your Johnny who tell people in South Brooklyn these things). A long black sedan with men in it got to him. (But, Dannie. Joey the Blond never got out of the car the night they beat you. Only the other three guys did.) That man Tom fell over gambling through (don't ever, ever breathe a word of this) my best girlfriend's UNCLE. And she's still my best friend although you may hate her. She hates you even more since you hit her. She never told her father or any of her uncles that. So maybe she doesn't hate you too much after all.

Dannie paused in his reading. Antoinette hadn't known about his bout with Scap and his encounter up on the Prospect Park hill with Anna. But he relished the revealing letter, the information in it about Gretti giving over details. He read on:

She called him her black haired God-face, and was worried frantic whether he had any scars from that sneaky, low-life night.

Dannie stopped reading. He hadn't gotten any scars. If he did they had healed. But the memory of his demolished bike—done on purpose as a facade—hadn't. He finished her letter. It was an unlucky night all the way, she wrote:

Unluckiest most of all for me. Cause I'll probably never see you again. And I don't blame you. But don't blame me for that night. On my word of honor I didn't expect it to come to that. Can you write me back and say you believe and forgive me?

She had signed the letter "With undying love," sealing it with a lipstick imprint of her initials. Dannie made a note of her Pacific Street address, but didn't answer the letter. He felt stuck! Antoinette and Anna both lived in South Brooklyn!

During the third week in October, Dannie made his fourth visit to Scarola's Italian Cuisine on Church Avenue. There was a table in the middle of the restaurant. A long one. With at least a dozen men sitting at it. Most of them wearing fedoras with the brims up. Rakish style.

The smoke from their cigarettes was curling up in thick clouds to the ceiling. Their talk, between their hearty meal and drinks, was subdued.

One younger, thin man, wearing a brown felt, 3-inch brim "bomber," who closely resembled a movie screen actor, seemed to be president at the head of the table. Dannie, looking up from his plate of linguini with white clam sauce, recognized him.

Dannie washed down his meal with white wine, knowing his fourth visit had paid off. But he wanted to leave, end the evening. There were too many guys around.

The man looked up for a quick moment at Dannie.

Dannie, trying to act nonchalant, paid the check and was putting on his charcoal suburban coat when the short, thin man approached, a cocky smile on his tight-skinned face.

"How ya doin'?" he said.

Dannie remembered the name of the actor. Richard Widmark. He also remembered the name of the guy before him. Joe the Blond.

"Seen your *padrone* Johnny Squint lately?" Joey was baring his teeth in that gracious, mean-eyed smile. "Sammy," he motioned with one finger to the tubby waiter. "This check's on me. Give him back his money."

The waiter spun on his heels.

Dannie suddenly wanted to do the same, but Joey Gallo's pale blue, deepset eyes were holding him to the spot. He automatically sat back in the booth at Joey's nimble "won't you join me" gesture.

The waiter was in a fright. He placed fifteen dollars before Dannie instead of the seven the meal had cost.

"Been a long while." Joey was smiling, ever-charming, as the waiter scooted away. "First, President and Fourth when Miss Schnozola came to your rescue. Then, Prospect Park when you beat the piss out of Scap."

Dannie sat quiet, Joey had left out the night on Ninth Avenue.

"Still not one for talking." Joe had that shrewd, wide-open grin on his face. "It seems the world wants your old rabbi and Gretti for takin' a rat out for all to see. Right out from in the midst of that two-bit Borough Park. Good for Johnny. If I run into him I'll pin a medal on his chest."

"If you run into him," Dannie said, "where can I find you?"

"For what?"

"To pin a medal on your chest," Dannie said, trying hard not to show any reaction to Joey's comment about Johnny and Gretti.

Joe Gallo laughed, his face illuminated by his gleaming teeth. "I hear John's *padrone* Costello is in the Federal Atlanta Pen after leaving Lewisburg Pen last month. He gets out in a year. V.G.'s the new war lord now. Fuck 'em both." He paused to think for a moment. "I'll get a medal someday for havin' your old friend Johnny Squint's arch enemy's brains in my hand. The mean Mr. Al-bert. I'm gonna nail him on the rack of this tough town of ours. That's when you can come around with the medals, good-lookin'."

Joey Gallo liked to talk. Dannie didn't mind listening for another few minutes.

"The check was on me," Joey said, "for the price of your old bike. And the bandages. Square? Consider it a 'pass' for old time's sake."

Dannie glanced askew at the clan of men at the long table and said nothing.

"I was doing Al-bert's ugly niece a favor then," Joey leaned towards Dannie from across the table. "But things have changed. I'm the Olive Oil King Joe Profachi's man now. My brother Larry and I. Take a tip there scapper. That snortin' bull Little Mike and

Gretti who's on the lam, and those lames with them, have jumped the fence to Al-bert's camp away from Uncle Frank. Gret got a medal—a Badge—pinned on his chest after the hit on Schuster. An Al-bert Button. When I see your old *padrone* The Squint I'll be sure to tell him that." Joey stood up. "It's all a loose-structured confederation. Non-connected Friendships. *Amicizia.* Disparate *friends.* I'm Profachi. Coffin-Gret is Al-bert. Squint is Uncle Frank. Three separate units. With not even the weather in common. And you're nowhere! But you kept your trap shut in the park that time. I know. Anna Banana told me. So take a tip. Stay away from four things. The Bulls. Smouldering Gretti. Borough Park, and South Brooklyn," Joey winked his right eye.

Dannie sighed to himself. It really was good-bye Antoinette. He stood up.

"And you can find me," Joey tapped the side of Dannie's shoulder, "a block from here. At Jack's All-Nite Diner. Across the street. On Church and McDonald. And if I hear from Scap up in the El, I'll tell him I saw that 'down' kid with the up-in-the-sky blue eyes. He'll get a kick out of those street memories."

"How is he?" Dannie asked.

"Comin' along. He'll be shipped from the Reformatory to Auburn State Prison soon. Be home in ten years. No sweat."

"Goodnight," Dannie said. "And I'll take you up on that visit to Jack's if you ever hear where Johnny is. And if you do hear from Scap, tell him I truly wish him luck."

"*Buona notte.* And *buona fortuna* yourself. And I'm not gonna ask why you're lookin' for Johnny all by your lonesome. That's your business. You gotta gripe with Schuster gettin' dumped? Inside talk is," Joey lowered his voice, "you may have played a part in that. Well, your retribution—your immediate vampires—and scores to settle are yours. My gripes are with old Dunsky's. If you hear from Johnny before I do, tell him about it. I could always use an ally, a good 'hitter' on my side."

Dannie was struck by Joey hinting . . . getting even for Arnold's death. He watched warily as Joe Gallo returned to the long table. He had been right about Joe when he had first met him. He could draw you in with magnetic eyes and pure, powerful charm, though Dannie wondered how those old Dunsky's would take to it. He turned, leaving the cuisine to face the treacherous, thundering rain outside.

1952

*D*annie hadn't called Eve or Eleanor for over six weeks. He kept thinking of the danger he would expose them to if the two crews or the police linked them to him.

But on the day of his sixteenth birthday, after days of hoarding every penny for fear he'd starve, weeks of doing extra body-straining push-ups, sit-ups, and after seemingly endless insomniac nights of downright loneliness, he gave in.

Naturally his mother and aunt were in a tangle of mania. Where had he been? How could he have done this to them?

Eleanor told him his mother had been in a near coma, paralyzed with fear and worry. She preyed on his guilt and anxiety. He was tied in with the Schuster murder, wasn't he? The 1947 Sutton escape? The incessant executioner Anastasia?

"Don't you see what came out of your association with that monster, Johnny Squint?" Eleanor nagged.

They agreed to meet at the Elegante NiteClub to celebrate his birthday. His aunt also wanted him to hear his mother's complete story.

Dannie planned on securing a job and seeing Kathleen after the birthday meeting. But that night he met his mother and aunt at the Elegante on Ocean Parkway, not far from McDonald Avenue.

His aunt had a birthday present for him. More like a birthday "grown up" message. She had gotten a phone call and a letter from Roscoe.

She had opened the letter, but at least she was giving it to him, and Dannie was grateful, thinking of them stowing Antoinette's letter, keeping it from him. He decided not to make a point of it with them.

The only contents of Roscoe's envelope was a postcard from Miami Beach, Florida, addressed to the Mazziotta children. (Not the fourth child, Eleanor assumed haughtily.) The postcard had no other writing on it. No signature.

It may be time to travel, Dannie thought as he placed the postcard in the inside pocket of his light blue suit jacket.

Aunt Eleanor had yet another "gift" for him as the three dined on prime rib in the sedate restaurant part of the Elegante. This one was from geep-creep Tony-boy. He had been outside the telephone company where she worked on Sixteenth Avenue waiting for her.

His message was for her elusive nephew from his "superiors." If you see him, tell him that the Borough Park cops were still mystified at that Doctor Fialks from Ninth Avenue's report that he had seen a boy with a gold jacket that night from his office window. But that doctor had been attended to. They were also working on the group of guys that wanted to go to a party at the Menorah Temple.

Eleanor, apparently, had raised her clenched fists at Tony-boy, telling him she hadn't seen her nephew; that he must be dead from hanging around hoodlums. Ordering him to "get your greasy self out of here!" Tony-boy had backed away to a waiting car. Dannie wanted to kiss his spirited aunt. He smiled at her from across the dinner table as he sat next to his pliant mother.

But he was going to hurry this birthday meal and get out.

The three of them stood on the sidewalk by Ocean Parkway's service road, the snow flurries attacking, cold, sticking wet, drying damp on their faces, outside the Elegante.

They wanted him to spend his entire birthday night with them. But as they walked swank Ocean Parkway toward their apartment, he begged leave to go it alone.

His mother would get down on her knees if he'd give up this demonic search of his. "It's the past," she implored. "We could still find happiness in the future. For the love of God, please, just walk away from it all."

He wondered about God and wondered if he had a future at all. Would Gretti, Mike and company, now Al-bert's men, kill him if they found him, to protect the past?

And if he found Johnny, Dannie grasped for hope, would he set things right through this V.G.—Vito Genovese—that Joe Gallo and John himself had mentioned?

He had the recurring thought to seek out Anna Banana, become close with her, and thereby buy insurance from and through her uncle, Al-bert. But it could backfire.

He was sixteen today, reaching the shooting height of six foot one inch, and filling out physique-wise. They served him drinks without question anywhere he went. Yet he felt like a child, certain that the police were going to swoop down on him and make him an accessory to a murder that had shaken the roots of the criminal justice system.

His mother shook him out from the depth of his thoughts. She was close to rolling into a ball on the snowy sidewalk. She stood five foot seven, but her body cowered within her clothes. She couldn't stand being without him today—a day she had agonized her womanhood, clawing her being, giving birth. She nearly collapsed on the sidewalk, but he supported her while his aunt flagged a passing cab.

He ordered the cabbie to take the two of them home to 426 McDonald Avenue. But his aunt said it would serve to kill her sister. She'd go into a seizure from the inhuman strain. She re-ordered the cab driver to the nearest decent hotel, reminding Dannie that he had a complete "story" to hear.

The cab driver took Ocean Parkway, the length of it, toward the Coney Island section, swinging left, eastbound onto the Belt Parkway. Eve Crosscavale was a bundle of shivers under her minty Arnoldton coat. Dannie wished with all his might that he could give up this hunt for Johnny. But then what? Face the FBI? Vindictive Little Mike and clan? His only saviour now, he felt certain, was John himself.

The Skyway Motel was for visiting dignitaries from foreign countries and for cheaters readily eager to trade bodies and lies for a few hours in the fashionable rooms. It was at the edge of Idlewilde International Airport in Queens, a stone's-throw, the driver said as he took the fare from Eleanor, from the Brooklyn border.

Inside, the lounge was cozy and intimately dark, full of overly made-up wenches and sharp wise-guys. Dannie walked on the sky blue rug, down the four steps into the dim, crowded lounge.

The maitre d' found them a small table away from the round bar jammed with customers after Eleanor slipped him five dollars.

Dannie ordered Seagram's Seven straight, his aunt a vodka collins, and his mother a glass of burgundy.

The two sisters had taken their identical mint brief coats off, setting them on a fourth unoccupied chair at the rectangular table. Dannie placed his charcoal suburban on top of their coats.

Eve and Eleanor wore identical outfits. Mint green three-quarter-sleeve sweaters and matching tight, trim-waisted skirts. To look at them, Dannie thought, you'd think they were twins, but you'd never guess the torn emotions they carried behind those seductive, haunting eyes. Dannie saw his mother relax somewhat as she touched her moist lips to the stemmed burgundy glass, his aunt chiming in, wishing him Happy Birthday, both sitting across from him.

It was small talk at the table. "Do you have enough money?" his mother asked as she handed him a sealed card. He flushed when he saw the three hundred dollar birthday gift from both of them. He owed them two kisses thanks, they reminded, and he told them he intended to get a job within a month.

His aunt took a birth certificate and a Social Security card from her kelly green, brocaded purse. Dannie set them in his suit inside pocket beside the postcard.

Eleanor spotted his thick chain-linked bracelet, and arched her eyebrows, demanding to know if it was indeed in the letter that Roscoe had finally given him? Dannie sipped his expensive rye and ignored the issue.

"And how is Roscoe?" his mother asked.

"Fine," he answered, and then ordered another round from the dyed ash-blond waitress.

His aunt reminded Eve that it was time to tell that complete story.

But the scene in the lounge, despite the sisters' eye-peeling attire, was more than depressing. It was demoniacal. Dannie noted the vacant look in Eve's stare as if she was attempting to tear the rind off the past.

Dannie gulped down the liquor, preparing himself.

Johnny had been fresh out of the Elmira reformatory when she had met him. Eve began to pour out her story.

"Four of us had first double-dated," Eleanor threw in.

"Johnny was dashing," Eve continued. "He drove a rumble seat car. Always dressed to kill. He was the . . . first man I'd ever kissed. My knees would buckle when we did . . ."

Dannie twisted in his seat as if straining his ears in order to hear her. Her voice was so far away.

"We laughed together," Eve went on. "Eleanor and I switched theater seats, he was so confused when the lights went up . . . seeing Eleanor instead of me. But he loved me. He paid my tuition to fashion school and never took the credit. Our courtship lasted five months."

Eve sat perfectly still, her green eyes glazed.

"You took sick," Eleanor prompted her.

"I took sick," Eve repeated, her voice coming from a trance of over sixteen years ago. "A seizure. A breakdown over an argument I had with my sister. Your aunt Eleanor. It wasn't her fault. Just an argument. I can't stand to argue, Daniel. The words that were exchanged were so violent . . . Finally I convulsed . . . I passed out from nerves. The blood had gone to my head.

"I awoke in Brooklyn Doctor's Hospital. They had pronounced me dead," Dannie saw her chin go so tremulous he had to reach over and squeeze it. He stroked her sweatered arm, waiting for her words to begin again.

"Her heart had not really stopped," Eleanor abetted. "It skipped. The blood pressure faded, the brain cells alive. Those idiot doctors mistook a stupor, a coma, for death."

"Your father made . . . love to me while I was in that . . . coma," Eve rambled, Dannie gagged! She could never destroy the life of a child, but at the same time, she could never marry Johnny Mazziotta. The rest of her monotone of rape left him feeling sick.

Eve went on: Roscoe Valencia was over twenty years her senior. She had, as Roscoe stated, originally met him through Eleanor. A good man. "He lent his name to you, Daniel," she sobbed. "He foresook his brother in the Bronx for me—a pregnant woman.

"When I gave birth he treated you as a son. His son. He never prodded me about the past. But I could never bring myself to give him what a wife . . . Sometimes I thought of . . . John's crushing embrace, but ultimately I dreaded sex. The touch of a . . . man. But I . . . in the long run . . . pictured myself . . . dead and violated." She stopped, and Dannie had to order a glass of burgundy for her. Making her drink it, he sat stiffly, letting her finish.

"I lay nights now alone." She drank half her wine. "As I'd lain sexually dead beside Roscoe. I fought sleep. Thinking a stranger, a vile parade, would enter me on my way to the freezer slabs.

"Roscoe had a better than good reason to leave. What kept him by me so long, God only knows. The enduring patience he had shown. It was inhuman.

"But with you, Dannie," she looked away. "I yearned for you on our old couch, because you were the only living man I could love and trust." She drained the wine glass.

"Then John recently proposed to me . . . marriage. I told him yes, hoping it would work, despite my hate for him. I would do anything to keep you, Dannie. Anything! He had a spell of some sort on you . . . blood going to blood. You ran from me. He could get you back, and I would take him in the bargain. But, Daniel, I could have loved him again. I could have been a whole woman, a giving, thriving . . ." her words trailed off, as she placed the empty glass on the table.

That's why he had been used, Dannie understood, sinking into that thought. His life-long hero, Johnny Squint, used him in the murder of Arnold Schuster just so he could bind Eve to him forever. A death bond. A bond of dark lust. A father's supreme betrayal of a son.

Made part of a killing, to be used as blackmail, a pawn—something John could hang over his mother's head to get her back and keep her. Dannie was distraught, repelled, and suddenly frightened for his very life. So far the blackmail had backfired. The lounge was spinning in his head, furious confusion revolving into a burning, spectral turning point.

The whirling moment twisted his passion for Johnny into fear, distrust, and anger. The payback for what Johnny did to his mother all those years ago, and now to him—the rape and the betrayal—were uppermost in his mind. Dannie wanted to charge into the Men's room and vomit. He could feel the drinks rising up . . . but before he could race to the bathroom . . . it was like turning on a light switch, flicking it when Dannie spotted *him*, dark lounge and all.

He had his fingertips just barely touching his lips in a limp effort to stifle any retching. He saw the discoloration in the face before he saw the actual face passing his table. The face gave Dannie a sideways glance, looked an alert second into his, and pushed slowly on through the bar's standing-room lounge crowd.

"Wait here! Don't move!" he told his mother and aunt as he got up to follow the man with the facial-fungus growing, spreading discolored. He footballed through the jam of people and saw the tall bookmaker from 40th and Eighth, Al Rispone, in the Skyway lobby.

An Al-bert man! A turncoat buddy of Johnny and Hugo Duce's. He walked straight up to him.

"Thought I was seeing things, kid," Al's lips were sticky with spit as he spoke. "At first I was glued to the two flashy dressed heads with you. I passed the table to get a better look. When I passed, I knew they weren't fuckin' material. Just two big-tit carnival cases as Little Mike used to say. Shame. They could make the French army happy if they were ... normal."

Dannie was thinking heatedly of the things Joey Gallo had said, trying to contain his anger at what Al had just mouthed.

"Shall we go?" Al said, the bulge under the left side of his shiny black Roma sport jacket protruding menacingly. "Talk over old times with Little Mike and the gang. Or do we involve the two lithesome freaks?"

"Johnny's my father," Dannie blurted.

"Wha . . ." Al's fungus glimmered under the lobby's chandelier lights. "Your father?" He was thrown off balance for the moment. "Are you as screwy as those two gypsies in there?" he said, regaining himself. "Come on. We'll let Mike and Tony-boy do the deciding."

"Why'd you go over to Al-bert?"

"Uhh?" Al was taken completely aback again. "Who told you that? You been seein' his niece?"

"Joe the Blond told me," Dannie fluffed it. He knew he had. He should have said yes. He was seeing the niece. That might have shook Al. But who knew if the near seventeen-year-old Anna was engaged or something by now. His head was in a turmoil. He saw his aunt, her eyes a blizzard, by the lounge's entranceway, and waved her fervently back.

"The Blond?" Al wavered. "That *pazzo* rebel shrimp. Al-bert's got designs for him. And they don't include no murals on a wall. Let's take a ride. Maybe Gret'll make the decision. Who knows?" Al grinned widely. "Al-bert himself went through a lotta trouble for you, Dannie-my-boy. The cops are blocked so far as to you. Al-bert's command. Burglarized the clothing store and clipped your custom-made-pants records, even. Maybe Al-bert will show himself tonight."

Dannie, pulverized, followed Al outside. For the sake of his mother and aunt, he'd go. What else on earth could he do? Al-bert himself!

He climbed into Al's gray Cadillac parked on the side of the Skyway, the snow flakes furious, pelting the car's whitening dome.

"Just on a lark," Al Rispone chuckled as he purred the engine to life. "Stopped in for a drink. No business. Just pleasure." He guided the Caddy around the Skyway, out onto the snowy Belt Parkway heading to Brooklyn. "And who do I spot? You, Dannie my lad. Your fuckin' nutty cunt aunt had lied to Tony-boy by the phone company. She knew you were alive and kicking. She oughtta get fuckin' slayed, laid, and parlayed by every soldier in Al-bert's Crew for that lie. Both of 'em. Just for the way they walk." Al, Dannie could see, was enjoying this immensely. He steered the car through the Belt's slippery traffic. "And you, kid. What's your hidin' game really about? You got notions concerning the dearly departed Arnold Schuster? Like it was gettin' even time? We gonna have a lot of fun with you! So just relax. Be like old times on the corner."

Dannie had visions of himself somewhere in South Brooklyn. Little Mike and Al-bert the masters of ceremonies . . . Johnny not there to defend him . . . his aunt, his mother being unmercifully, brutally raped later. He lunged at the Caddy's steering wheel, the car going haywire, Al in near shock trying to steer it through the hectic-splashing snowfall. He tried to elbow Dannie off him. Dannie felt the impact, heard the crashing, grind-skimming of metal, as he fell sideways, upside down under the fancy dashboard as the car went over on its top.

He was living in an upside down world for two minutes. But living! His right shoulder ached the life out of him.

He hazily saw, felt a pair of hands pulling, reaching, touching him. He let them guide him through the car's shattered side window. What happened? He was on his knees on the slushy Belt Parkway. Traffic to Brooklyn at a dead standstill, the array of headlights all but blinding him.

"The driver looks as though he's dead," a strange man said. "He looks like solid, frozen glass."

"Seven cars," Dannie tried to stand, while hearing another man's voice. "Four injured in the other vehicles, one dead as the proverbial doornail here."

Dannie heard the screaming of a police car's urgent wail. The irregular static of its siren.

That's the one thing he didn't want. He bounded limp, but free, of the man holding him, crossed the Parkway's divider, and inched through the crawling, rubber-necking traffic of the east-bound lane. He fled, half-dazed, along the Parkway's snow-laden shoulder.

He felt his own shoulder a mass of swollen tissue, but he ran, groggy huffing, feeling pieces of glass sticking in his body, jutting through his suit jacket, bruising, piercing him further with each night-quickened stride.

He saw the Skyway. The misty blue lights of it Heaven itself.

1952

Midnight Mass, December 24

The bells of St. Agnes Church were ringing parishioners to the Christmas Eve midnight mass. Dannie sat in a pew on a side aisle, his head turned to the main entrance. Among the Christmas worshippers filing in he hoped to see one face. That of Kathleen Mazziotta.

He was seven short streets from the corner of Eighth and 40th, and two shorter blocks from Schuster's home in Borough Park. But Eighth Avenue was the parish dividing line. Saint Catherine's on Fort Hamilton Parkway was the church most people in his old neighborhood attended.

But this smaller one on Seventh Avenue was closer to Kathleen's house. She had said in the past that she knew it was a sin, wasn't right to go to a church other than her former school-parish one, but that God would understand why she needed to save her strength and take the shorter walks.

Dannie wondered now if that same God would understand why *he* was here, the joyously-solemn, holiday-filled church a sanctuary of refuge from any other familiar faces that he didn't want to see. He stood with the crowd as the pious tinkle of a bell announced the beginning of Mass.

He hadn't seen Kathleen among the throng of people coming in, but if she was here, she'd be receiving Holy Communion. He'd see her at the altar rail. He knelt on the knee rest of the pew, the sacred Mass re-enacting the feast of Corpus Christi before him. He closed his eyes to the altar and wondered if the symbol of the tabernacle would understand, on this the eve of His birthday, the events of the night of his own birthday. Dannie tried to assuage his terrible guilt over those overwhelming surges, feelings about that night in the International Hotel with Eve and Eleanor.

He was trying to cleanse himself from the sensations—trying to feel decent about himself again. He felt so soiled. Yet, all during the Mass he was also thinking of Arnold Schuster. The eyes and the balls. The body and the blood.

And he needed to see Kathleen. To feel "normal." He saw himself running from the accident, bruised, the bits of windshield glass cutting into his scalp.

His mother and his aunt had been outside of the Skyway. They cringed in unison from the anguish of pain on his face, the blotches of blood on the right side of his neck.

They wanted to take him back inside the Skyway, but he steered them clear of it. Who else was in the lounge that could place him. The waitress, the maitre d', maybe even the desk clerk, could well place the three of them as being there; him talking to, and walking out with Al.

He was still unsteady, walking between them toward the Airport proper, not knowing which way to go. The pain from his right shoulder had made him want to keel over. Without his suburban coat, the chill from the pelting snowflakes caused his jaw, the inside of his chest, to quiver.

His aunt, quick-witted, had told him and his mother not to move. She had run around the building and had returned in ten minutes, leading them to a side entrance of the Airport's International Hotel.

The room wasn't that rich in luxury, but it was a haven of comfort against the slats of glass which bit through his suit pricking into his skin, and blinding him with burning, stinging cuts.

But the bed he was stretched out on was hard, warm, and comfortable.

"Al Rispone is dead," his Aunt Eleanor had said, sitting on the bed beside him. "You've been delirious for an hour. The television set comes with the room. The broadcast thought it a Mob killing at first, but later said it was merely an automobile accident. I didn't realize you had more such famous men on your friendship list." She brushed the strands of hair from his eyes with her silky right hand.

He was coming to, recalling his fleeing, stumbling back to the Skyway, his aunt and mother sheltering him from observing eyes.

They had led him into the room, undressing him down to his boxer shorts. His blood stained T-shirt had been cut from him with his mother's nail file. Both of them were harried over that gangster bookmaker cohort of Johnny's and Hugo Duce's, fungi-faced Al.

His mother had offered him a glass of Seagram's Seven Crown whiskey that she had ordered from Room Service. "They don't stock Three Feathers," she said apologetically.

Al was dead. It was a highway miracle that Dannie wasn't. He had run and faced Al in the Skyway lobby to prevent him from originally making a telephone call that would bring others. He had gone with him to keep his mother and aunt from being left stranded and in possible danger if he had fled from the lobby.

His mother and aunt had both tended to his wounds as if he were their son, their conquering hero, their lover, and their husband.

"He fractured his collarbone," his aunt had said of Al Rispone, squeezing the skin on the side of his neck, probing with the match-heated point of the nail file for any other tiny slivers of glass that might cause infection if they remained in him. "The report was conflicting about another man, a younger one being helped from the car. Missing. Leaving the scene. You've broadened that much since March. Those animals, Al's 'associates' may never put two and two together." She had told her sister Eve to telephone downstairs and renew the room for another day. She had registered under the name of Mr. and Mrs. E. Hunt. She didn't know where she got the name from, she had reservedly said to him privately, it just sounded so average.

"Much too late." She had completed her probing. "The likes of that jungle-smut Al should have died years ago. He looked at me in that lobby as if he had gang-rape in his putrid eyes. They should cremate instead of burying him." Dannie had drunk the Seagram's Seven poured by his mother from the set-up room service cart.

It was smooth, full-flavored without the bite or sting of Three Feathers, and it dulled the piercing of his aunt's digging into his shoulder.

Al was a goner. Gretti would never know the circumstances, he had kept his mind busy, his mother's compress soaking his bare shoulders in between the excruciating splinter extractions.

After midnight they had decided that the fine wounds were clean and cleared of glass.

They had taken the ice from the white cardboard bucket, had packed it in a towel, and had let it rest cold against the swelling black and blue of his shoulders, his aunt was leaning over him on his right side, his mother's weight on the left balancing the bed. At intervals, she had wiped at his sweat-brow.

"What really happened tonight?" Eleanor had asked, her voice miles . . . years away.

"An . . . auto accident," he had answered.

She didn't believe him.

He had told her to believe what she wanted, and had tried to sit up, both of them holding him down.

Eleanor had pushed. "Did you go with that fungus face for our sakes?"

"Let me sleep," he had lain back under the pressure of their hands on him. "What's the difference why I went. It all has to do with finding Johnny. Otherwise I'm as dead as Al is now." He had known that he was in no shape to go anywhere that night, and didn't relish any exposure after the crash. He had rested, and tried to think straight, clearly, on the bed.

But from his position, under the hotel room's golden lampglow, his sixth shot glass of Seagram's in him, he saw a magnificent sight: his aunt and mother undressing unabashedly before him.

They had discarded their clothing with an almost animal sensuality to their movements. Slow stripping their sweaters off, primping their sparkling black hair in the vanity mirror, circling the bed, sitting, knees high, sheer stockings rolled, peeled, and shed. They had turned, with the rehearsed coordination of a stage duet, unhooking their mint green bras, their backs to him, but their bosoms bare, partially reflecting in the mirror. Their daring, minty half-slips had wiggled curvaceously up to their bust lines, seemingly molded into them. Then, by turns, they had taken long, steamy showers.

They had knelt on either side of the bed, collecting in turn the birthday thank you kisses he owed them from the gift-giving Skyway lounge. He felt the desire, the indulgence, gathering around them, and had savored it, feeling that the trio he was part of was somehow separate and apart from the rest of the world.

Both sisters had lain down on either side of him, the perfume of their bodies more intoxicating than all the rye ever packaged.

They had begun talking about the past, dreaming about the future. The three of them were alone in the world, having no one but each other.

His aunt had by then shut the lamplight, but the same old questions had returned to him.

Why hadn't Eleanor Cross ever married? Had she been a virgin the times he had fought her and nearly made love to her?

The same old answer came to him. Eleanor Cross didn't trust men. He had asked the question of virginity, and she had sidestepped it.

But there were other questions to be answered. That much more about the past that had made them like this, caused them to be as they were now. He had needed a Seagram's Seven, but hadn't moved from the bed to get it—he didn't want to have to climb over either one of them.

Why only him? They could both wink and have an Air Force of men. Swing-walk, sway, and they could own the men looking at the tight bays of their skirts. But why only him? He had to find out.

"You're as tall as your grandfather was." His mother had turned, curling on her side to him, her toes scraping slightly against his shins. "Past sixteen. And so tall."

He had asked in bed about his grandparents and had moved his right leg a hair's breath away from the touch of her.

His grandfather's name was Dominic Crosscavale. (Hence, *Valen*cia to Vale.) A man who possessed extreme savoir-faire. He had died of pneumonia when Dannie's mother was fifteen. The two sisters were without anyone after that. Their mother, Scotch bred— her name was Eva—had passed away a year before. From childbirth. It would have been a son. "They both . . . died," her echoes had filled and haunted from far past the warm room. "We were left alone, with a Police Academy Delenty Graduate foot patrolman soon courting your aunt and a gangster courting me.

"And since then," Eve was lulling the words that did not come easily to her now, "there has been no Crosscavale blood strain flowing but yours. no man that we could both truly lean on. The rookie patrolman . . . left your aunt. The gangster slept with a corpse. Who else is there left, but our own? Who else, Dannie, who else can you rely on for love than your own blood? Tell me!" Her echoes had faded in the hotel room.

It had been a sad story, a sadder one still that he had closed his eyes to their undressing.

His mind had fought to not say the things he wanted to say while his body had lost ground to the things he didn't want to feel. His aunt had kissed him goodnight, her mouth open upon his.

He had returned his aunt's kiss wanting much *more*, but trying to maintain control, had gently pushed her prone on her back.

After Johnny, after he found his father, he decided, he would have to solve the enigmatic desire of the bed he slept in. He'd have to, or he'd either be a prime candidate for the Long Island, Islip Nuthouse or an utterly satisfied incestuous bastard that deserved whatever the *vendetta portore*, Little Mike and friends had in mind for him. Eve had sweetly pecked his lips goodnight, but after the sorcerous-like . . . kiss, he had prayed that when he found his father, it would give him the answer to his mother.

He hadn't slept well at all, Al's broken neck, him, an eyelash away from the same fate, the incubus-filled night a contest between Eve's tossing death-throes, and his ever-present view of Arnold, eyeless.

He recalled well the two women falling asleep and his futile attempts to disentwine himself from them. Eleanor, half-asleep, had caressed his wounds, his body anew. He had felt her unashamed desire for him—and his for her. Eve, on the other side, had clung to him. He had lain most of the night, limp, immobile between the two of them. The all-embracing mystique, the ecstasy in the room unbearable to him.

As he contemplated getting out of bed he had felt his aunt's left, bare leg entwined over his right one. She had worn no sweet panties and he had felt her sweltering pubic bareness against his groin. He would have rolled her backwards and entered her, his fettered desire was that bad. But he had recoiled, the thought of Johnny Squint entering his mother in a plush death-sleep freezing him.

He had managed to delicately inch and squeeze straight down along the bed, trying his best not to wake them both. How he had wished that they were just apparitions, just darlings in the dark, nothing earthly, nothing less but never anything more.

He had been on his way to the closet to get dressed when they had awakened.

But neither his mother's exhortations nor his aunt's cunning demonstration that he was an ingrate had kept him there.

He had dressed, hating himself.

Shielded by his charcoal suburban, which Eleanor had been sharp enough to take with her from the Skyway, he had left the hotel. The guilt of his feelings he could never leave behind. That decadent birthday night of his, he had consciously and inexorably bound himself to his mother and his aunt. He had almost made love to Eleanor again. How was he to achieve that slippery manhood—free himself from the bondage of them? Find a woman of his own! Could he make all of that possible?

He strained his brain, trying now to leave it all behind him as the people filed up the church aisle to the sanctity of Communion. Kathleen was among them, a white kerchief—required headdress—atop her head, knotted under her chin.

He watched her go to her kneeling, altar-rail position and wait for the robed priest and altar boy to serve her, her open mouth and extended tongue receiving the wafer that would make her trip to Heaven that much quicker than so many others, him foremost among them.

He waited for the Midnight Christmas Mass to come to an end and remembered how he had fantasized escaping to some idyllic Heaven with Kathleen. Now he might have to get out of New York on the strength of Roscoe's postcard. He felt in his gut that his old days of innocence were over. He needed to get out of New York to find Johnny.

Kathleen took Holy Communion, but the only body and blood Dannie could think of was Arnold Schuster's. Why was he killed?

Kathleen wasn't stunned when she saw him in the crowd on the sidewalk outside the church, but she exhibited a feeble surprise. A happy glow emanated from within her rather than without.

As bad as his eyesight was, as much as they said he was as blind as hell, he could see that Kathleen was dying. Her face, her almost lifeless body movements seemed more in the grip of death than the day he had met her.

"You shouldn't have come so close," she said as she limply took his hand. She led him back up the church steps, guided him to a rear pew, and sat with him. She had genuflected and crossed herself four times. Once at the church's entrance by the Holy Water, again at the threshold of the center aisle, a third time by the pew, and lastly when she knelt inside the pew itself.

She was going to Paradise non-stop, Dannie reflected as he strangely wished he could think more like her. He withdrew in the solemnity of his surroundings, not wanting to burden her with searching questions of her uncle John.

But Kathleen Mazziotta didn't speak as one about to go so quickly to her Heaven. Rather, her words were those of one sent fresh from the sky above.

She thought her uncle John was in Miami Beach, Florida. In hiding. Her grandfather Felice, seventy-seven years old, had tried to kill himself. He had slashed his throat with a razor.

Her aunt Millie, on her father's side, had found him in the bathroom. That was two o' clock in the morning on October 4th. Dannie listened, the swish of the custodian's broom, the knocks of its wood against corded knee rests melting in the sounds of the church's bell pealing Christmas tones. Kathleen apologized for talking in church by making the sign of the cross, again. She continued whispering the events to Dannie:

"My grandfather was in the papers. If anyone on my father's side of the family so much as sneezes, they print it. Because of my uncle John. God bless him." Kathleen crossed herself. "He's not guilty. Only God has the right to say that. Not reporters, or commissioners." She took a picture postcard from her leather pocketbook.

Dannie took the one Roscoe had sent to him from the inside pocket of his powder blue suit jacket. It was addressed to the Mazziotta children, 345 Fountain Avenue, Brooklyn, New York.

The one Kathleen had handed him was addressed to Felice Mazziotta—744 39th Street, Brooklyn, New York. Both had no writing, no signature on them.

That's it! Dannie jumped on the fact that it complimented Roscoe's information.

Her grandfather was rushed to Israel Zion Hospital then, critical, to Kings County. Dannie gulped, worried about . . . his grandfather.

"But my aunt Millie Bandille," Kathleen hushed on, "her marriage name, had saved his life. If my uncle John read this, or was told this, I don't know. I only know the card arrived four days later. I took it from the mailbox a half hour before the police got there. I had just finished cleaning my grandfather's apartment. The FBI visit there regularly. They hound him. That's what may have caused his suicide attempt. And maybe because of Arnold Schuster. My brother Jimmie shopped there twice and Arnold's gruff father, Max, was so good to my mom. He gave a second pair of high-rise tailormade pants free because mom was short money that day. Guilt, Dannie. My grandfather found out about the nice, respectful gesture to his own grandson by a man whose very son was cruelly killed, they hint, by his son. Oh, God," Kathleen winced. Her face ashen, she continued.

"And he had this awful, empty depression from his worry about his missing son, my uncle John, who, God pray, is innocent." Kathleen made yet another sign of the cross asking God for probably the tenth time, Dannie guessed, to forgive her for "taking" that postcard.

"Why did you tell me all this," Dannie said, "before I asked. How did you know?"

"Know that you were looking for my uncle?" she said. "Because my ex-aunt Rosa says that you're . . . my uncle's son. She believes that wholeheartedly. Because my uncle was leaving his second wife, my aunt Betty. She says he was leaving to marry your mother and claim you. It's all so complicated, Dannie. If it's all true then we're related. We're . . . cousins. It can make your head swim when it's all so untrue."

"What's untrue?" Dannie leaned forward.

"Relatives," Kathleen said. "We truly have none. We are all related, but only through God. We are all His children. The rest is earthly nonsense."

Dannie saw the sinewy custodian by the pew. Leaning on his broom. Waiting.

He led Kathleen from the deserted church. She genuflected "Happy Birthday to Our Lord" outside the church steps.

"Dannie," she fidgeted, adjusting her white kerchief. "The Police Commissioner is hinting at a solution of the Arnold Schuster case. He said it at the swearing-in ceremonies of the new police recruits. He has good reason to want to solve this. That's his job. It's a sin, but he had to arrest and indict those two working men—the two longshoremen on the piers that said they sold my uncle those guns. The gun that made my uncle the link to the killers. The same gun that was used to break the Fifth Commandment. But if you are out looking for someone you call your father, you're looking in the wrong direction."

"Kathleen," he glanced down the decoratively lit Seventh Avenue. Squinting, he spied Rocco Bruzzese, that neighborhood bedbug, the flamehead *gabadorsch*, lurking again across the street by a skeleton of a tree, watching them. Dannie was thrown from his train of thought. He remembered the old days when he had told Rocco to buzz-off! But now he knew he couldn't start any disturbances that would lead to the cops coming.

Kathleen told him that she'd finally decided Rocco is harmless anyway. Just "horny."

Dannie was embarrassed to hear the one he had thought of as so innocent using that word. But she was still his model Saint. She begged him to go on with what he was originally saying.

"I think I know who you meant before," he began again. "You may have meant God. The Father. But that's later. The now is I need a saviour. Not the one in the church behind me. But the one I'm looking for, Kathleen. I trust you with my life. Let me be frank and open. Tony-boy, Gretti, a cadre of them, your father, Jamesie, others may be looking to kill me. Your uncle can . . ."

"My father?" Kathleen's voice was languid, only her fingers, entwined in Dannie's, came to life. "That can't be true. He doesn't speak to Little Mike. I can see they hate each other now. Gretti's friends and my father's friends are enemies. Dannie, you mistrust everyone."

Dannie saw an Austin pass by. The four-door Deluxe had passed the church, U-turned, and was circling again.

"I'm sorry I said that about your father," he said, freeing his fingers from hers. "The break-up makes sense from what a fellow named Joe the Blond told me. I've got to go," the Austin went by the front of the church stopping on the far corner. Dannie's mind flashed to Al Rispone's inadvertent slaying.

"That's my uncle Pietro M. and Mush come to get me." She followed his eyes to the car. "They don't speak to that counterfeit Gretti or those others now either. How can I prove it to you?"

"God'll show you how," he near-snickered, watching the car, no one exiting from it yet. He stood, ready to turn up the residential street. "I didn't mean that. You have nothing to prove to me. I believe you."

"Dannie," she began. "Your conscience. Is it your guilt causing you to turn on and move away from Our Lord?"

"Guilt?" he gulped openly. "Guilt about what?" He was suddenly nervous.

"I don't know, D." There was sweat on her peaked face in spite of the cold. "Like my guilt," she groped for the words. "About Arnold. I went to visit his family, because of my uncle. You disappeared when he did. Have you anything to atone to Arnold's kin for also? Oh, Dannie. I don't know what I'm saying." Dannie half-turned trance-like to leave.

"Where are you going?" Life came to her eyes, guilt giving up its grip.

"Maybe Miami Beach." His eyes were fixed steady on her, his mind halfway back to that pitiful, infamous night in March—and that car now on the far corner.

"I'll show you the truth about my father, his true friends, and my uncles. They go to Miami often. I'll show you. I'll give you faith. But give me one thing."

"Anything," he said quickly, his eyes still on the Austin.

"You can't," she had changed her mind. "And I only wanted it as a going away present. I'll never see you again, Dannie."

"What did you want?" he asked, moved by the finality of her statement, as if it would be through her guilty fault that they'd never see each other again. Her fault through her . . . dying. She was close to him by the church steps.

"A . . . kiss. But you can't. We may be . . . cousins. And you'd kiss me like one." She plaintively wished for a real kiss . . . "from only you, Dannie." Her head bowed, she sadly bade him Godspeed and gave him Gloria's undying love.

He wished he were close now beside mouth-watering Gloria, who thought his "disappearance" from her life had to do with his jealous aunt. He reflected on Kathleen saying "cousins." What did that matter after his perverted December 9 birthday in a hotel room—not to mention the times before! He kissed Kathleen as if she were sweet clay that he wanted to breathe fire, life into. "We're all God's children, remember, so it doesn't matter, does it?" He couldn't believe she was ardently kissing him back, tongue-to-tongue, actual vibrant life flowing from her moist mouth into his. The Austin shifted into reverse and was coming their way. Dannie released her.

"Thank you," she breathed, "for my last Merry Christmas." She made the habitual sign of the Cross as he turned the corner, leaving her and tearing the hell up the street.

He raced, making up his mind. He would have to go to Miami Beach.

He'd need travel money, he figured as he zigzagged toward the safe-darkened subway train cuts.

But no cash from his two spellbinders: stunning Eve and rambunctious Eleanor. Better leave them be. Safer too, for them, he feared!

1953

January-March

In January, Dannie acquired the job he had promised himself he'd get.

Any job just to earn and save money for his planned trip to Florida. He shined shoes in a shoemaker's shop on Vanderbilt Avenue in the Crown Heights side of Prospect Park.

He had seen a sign in the window, "Boy Wanted," while walking aimlessly one day, and when he discovered that sleeping in the rear of the store came with the job, he had jumped on it.

It would save him furnished room money, and it would give Mr. Ammodio, the proprietor, protection from the "young colored *roofians*" that were moving into Crown Heights.

He had to show his true birth certificate to Mr. Ammodio to prove he was Italian before he secured the position. The gray, trim mustachioed storekeeper trusted no one but his "own."

Dannie wondered about that as he shined, careful not to get the polish on the socks of the men whose shoes he was rag-buffing, spit-polishing.

His own: Al-bert Anastasia seeking to dethrone Uncle Frank (Frank Costello) and Vito "Don Vitone" Genovese from their other group positions in order to assume the title, Boss of Bosses.

He wondered, as he delivered rebuilt shoes to nearby brownstones.

His own: Little Mike, Gretti, and Tony-boy at odds with Jamesie, Pietro M., and Mush. They belonged to two separate organizations now.

Joey Gallo was aspiring to topple all of his own with the aid of his two brothers, Larry and The Blast.

Scap, with the wild pistol, shot at his own James Fortunato in nearby Prospect Park.

His own aunt had enticed Roscoe with false allure, using the devilish, phony hint of hot sex to get him to marry her pregnant sister.

His own father. John. He had set out to find him. Then, finding out the way in which he became his parent, he wanted to . . . kill him for it! But it was his father alone who could keep him alive.

And on and on with His Own.

Dannie worked six long days a week well into February before he took an official holiday off to make good his promise to lithe Fran on Staten Island. He'd see her. Maybe she had some inside information for him concerning John's whereabouts, maybe it would coincide with the Miami Beach set of postcards.

On the President's belated birthday he ferried it to Staten Island and made his way to the boarding house on Bay Street in the Stapleton section where Fran lived.

She radiated an inviolable air in silver brocaded jacket. At her suggestion, they went to see *High Noon* with Gary Cooper. While Cooper tried to gather men for the 12:00 p.m. gunfight, she started nibbling on his left earlobe, running a slender hand through his hair.

His face went crimson in the dark movie theater at her own feline lip-licking. Sweet oblivion, it could come with her. It would be like fucking fire but he couldn't . . . perform the foreplay. Dannie wanted to crawl into a manhole from sheer humiliation when she rashly kissed him.

On their walk home, Fran spoke of keen Willie Sutton, quoting him like a priest reading from a bible: "Most laymen," she said, "are a bunch of flakes snowin' each other."

"Willie," she continued, "was noticed by his part of the world when robbing banks. He was a genius," she asserted, "not a scoundrel." Yet she was classy enough not to allude to Dannie's. . . dead-flesh during and after the *High Noon* shootout.

Dannie kept prodding her with questions, seeking some kind of lead.

Marge: Willie's paramour. She'd tell all she knew to stay in this country.

Angel: Where was he? A loyal *meshugener* never in it solely for money. Nobody knew.

She made no mention of Johnny Squint, and Dannie felt the trip all but wasted. But he did find light on the topic of Gretti. Fran knew that Gret was always down on Dannie because Dannie had supplanted Gretti as second closest to John.

Meyer Lansky: Willie the Actor got on his good side by helping to fund the Zionist movement. Mr. Lansky would know exactly what to do with wheelbarrows of fresh cash Willie was bringing in.

Then the subject shifted to escape and the money they'd need to bring it off. Did Dannie want to shovel, search with her, for all the hidden money, more than likely in the marshlands.

Dannie's mind kept returning to Tony-boy's greedy insinuations when the Actor was apprehended—where were Willie's millions really hidden?

"Fran," Dannie tried not to stammer. "Others want that loot, that money, for other reasons!"

"The Anastasia people?" she countered, unflinching. "That mushroom face, Al Rispone, was here once askin' about it. Now his spongy face is buried along with the rest of him."

Dannie choked inaudibly on a gulp. Fran's coolness reminded him, somehow, of his aunt. And it frightened him. He planted a peck on her sculptured cheek, and wished her luck. *Buon caccia*!

A week later Dannie took a day off to have his eyes examined. "You have an astigmatism," the eye doctor told him, discussing it as nothing serious. "We're born with it—some of us—it's a hereditary factor."

Dannie ordered three pair of dark glasses. Prescription sunglasses. Gray, green, blue tints, as Johnny had suggested over a year ago. How he wished that he had them the night Schuster was brutally slain.

He telephoned his aunt and mother once, and he was glad he did. His aunt had a letter for him from Kathleen Mazziotta.

He was planning on leaving soon, so he gave in and met Eleanor on a lone Sunday by the Boathouse in Prospect Park. It was close to the place where memorial services had been held for Arnold. Dannie shuddered by the frozen lake, concentrating on his aunt before him.

He asked about his mother. "Not well at all . . . emotionally," Eleanor answered coldly, her long hair mostly defying the attacking windstorm.

He didn't have to tear open Kathleen's letter. It was already open. He read the body of the letter—the list of places where men like her uncle John may be found on the tail end of the gambling, southern Gold Coast. She had gathered them from her father, Jamesie.

She had signed off with "I'll see you in a minute."

"You're going to Miami Beach on a wild-goose chase," his aunt said sternly.

Yes, he nodded, pocketing the letter.

"You're leaving your mother and me!" she demanded.

Yes, he nodded again. Aside from Johnny, he couldn't think of two better reasons to leave! The sight of Eleanor before him wrapped in a tight-fitting lime winter coat, sparked thoughts of her curvy, tasty contours. But brushing his dark thoughts aside, he took leave of Eleanor. Filled with fury, she reached and spun him around.

"You're running to something you'll never find," her eyes tore into him.

"I'll find him!" he swore.

"You'll never find your father." She wanted to strike him, her gloved right hand rising, falling.

He turned away.

"We know what you're running from!" her voice punctured the wind. "But you'll come back for it because you'll never find it anywhere else. With anyone else! Neither will we. Goddamn us." She was screaming, her voice cutting piercingly through the Park.

He ran away, his back to her, sprinting like a track star, the lure of incest chasing at his heels.

The night before he left for Miami Beach he dreamt again of his own eyes and balls being blasted to bits. The identification with Schuster was gaining ground, growing strong.

1953

Miami was a burst of sunshine. The hot ocean air felt good as Dannie got off his National Airline's flight. He stood outside the airport terminal, his eyes protected from the sun's harsh rays by his blue-tint prescription sunglasses.

The warm breeze wafting in from the pale green Atlantic gave him a good feeling that he'd find Johnny. Why else the two postcards with the same handwriting? Thank you, Kathleen, he smiled. He stood there with the three suitcases his mother had brought him on the day he had met her and his aunt at Gregnano's Under-the-El restaurant.

He had telephoned his mother to say he was leaving when he knew that Eleanor would be working. He asked how she was, and she had told him it was urgent she see him in person before he left.

Unable to ignore the urgency in her voice, he agreed to meet her at the National Airlines Terminal at Idlewild Airport, twenty minutes before his plane was scheduled to take off.

She was already there when he arrived.

She seemed well, stable enough. She had another letter from Kathleen. In it was a much older letter written by Johnny to his father. Kathleen had found it in her grandfather's apartment.

The letter was worn, soiled. The postmark a twenty-year-old

faded imprint. It had come to Felice Mazziotta from Elmira Reformatory. It was from Johnny Mazziotta, and the writing seemed exactly the same as on the two postcards as he compared all three, sitting in the bare but snug restaurant of the Airline Terminal. The double T's crossed the same way, the small I's dotted to the right side, and the capital M's a perfect match.

There was also a note from Kathleen, the end of which asked Dannie to *trust* the Mazziotta's. She had signed it: "I love you. P.S. Even if we are cousins. (God forgive me) but I do!"

Cousins. He had walked with his mother to the flight gate. Seemed the joke of love was on him so far. We're all God's children, Kathleen always said, but he had all kinds of promising luck with the wrong children. He had kissed his mother on the cheek as the speakers blared that his flight was now boarding.

His mother, at first, had kissed him calmly on the cheek in return. She had said she was withdrawing from the world, from people. But not to worry, she'd never withdraw from him! The moist, stinging bite on his left earlobe she had given him after that made him carry the weight of their bizarre relationship with him as he walked up the flight ramp. He had hoped the plane would crash, but prayed it wouldn't.

He stood now in Miami, Florida, and the warmth acted as a balm to the scars of New York. He hopped into an airport cab, sharing it with six other passengers. His destination was the Barcelona Hotel on Collins Avenue—the Miami Beachfront picture on both postcards.

It took him five minutes to secure a room at the Barcelona. The ten dollars he palmed the desk clerk, as he had seen Eleanor do to the maitre d' at the Skyway, made up for his lack of experience in not telephoning ahead to make a reservation.

It took him twenty minutes of browsing and chatting with the lady clerk in the Barcelona souvenir and card shoppe to discover that Barcelona Oceanfront postcards could be purchased in ANY hotel, drugstore, or card shoppe anywhere in Miami Beach.

And it took a week to go through Kathleen's list. A week of taking buses and taxicabs. To the Dream Bar, Remo's Restaurant Motel Row, the Dream Lounge on the 79th Street Causeway, the Five O'Clock Club "fronted" by comedienne Martha Raye—Sally G. Burns of the Costello Group and Frankie Dio of the New York Harlem Crew as Silent Partners.

Dannie covered all of the dark clubs eavesdropping Kathleen had informed him Johnny Mazziotta might hang out in. A drink in hand, his head would twist and search for a familiar squat figure—a silhouette, profile in a shadowy corner.

Nothing.

It took him just thirty seconds to count his funds and know that he could never last at the Barcelona.

For three months he lived like a miser in a furnished room. He had scouted betting parlors on Washington Avenue, Lincoln Road, the side and backstreets of Miami Beach.

To him the Beach City was a place in which to spend money, not make it. Honeymoon couples had the wedding profits, tourists had their vacation money, and elderly people had pensions, or wealthy offspring paying their downtown hotel row bills from New York's garment district.

He had applied once for a job as a bellboy at the Barcelona, but he needed a police card to work on the Beach.

He never tried that again.

Oddly enough, it was books that kept him going. He'd burrow away in the Public Library, studying handwriting analysis and graphology, anything that might aid his search. He studied T's, inverted strokes for M's, line values, loops, and breaks between letters and words. He compared until he was blinking himself blind behind his tinted eyeglasses. Each time, the writing in the original letter matched the writing on the two postcards.

But where could Johnny be? Dannie walked the streets and prowled the beach. He checked the "smart" men's clothing shops and shopping centers by day and lurked by the race tracks, outside of fine restaurants, bars, and key-clubs nights.

He grew to know Hollywood, Hialeah, Hallendale and then Ft. Lauderdale, Coral Gables, the Tropical Park, thoroughbred Gulfstream racetracks, the Flats.

He watched the dog races, the Jai Lai game, and the outskirts of the city and the outside of more places than he had known existed. And always there was the inside of his cheap, dingy furnished room where, night after night, he overworked his troubled head.

Had John moved on?

Would John have taken a chance and sent those postcards from here and stayed?

Had he gone on to Cuba or the Bahamas, where there was lucrative, legal gambling?

Had John's *padrone*, Uncle Frank, secured him a spot in the Caribbean or overseas? Maybe Russia? Dannie clung to that straw. With that ruby-gold ring from the Princess in Sunset Park, "as good as a passport, if you get past the border," he recalled the tall blonde's words.

Where do "wise-guys" run?

Were the police protecting Johnny now as they had shielded Willie Sutton for five years? They had refused to protect Arnold Schuster for less than three weeks. Dannie knew he needed help—a kind of help that John must be getting. He tossed between the promising Joey Gallo, and his faithful duo, Eleanor and Eve.

His nights were haunted by craving dreams of his two black-haired . . . relatives. And with nightmares about Schuster. He could feel his own descent into a dark, lonely night-world of hell.

Reach out! He had to. And he realized after he did it that he made the same mistake as Johnny.

He had sent a postcard. A Barcelona one. Why not? They sold them at any hotel, motel, drugstore on the beach.

He sent it to his mother, asking her to contact Roscoe Valencia, Kathleen Mazziotta, and Joe "The Blond" Gallo from Scarola's Church Avenue restaurant.

A week later he telephoned more instructions to her. The collect call must have cost his aunt plenty, especially since he was barely able to get a word in as his mother screeched and fell apart on the phone. He told her he'd call her back within a week to see if she had any positive information for him, and hung up, afraid that he might give in to her. She wanted him to come home and go away with her and Eleanor. But he couldn't give up on Johnny now. Finally, three days later, he blessedly found a job.

The Place Pigalle, just off Collins Avenue, a Nite-Club. Raucous. B-girls hung around the bar waiting to suck you into buying them a drink. They led you to an expensive, cover-charge ringside table, and had you order watered down champagne, teasing you, making you feel like an appealing million bucks, only to leave you high and dry when either your money ran out or the night was officially over.

The club boasted risqué entertainment: Pearl Williams telling dirty jokes at her piano, B.S. Pulley and his sunken-cheeked, cordial partner Andy Gump reciting filthier jokes, all to get you in the gay mood for the on-stage strippers and the off-stage cockteasers.

The "Place" had a greeter. A captain, and a doorman all in one. His name was Art, and he knew the art of being where you were from. Be it the Grand Concourse in the Bronx, the loop in Chicago, or Green Street up in Albany, he was from there to make you feel at home.

He was sixty years old. But he and his shiny brown suit both couldn't take the blood flow and the blood stains that came with the job anymore.

He was the club's bouncer, too. Groups of out of town fellows got nasty when they got the padded bill for treating the girls who had no intention of giving them a "treat."

Dannie had been in there three times before. The Place was on Kathleen's list. He had nursed a drink at the crowded bar, refusing the advances from the working girls, choosing instead to look for the five-foot-six man with trademark Brito brown-on-brown shoes.

He had been tempted on his third trip there to buy one of the girls a drink. A redhead, nearly as tall as him. And it wasn't her bad whiskey-breath that had turned him off. He could have possibly gotten past that. Her hair flowed down to her rear and she was built, her bust tearing at the lamé blouse she wore.

What it came down to was the fact that he was hoarding every nickel to survive in this free-wheeling, free-spending town.

There was another fact thrown in with it. The fact that she didn't have Crosscavale black hair. The scent and shapely beauty of Eve and Eleanor hounded him!

On his fourth trip there he tested the greeter, saying he was from Pacific and Fourth in South Brooklyn.

Naturally, so was Art.

Dannie nursed his rye. The redhead recognized him. Her "name" was Betty Allan, but Casey, the in-the-know bartender, called her "Mamie Stover."

She plied her wares, working at her bar-trade, but Dannie didn't buy her a cocktail. It would have cost him the price of a meal the next day.

Betty moved along, trouble seeming to move along with her. She took three fellows from Boston for a ride. To a ringside table, and a $160.00 tab. Not only didn't they want to pay the Place, but they wanted to drag her out of it. She was "big enough to handle the three" of them in the backseat of their car.

Dannie said it again and again. To himself. The golden rule of the street: MIND YOUR OWN BUSINESS.

But one of the fellows had punched Betty Allan bloody. The other two had wrecked Art the bouncer, along with his shiny brown suit.

Dannie had his own Borough Park beating in mind. Get mad, was Hugo Duce's battle instruction to him through Johnny. "Take it personal when fighting. But try at the same time to stay cool . . ."

He had no Ronson lighter with him to palm this time. He watched the redhead's mouth bleed a finer red than her hair. Her lips had fattened and her mouth had swollen in the course of several moments. She was in a semi-stupor, being dragged to the front door by a burly Boston customer.

It took those drawn-out moments to get Dannie mad enough to break the rule he tried so hard to practice. He jumped out of his seat and raced towards the door. He got lucky and sucker-punched the guy that had the redhead in a choke-hold around the neck.

But he caught a nasty whack from one of the other two. It knocked off his dark glasses, sending him staggering like a Scap blow of old.

All he needed to stay on his feet and come back was a girl's cry! He got it. It wasn't Antoinette's or Anna Banana's, but Betty Allan's. And he fought, not flatfooted, but balanced on his toes, peppering his adversaries' faces with sharp jabs until they were bruised and bleeding.

No arrests were made. Harry Rich, the owner of the Place, saw to that.

The trio from Boston were dragged limply to their car, the beige uniformed police were staked, and Dannie was offered two things. The first was from Harry Rich, an intimate confidant of KG's (known gamblers). He was a corpulent, cocky man who also liked to mix with "good people."

The offer was a job as bouncer to back up Art. Dannie took it. Sans fictitious I.D.

And he took the second offer, from the redhead, Betty, taking her home to her apartment in Miami Springs where he soaked her lips with a hot compress, and iced her mouth for the swelling to go down, the contusion to heal.

Her massive breasts pressed firmly against her red satin brassiere. Her breath had sweetened with the compresses and surrounding fresh ice, and as she lay on her back her experienced hips made him want his satisfaction so badly he could have tasted it. But he didn't take the offer.

Goddamned Eleanor's vampire thighs distorted his vision, killed instead of whetted his appetite for sex. He'd kill her someday, he decided as he left delectable Betty safe, but unsatisfied, on her bed, and secured the job at the Place Pigalle because, as Harry Rich later said, "he was a kid . . . a man who was . . . wise. South Brooklyn wise enough not to mix business with pleasure." He should only know his motives, Dannie thought.

Dannie, backed up by Art, became the Place's bouncer. Harry

Rich saw to it that he needed no police picture-print work card.

As hard as it was to refuse the Pigalle's B-Girl's repeated playful come-ons, Dannie somehow managed to go home alone each night. His memory of his bastard aunt saw to that, taunting, tempting until he gave in and telephoned Eve.

She was on the verge of a breakdown over not seeing him for so long, but ecstatic at his being safe and sound. And working.

"Are you lonely?" she finally asked. Dannie caught the teasing intonation and quickly switched subjects. But Kathleen had nothing new to report, Roscoe knew nothing further, and Joe Gallo had said, "Take care, kid, wherever you are." He would keep him apprised." Dannie hung up on his mother after he was forced to tell her he loved her more than life itself. Hesitantly, timidly she had asked, "As much as . . . you love Eleanor?"

Dannie worked the week away, making enough money to roam down Kathleen's list again, looking for Johnny. Harry Rich had inadvertently added to it by mentioning where the eastern Badge men hung out.

Dannie walked to his nearby room, the mystery of him between Eleanor's inviting legs causing his mind to spin. That night he dreamed a horrid wet dream and swore, soggy and sick in the night, that she couldn't be his *Aunt*.

Other nights he tried with Betty Allan, taking her home when the Place closed. So she was a regular Mamie Stover, like the known madame of Hawaii fame. She was still a "down," an O.K. girl with him.

But he couldn't get hard during the foreplay and had to conceal his feelings of inadequacy behind a conscience-stricken decision that he couldn't allow himself to mix business with pleasure. He took off from Betty's fashionable apartment like he had run from zesty Eleanor in Prospect Park. Only for an entirely different reason.

He "cleaned" himself early in the morning after a night of see-ing . . . her, so wanting, sleeping by his bed, the blanket barely cov-ering her naked form. At least the dreams told him he could get hard.

Life had played a son-of-a-bitchin' trick on him. His dreams cer-tified it. He knew peaceful sleep was out of the question as he said a quick prayer that he'd find Johnny before he killed himself.

"LOOK AT THAT MOTHERFUCKER!" DANNIE HEARD the voice of the young man beside him as he lay prone on the rented, wooden beach chair by the Barcelona swimming pool.

He had two days off and chose to spend them as a non-guest at the ever-hopeful Barcelona Hotel. He lay on his back, eyes half open beneath his blue-tinted sunglasses.

"Am I seeing things?" he heard another voice say, and twisted slightly to his right to get a view. Two guys in their early twenties, reclining on cushioned pool lounges, were admiring the "scenery" on the Barcelona's pool deck, the Atlantic Ocean as a backdrop. Dannie didn't turn full round, but he closed his eyes, the poolside comments brash, slurred, nasal in his ears. They must be New Yorkers, he figured, the southern sun browning him.

"It's a mirage," he heard. "I'm seeing double. You hold them and I'll fuck 'em. We'll take turns."

"Why don't you two jerks turn in your wagging tongues." It was a young woman's voice. The last thing he wanted was trouble out in the open without Harry Rich around to smooth things over. He turned on his other side, keeping his eyes shut tight, but saw in the memory of them the back of the woman that was speaking.

She was laying on her stomach on the third chair on his right, just as he had passed her earlier. Her bikini revealed a real shapely half-moon rear, and Dannie was also stricken by her long satiny, chestnut-brown hair. He loved long hair. But hers couldn't be long enough to get involved, even if the two guys wound up killing her in public.

"Keep that fuckin' big beak of yours out of this," the husky guy by Dannie snapped.

"We're watchin' paradise on the pool deck and you got a face like fierce piss," the second guy jumped on the bandwagon. "Shut up cucumber nose and try to hide your jealousy in it."

"Both you fags," the young woman broke into a torrent of anger, "are gonna be in Paradise before the day is up! You won't be hiding in sand. You'll be buried in it. Up to your fuckin' lower Manhattan big mouths!"

This was going to be a whopper. Dannie kept his eyes closed.

"Hey, Beansie," Dannie could sense that the guy nearest him had risen. "We got a killer-diller broad among us. If we fill her schnoz with water it'll drown her."

"And give us time," the other fellow had also stood up, Dannie could tell by gauging the voice distance, "to make the two black-haired witches and beat the hotel at the same time!"

Dannie opened his eyes, blinking them clear under the bright blaring sun. He saw what he knew!

It took him a moment with heated, fogging tears under his sunglasses to take out his madness on Beansie and friend.

A one-sided battle, the insane fury in him made him hit harder than he ever did even with Hugo's lighter. His punches shot out in flurries until Beansie fell back into the pool, his blood turning the water around him an ugly red; the friend decked into a paradise of his own by the pool side.

The lifeguard dove in after Beansie. The friend just lay there, incapacitated.

"You're not skinny anymore," the bikini-clad young lady stood smirking before Dannie, as hotel waiters, two security guards, and an assistant manager approached. "Coincidence?" she said. "I laid in wait on you. Checked out of the Eden Roc up the street when I spotted your mother outside by the bus stop. Who could forget that *bella* woman's face and figure during the days I was scouting you and your Borough Park neighborhood?"

Dannie stood mute amidst the crowd. It was Anna Banana doing the talking. The girl who had dry-laid him in Prospect Park. Alburt's niece. The last girl he wanted to see. Anna buzzed the assistant manager's ear, while Dannie turned his head slightly and saw the two black-haired witches that Beansie and friend had been drooling loudly over. He froze. It was his mother and aunt.

"No sweat," Anna said to him. "The manager *knows* that this is a dead issue. Join your mother. But be on the beach at ten." She half turned into the dispersing crowd, but looked back with a smile. "Unfinished business. Remember?" She bikini-swaggered through the gaping tourists.

Dannie strolled slowly with his mother and aunt in the moist sand on the Barcelona beachfront. They were adorned in low-cut twin lemon-shaded bathing suits, and he was painfully aware of the jealous glares of passers by while his mother hung onto him like a drape. His aunt castigated him like a trooper.

He was inconsiderate, an ingrate, on a wild-goose chase. He didn't even have the decency to follow up the calls he had made seeking information. From them. From Roscoe, who married the harlot Rosa. From Kathleen Mazziotta, who is related to a mercenary bunch despite her protestations of the opposite. From the pale-eyed skeleton of a gangster, Joe Gallo (dubbed now by the New York Metropolitan newspapers as "Crazy Joe"), who proclaimed he only cared about his "friends," his "followers," when in reality he only cared about himself.

"We have come to *you*!" His aunt was her old self, bringing to bear the forceful, uncertain seasons of her temperament. "You sent us what? A Barcelona postcard? Three days here looking for you only to find you fighting over a young girl with a nose a size larger than a palm tree."

If his aunt wasn't such a crank and so nutty, she'd be funny, Dannie thought as her words punctured the relentless thunder of the ocean's waves—an ocean he'd have liked to drown her in. Eleanor kept going till the afternoon sun set.

He had two appointments—two "dates"—when the day went to dusk and the harangue ended. One with Anna at 10 p.m. on the beach. The other with the two sisters by the pool at 10 p.m.

He kept neither.

TIME TO LEAVE MIAMI, DANNIE DECIDED. HE DIDN'T have the Gold Coast inside track of information after all. But go where? Back to New York? To see Kathleen? Roscoe? Had his aunt lied? Two postcards and a letter was all he had to go on.

Casey nodded to him from behind the bar of the Place Pigalle—a safe two miles from the Barcelona. It was a slow night, off-season, everything cool. He saw Art by the entranceway, greeting a foursome. He heard the word Cleveland and knew Art was from their home town. Hungry, Dannie went into the kitchen for a snack. A roast beef on white with mayonnaise, a kosher pickle and a bottle of Bud.

When he came out, he saw the legs first. Crossed. The right one kicking gently, provocatively, a back and forth steady motion of desire and determination.

He walked steadily as he approached her bar stool.

"You working bars now?" he sneered, wanting to drive her the hell out.

Eleanor Cross did not dignify the remark with a response and he was sorry he had said it.

"Friend of yours?" Casey muttered as he sauntered over. Dannie nodded.

Casey refreshed Eleanor's vodka collins. "On the house," he drifted away.

But Betty Allan had drifted over. "You're working the wrong side of the street," she slurred, drunk and dead serious, to Eleanor. "This one doesn't lay girls," she jabbed an elbow at Dannie. "He calls it not mixing pleasure with business, or however it goes."

"How would you know?" Eleanor was colder than the frost on

the glass of her mixed drink.

"Firsthand," Betty swayed, hefting herself to a stool.

And she nearly toppled from the sudden whack in her face from the flattened back of Eleanor's right hand!

Same sweet aunt, Dannie smirked as he stopped the commotion before it began. He took Betty into the kitchen and told Lionel, the short order chef, to sober her up with as many cups of black coffee as he could get her to drink.

"How did you find me?" he said, trying to remain cool as he returned to the bar.

She strawed the drink, lifted her head to him, her depthless blue eyes daring him to rush right in. "You keep lovely company, Daniel. Has your taste turned to redheads?"

He didn't answer.

"I waited two days after you ducked all three of us, but found you with the help of that one with the nosey attitude and bigger than life nose," his aunt twirled the plastic stirrer in her glass. "She was on the beach at ten while we were by the pool. But we met again and she said it had taken her one hour on the telephone to locate where you were. I've been a telephone operator and supervisor now for nearly half of my thirty-three years. But she must have known WHO to call."

Great, Dannie removed his blue-tint prescription glasses, rubbing his eyebrows with the thumb and middle finger of his right hand. Anna knew where he was. Just great. He wearily rubbed the corners of his left eye with his fingertips.

"Give this up," Eleanor persisted. "The friends you've made kill each other from sheer boredom. They thrive on it. Johnny Mazziotta is dead. He must be. He has those kinds of friends," his aunt's voice had a pleading, tender tone. "If the police of ninety nations can't find him, what makes you think you can? He killed a law abiding citizen and got his just reward. Death in return. Come away with . . . your mother and me. I'll get a transfer or a new job in any state you name. Your mother can't work in the emotional state she's in. She's afraid to leave the house. She lives in dread of rape. For Godssake give us what we gave you."

Dannie followed her every word. It wasn't that easy. There was the Law to contend with somehow, someday. How could he involve his mother and aunt.

What was worse, there were the likes of Mike and Al-burt and all the other Badges of that Crew that could make mincemeat out of the three of them if it came to that. The Sutton-Schuster case was still a hot issue from coast to coast. The post offices around the country were still plastered with bigger than life mug shots of Angel Tenuto and Chappy Mazziotta. He had been on the verge of giving in. But that would get him nowhere. The same nowhere he was living in. He felt so lost in between.

"Where do you live?" Eleanor seemed to read him.

Nowhere, he almost answered, but caught her meaning. He glimpsed across the bar to a now sober Betty, a glistening redhead, to the customer buying her a drink. He thought of the nights he had tried with her, and gave in, telling Harry Rich he was not only taking off for the rest of the night but that he would be quitting soon.

Harry Rich had been good to him. Taking him in the way he had. He asked Dannie a personal favor. To stay on for just one more week. For time to get a replacement. Time to lend him out to the nearby Five O' Clock Club for a one night private party.

Dannie said yes from gratitude and left with his aunt.

He walked the ten blocks to his dowdy furnished room with her in silence. Her arm was hooked into his like he was her beau, and the perfume and body contact made him quicken his pace.

"Will you go home with my mother after this night is over?" he asked her in his room.

"If you must have it that way, yes."

And he was stuck on how to start the night. He stood out of place in the room by her. Did they have to battle to begin, he trembled. Would that touch it off? Who were these two sisters, really? His thoughts darted to the lovely, almond-eyed Eve, the same old guilt in his head causing him to cringe

Eleanor sat down in the one chair and crossed her legs as she had done in the bar, her right leg kicking back and forth motions, her right hand by her knee.

Did Eleanor have to be in a clinging, shortie negligee on a bed beside him for the *proibire* blood line to be crossed. No; he felt himself getting hard, her Jasmine scent permeating the room.

Was it some kind of contest? He just stared at her. He must have been overthinking from the moment she had asked where he lived. He'd chalk up the night and let it stop here. He could live in peace without her. Then, suddenly she stood, turning her back to him, and he saw her hands going up under her hair to the top back of her dress.

"Stuck," was all she said, fine strands of her long coal-dust hair were caught in the teeth of her dress zipper.

He stepped forward at the wincing sound she made and helped her.

"You pull it *down*," she ordered with her back to him, her hands up behind her, holding her hair out of the way.

"I know." He unzipped the dress to her waist.

"And you do anything you like," she turned to him, her hair still upswept, the effect accentuating the depth of mystery in her blue eyes. "And I'll love everything you do!"

"And you loved the torture of the last five minutes," his eyes held hers. "Sitting in that chair. Waiting for what?"

She let her hair cascade down. "Waiting for you. Like I've been sitting in chairs waiting for eighteen months since the last time we nearly loved each other. And now that I've made the first move, you make up for the rest, you bastard, redheaded lover!" Then she was on him—making Miami a heaven of her.

He made love to her. And it was as if the first time for both of them!

Eleanor was as wild-vicious in the lovemaking as she had been during their fights in the past. She drew blood from his lips with her teeth as she tried to devour him.

Her legs locked him to her in an ecstasy of rhythm as his semen gushed. She was satisfied, aglow, then, not satisfied, shrieking her satisfaction with fierce agony as he came again!

They held each other until the beach sun filtered through his shoddy window shade. And again and again she made him repeat that he had not made love to that redhead! Her stroking hand, a tease of fingertips, scintillated him to erection for the third time since dark, trying to satisfy the years of longing stored in her fire-body. They lay side by side breathing in, tasting each other, the luxury of her pink, open flesh his.

"Let me be your breakfast," she held his dampened head to the nectar of her ultra-swollen breasts "And give me a chance for you to be mine some other morning, darling."

The words led him automatically to lay her on her back, and she, just as naturally, wrapped her thighs and legs around him. It took them twenty minutes of deeper than body rapture to come in unison—together. After, he wondered the future of that last word—together!

"If I become pregnant would you shoot me like you said you would that time by Gregnano's restaurant in Brooklyn?"

He had never actually dreamt of that possibility. "No," he said. "I'd probably shoot myself."

"In any case don't waste a bullet," her voice was truly light-hearted, she stroked the back of his neck, his head cozy on the sumptuousness of her naked bust. "When we're married I'll tell you why."

God never made a greater nut. His eyes were wide open along with his mouth. He let her indulge in fantasy while he enjoyed her sensual caresses. That was *real*. He began to fall asleep holding her tight around her blissful waist.

THEY WERE GONE, ELEANOR AND EVE. AND HE HAD A half a week before he left. And a "private party" to aid in overseeing before he did. And he knew standing inside the Five O' Clock Club's foyer that the party was no party at all. It was a Meeting. A private one that he, with two other selected bouncers, were to keep Private.

And when the curvy, tanned, nose roaming all over her face, Anna came in, he felt he knew just who he had been selected by.

Anna sauntered up to where he was waiting, elbowing the huge, circular bar. She gestured to a polished, silk-suited, but rough looking fellow.

"He'll brief you," she said to Dannie. "And of course you figured out by now that it was me who landed you this position."

"Of course," Dannie didn't smile. This one was dangerous.

She hit him with a barrage of questions: Why was he still wearing her girlfriend's I.D. bracelet gift to him? Why hadn't he shown at the Barcelona beachfront? Where are the two *splendido* ladies now, that he had also stood up by the pool? And where did he learn to fight so handily since the days of Scap and rolling in the Prospect Park lake? He gave no answers, slightly amused but more anxious over what he had gotten himself into tonight. The silk-suited fellow was coming toward him.

Anna grandly kissed Dannie, a prolonged one, making him, ostensibly feel like one of the "family" before she sashayed away.

Lou "T," the second bouncer, introduced himself, firmly shaking Dannie's hand. He pointed to a gargantuan guy by the bandstand, a third co-worker, nicknamed Jinga Betz. It would take four giants to ever corral him, Dannie observed.

Lou T's briefing was simple. Simply stated. Under no circumstances were they to allow anybody in: Feds, local cops, tourists, or strangers. In short, keep the non-invited out. At any costs.

"*E inteso*," Dannie nodded, playing it coolly, trying to act professional. He walked slowly around the bar, nodding once to Jinga Betz, whose size made him feel as though he had shrunk six inches.

Dannie's mind drifted back to Eleanor. He envied her nightgowns for holding her beautiful, hot 37-inch tits day in and day out.

He couldn't help thinking that crude way, somehow it seemed natural. He knew he lost his shot at eternal life for committing that filthy sin. Dannie sweated, trying to regain a facsimile of composure.

Unobtrusively, he took in the Five O' Clock Club. He spotted the front, side and rear exits and entrances, saw the booths circling the bar, and noticed the wide archway leading to the dinner tables in the main room.

The rust lampshaded dim lighting was fine with him. Dannie roamed inconspicuously like a cat through the crowd that was filing in. He kept a sharp eye out for bulky, round-faced plainclothesmen with guns protruding from the hip holsters under their drab sport jackets. Shades of spotting for Johnny Squint. Lou T stood in the foyer by the wide front doors. Jinga Betz had taken up a position by the rear exit, and he was so large no one would know there was a door behind him. Dannie stationed himself by a side entrance, thinking how he had allowed himself to be trapped by the overly friendly Anna. He was a fool. She was coming toward him now, leading a short, stocky, gray, wiry-haired man by the hand. The milling crowd parted as they passed.

Gaily she introduced him to her uncle Tony. Anthony "Tough Tony" Anastasia. He shook hands solidly with the union boss of Brooklyn Longshoremen, who he hoped to hell hadn't been in the Buick that time in Prospect Park.

"Tall, blue eyes, nice-ah-boy," Tony shaking, commented. "How old are-ah you?" he asked, cordially.

"Twenty-one, sir," Dannie lied. Anna hung on her uncle's arm grinning.

Tough Tony looked at him skeptically. "You boyfriend to-ah my niece? You too old for her?" Tony asked.

"We know each other from Brooklyn," Anna saved the moment, leading her uncle away. From halfway across the jammed room, she turned, beaming him a smile. Then he caught sight of the pudgy, fedora'd man who had entered, surrounded by an entourage of subservient greeters, the man's diamond pinky ring glittering star-white under the lamp glow.

Dannie instinctively backed against the side door, wishing he had warn his dark prescription glasses. He keenly watched Al-bert and Company walk to the rear step-up platform-balcony where Jinga Betz compliantly seated them for dinner.

In the course of a wary hour Dannie met several of Al-bert's prime henchmen: little Augie Pisana, Carlo Gambino, Johnny

"Roberts The Mortician" Robilito among them. He remembered those three from Fiola's.

He was also introduced, by Lou T, to two Costello Group men who he immediately felt somewhat comfortable with, Salvatore "Sally Burns" Granello and Salvatore "Pedro" Di Pietro. From what Dannie gathered during the fast chatter, they had a lock on Cuban gambling casino's which were fronted by the grand actor George Raft and insidiously backed by "Don Vitone" Genovese.

While Lou dined, he covered the front door. He wanted to walk the hell out, turn his back to Madhatter Al-bert. But he stood pat. He slipped on his green-tint eyeglasses. To instantly leave in the middle of a "job" might prove fatal.

When Dannie relieved Jinga Betz in the rear, he garnered more than an earful from the diners. Cuba, parts of south Florida, Hollendale, the big boats out on Biscayne Bay, the Bahamas, Gambling.

It was just like old times on the Eighth Avenue corner, only this was on a grander scale.

Then came his time to eat. With Anna. At a table directly across from Al-bert Anastasia.

Dannie supped on milk-fed veal a la franchese, nervously taking in Al-bert's flashing ring, dark glasses and shiny suit.

Anna still gabbed about the coincidence of him being down here, about Scap serving all that time in upstate New York, and about the last time they were together in Prospect Park. He saw Al-bert rise, Dannie and Anna followed suit, leaving the three of them standing in a semi-circle.

"Mr. Anastasia," he heard himself saying to the feared and hated gangster, as he shook his hand. And he saw a blurred bear-like hand by his face. Felt the taps, pats on his cheek. "*Buono guardare,*" Albert Anastasia had greeted Dannie. A few warmly bestowed slaps meant rough, but fond, acceptance—not exactly the smack Willie Sutton had received. Mr. Al-bert trundled off toward the bar. Dannie heard the phlegm-filled coughs over the strains of the six piece band before he actually saw the all too familiar balding Gretti approaching Al-bert through the bar's throng.

He saw flashes from a revolver's barrel as he actually had with Schuster. This time, though, the gun was aimed at him—his eyes, his testicles. He nearly lost control of his bowels. He was as dead as Arnold if Gretti spotted the kid who could incriminate him. Dannie fished in a panic for some semblance of outside calmness. Yet, he knew he deserved this punishment—for the night and the morning with Eleanor!

"Sorry about the beach date," he fibbed to Anna. "I'd like to make it up, but I'm leaving early in the morning," he tried. She had inadvertently gotten him into this, maybe she could get him the hell out. He saw Gretti, bull-neck Mike beside him in the distance, both taking turns embracing their superior Al-bert. "Too busy here to make it tonight," he ventured.

Anna squeezed his arm, seizing the hidden offer. She all but dragged him to the rear door buzzing, on tip-toe, Jinga Betz, who stepped aside unveiling the exit, as if the rock of Cyclops cave had vanished. Dannie, in Anna's tow, made it into the fresh, night, free open air.

He hailed a cab to the Singapore Motel. He didn't want to go to the Barcelona, where she was staying. If Gretti had seen him, it would be a matter of minutes before they converged there.

He walked her around the elegant Motel to the private beach front. They sat on the sandy beach while he repeatedly thanked Kathleen's God up in the cloudless night sky, for getting him safely out of the Five O'Clock Club.

Anna was coiled on the damp sand, not concerned with the condition of her tight red velvet dress. She kicked off her high heels and rested her head on his lap, her brown eyes and eagle beak facing up to the night sky.

"Did you know that you were the first one to ever kiss me on the lips?" she breathed into his crotch. He stared out at the dark, splashing ocean and didn't answer her.

"I saw Joe the Blond last month. That shrimp smartass," she tried.

"So?" he bit, after a while.

"He told me he saw you. Aww, let him go take a flyin' fuck."

He didn't know why he did it. Maybe to coax her. But he laid his left hand on her satiny hair, while his right caressed her cheek. His thumb lightly traced the outline of her nose, and he wanted to laugh like all hell at the contrast between the setting and the awful size of her prominent nose, but he managed to stifle it.

She rambled on about Joey Gallo and his two brothers. Larry and The Blast.

Larry was smooth, the oldest. A Captain now in the Brooklyn Profachi outfit. The Olive Oil King.

Joey was *spustadt*. Foxy, crazy, wildly ambitious. "Made"—they had dared initiate him.

"Kid Blast is a creamer. But not near as good lookin' as you,

Dannie. Even my uncle Albert said so," she gazed up at Dannie a moment. They were alone, arms around each other's waists, the darkened beach deserted except for an occasional couple strolling by and a couple frolicking nearby in the water.

Anna stood up, suddenly, brushing the sand from her dress. "Be right back," she took off toward the rear of the Singapore. "Tell you what nutsy Joey said about you!" her voice carried on the slight wind as she ran up the concrete steps by the pool.

His first thought was to run! Clear out of Miami.

But he stayed pat.

Maybe, just maybe, Joe the Blond had said something to Anna that might help him, help in the long run to find Johnny and keep him alive! He watched for her to return—for Gretti to pop up from out of nowhere. He was sweating in his black suit, thinking he might be dumped dead in the ocean in it. Where the hell had she gone? To betray him? The damp cold perspiration made him shiver.

He was about to rise, when he was relieved to see Anna carefully climbing down the steps, a heavy tray balanced in her two hands. "Whew!"

They sipped the champagne she brought. And after three drinks apiece, she told him that she knew, from what Joe Gallo had said, that he was searching for the wanted Chappy Mazziotta.

He drank, making no reply.

She was growing heady, giddy, lapsing into that night in Prospect Park, when they were both naked, and his little friend had broken up what never really began. . .and Fortunato accidentally getting killed that same night. She emptied the remainder of the champagne into her glass, flinging away the bottle.

"Eighteen" she lamented, "and still a virgin." But she saw now she had to stay that way. On commands from her parents and uncles.

Especially her uncle Albert. He had special designs for her. An arranged wedding between her and a "good fellow's" son. One in either his own Crew to insure his strength by the marriage tie and the eventual blood-tie in, or in another outside Group to cement that relationship. He wanted to keep the loose confederacy he belonged to bound tightly around him.

His gift of her, with virginity intact, was a must to show the purity of his intentions.

But what of her? She was more than tipsy now, a mouthful of the clear champagne left in her glass. What would her husband-to-be look like? Who would he be?

"Maybe Joey Gallo?" Dannie offered, half smiling, but trying to get her back on the track of what Joey had said. She raised her glass, right arm bent, and placed her left palm smack on her forearm. "Fuck him! He won't live long if my uncle has his way! And he told me where Squint was," she was staring glassy eyed now at her glass.

"Where?" Dannie said, automatically.

She kept looking at the glass then at him, intermittently, as she spoke.

"Johnny was supposed to be down here in Miami Beach. But the bulls were close on his tail. So he skipped the country. Mexico. Jaurez. The border town by El Paso, Texas.

"Hugo Duce had told Joey. Or he had heard it second hand. Joey had even said to mention it to the "young Cary Grant kid" if I ever ran into you. And lo and behold I did. But what do I do with you now?" she was more talking to herself and the unfinished glass than him.

Hugo Duce out in the open? On the scene? It hit Dannie. He listened, heart thumping.

"Juarez. Mexico." She was coming out of it. "The sin capital city of the world. Sure that's it. Champagne and all. The first time with champagne to the first one who ever kissed me," she placed her wide lips to the glass, tipping it to her mouth, and then flung it away. Dannie was soaring with hope. Mexico. It made sense, especially coming via Hugo Duce. Dannie looked. Anna had the zipper of his fly open. His neck cranked around the beach. There was no one nearby. He felt her moist mouth, the champagne still in it, swirling, swishing around his soft penis.

He lay back. She was writhing her hips, her pelvis as she "went down," "blew him," as he had heard them say on Eighth Avenue.

It felt great, tingling. But she was "blowing him" to no avail. He couldn't get hard.

He thought of Antoinette; the tight slacks, so form-packed, that he never got into. Beautiful, black-sexy breathtaking eyes. But it didn't work.

His aunt, goddamn her. He was getting from Anna what he had never gotten in his life, and he couldn't get an erection. Anna was sucking hot, wet, her hands eager, half around the base of his cock.

Eleanor, you hinted to just this in my room—you sweet middle-aged hump. In his mind he tried, near fucking Anna's mouth. She had let up long enough to pull his pants and boxer shorts down past his hips, before she went back at it with a body-gyrating passion.

Eve. Should he think vividly of his super luscious . . . *No!* . . . at any rate . . . he didn't have time. Jinga Betz's voice was carrying, booming from the rear of the Singapore to the oceanfront!

"Whoa," he turned on his stomach to see, Anna's face, mouth going directly into the sand. Three of them were searching, slowly coming their way, the mountain of Jinga Betz in the forefront.

Dannie made it up to his knees. He began hopping along the beach trying to stand, pull his pants and his shorts up.

He ran, bare-assed, closer to the water so as to get a grip in the firmer sand. Mexico! ran in his head.

He deserved to be chased, hounded, run out of Miami Beach for having the dirty gall to have Eve cross his mind while Anna was sucking his dead prick.

He ran from Anna, Al-bert's three goons heavy on their heels after him, crying, the stinging tears, and ocean spray mixing on his reddened cheeks. Johnny's own words "finish what you start in life, kid" kept Dannie going, racing along the sand. The only thing keeping him from running straight into that Ocean was that he had safely avoided becoming, so far, another Arnold Schuster. So far.

1953

El Paso, Texas, and Juarez, Mexico,
November-Christmas Eve

For five dollars Dannie could have his pick of any sensuous, full-breasted prostitute at the L.A. Club and Bar in Juarez, Mexico.

The women there ranged in age from sixteen to forty-seven. They seemed to have all come straight out of American magazines, like high-style models. The pick of the sensational crop from farms across Mexico. Long black, brunette hair, exceptionally shapely bodies in white, pink, tight dresses contrasting appetizingly with deeply tanned flesh.

They were "clean" and legal too. The state regulated and examined them, issuing health working cards.

But Dannie shied away from them as he traveled from bar to bar. Not only because his foremost purpose was seeking Johnny, but he hadn't gotten hard in three weeks of gazing at them—not hard since the love tryst with Eleanor in Miami Beach. He had more than damned himself by ever touching her to begin with.

Castrated by two sisters. He could never travel far enough to get away from the thoughts which had turned his mind into a labyrinth of guilt. The thoughts had followed him to the sin capital of the world, as Anna had put it the night he had run half naked—again—

from her.

The clarity of Anna's desires resembled another twisted embodiment of love and death, sex and violence. He shivered, feeling that his once rich soul had gone stone cold broke.

Dannie hadn't dared to stop at his room that night in Florida, for fear that Jinga Betz and friends would have tracked him there. Maybe even Gretti and Al-bert.

Either way, he would have been mashed by the former for tainting Al-bert's niece, or slain by the latter for witnessing Arnold's murder.

The U.S. newspapers nationwide were still recounting that it was Albert Anastasia who had flaunted the law by ordering the hit on Arnold Schuster.

Dannie was the direct link to Johnny and Augie. Hugo was supposedly still back in Brooklyn. John and Augie were not, and they were the links to the Madhatter.

But why had Gretti, Little Mike, Tony-boy, and Hugo Duce all surfaced, but not Johnny Squint and Angel Tenuto?

Maybe Johnny was dead. Killed to cover up. That's why the two cars—the Lincoln and the Rocket Olds—had still been parked on Ninth Avenue by the cuts overpass.

But what if he was alive? Dannie had had no recourse but to hitchhike from Miami to Mexico without clothes, extra glasses, or luggage. And no bus, train, or plane.

Although he had all the money he had made at the Place on him, he saw the benefit of hitching when he obtained his first ride in Bal Harbour, Florida. It was cheaper. And from past experience he knew how expensive it was to live on the road. When the money ran out to zero in a foreign country, he'd be exactly nowhere in the world.

It had taken three days and four separate rides to get him to Logan Heights, El Paso, Texas. The last ride was from two young soldiers stationed at Ft. Bliss, Texas. They advised him to live in El Paso and walk over the bridge to Juarez. Less of a hassle that way, legal and otherwise.

They also gave him the rundown on sin city. The jails had open roofs, the broads could be bargained with, and the cockfights were a gambler's dream. But they warned him to stay away from the hand-tattooed gang—the *pachokos*—and generally the food and water. All three could kill you.

Dannie had rented an efficiency in El Paso by the Green Frog Café where the soldiers hung out before and after their sojourns into Mexico. He had been warned straightaway not to venture to the outlying areas of Juarez, and he heeded the foreboding advice. The peasants would do just about anything for Gringo money.

It cost him two cents a day to cross into Mexico via the short bridge over the dry Rio Grande. A penny to return.

He prowled the bars, cafés, and clubs for a chance of seeing Johnny. Where else could he look for a man like Johnny? Dannie scoured Juarez under the assumed name of John-John Mazz for John Senior, letting it be known he was seeking his *father*.

He let it be known to the legalized beauties, bouncers, waiters, bartenders, cockfight gamblers, cabbies. It might lead to Johnny finding him.

The tequilas, salt and lime on the side, nearly blew the top of his head off. And as for the variety of available and highly alluring ladies, he had no real problem. He played drunk, ineffective, impotent when they solicited him, teasing him with their eyes, hands, fingers along his crotch, baring their low-cut braless busts. They were all beautiful when you're about to "come," Johnny had philosophized.

But Eleanor Cross had somehow done her part to wreck him when it came to having others.

Over the course of 44 days, Dannie didn't have a shred of luck in covering the endless rows of Juarez's backstreets. Finally, he telephoned home—collect—to see if Eleanor could ask Kathleen and Roscoe if there had been any postcards from Mexico.

Aunt Eleanor had a fit on the phone. "A foreign country, no less!" she went into her usual tirade. But she would comply.

His mother was more mellow, stable, as if she had made peace with the inside and outside worlds.

Both women seemed that way after getting over the initial shock of his first call in so long. Almost blissful, with no intimations of . . . sex . . . like his conversations with good ol' Eleanor in the past. Maybe she finally found a boyfriend. High time!

And it was high time that he attended the most likely place a diehard gambler would go in Juarez. The cockfights!

He had avoided going until now. The raw violence of two male birds fighting to the death, taking each other's eyes out, brought visions of Schuster, his face gorged by high-powered bullets, his testicles a bloody pulp

Before the spectacle began, he scanned the jammed gathering. Most of the native Mexican men he encountered were short, swarthy, compactly built, and dark skinned. Johnny and Augie would not stand out. They were counterparts, Dannie mused, except for the voice inflection. When he thought he saw a close resemblance, Dannie would sidle closer, short of breath, anticipating, only to see hope fade for that moment.

Johnny's chiseled jaw, Augie's scar over the right eye. He searched, hoped, as the fight began. Big bets were laid down, bankrolls flashed, the excitement building. But Dannie scooted out of the arena before the spectator-screaming finish.

He was weak with nausea. His stomach churning, the vomit coming on a narrow Juarez street, eyes tearing, head filled with the blood, brawn, and innards of the fiercely trained cocks.

He hazily walked the tourist-filled streets, as if in a cloud of choking cigar smoke from the crowd of fowl-gamblers.

From now on he'd stay outside of the cockfights and haunt the entrances, back doors, and alleyways, on the lookout for that handsome, rugged face, the powerful build and the sharp manner of dress.

Besides, hanging outside was cheaper than the bars. As usual his money supply was dwindling, and he was down to dime-pinching. Time was running out on Mexico. As he watched the masses of men, Dannie tossed in his thoughts, trying to figure Johnny's moves.

Why another country? Why not, if the FBI had indeed traced John in Florida. And why Juarez? Because it had an overflowing throng of tourists?

Why would Hugo Duce tell Joe Gallo? Johnny had no love for the "shrimp," as Hugo knew all too well.

Dannie knew that Johnny would need money. Was Hugo, Frank Costello, or V.G. "Don" Vito Genovese supplying him?

Dannie passed the days exercising in his room, reading the newspapers, glancing at True Detective magazines covering the killing of Schuster, and finally again, this time on his seventeenth birthday, retreating in defeat to call Brooklyn.

His aunt had reluctantly spoken to Roscoe. Her former brother-in-law had nothing new to add. The various law enforcement officials were still keeping close tabs on him, Rosa, his wife now, and the three children. Plus the adopted fourth.

As for Kathleen, she was busy chumming around with, as Eleanor put it, "blonde-streaked, braless-half-the-time" Gloria Bruzzese. That "tart" had frequently asked sweetly for Dannie, but Eleanor had smacked her silly when Gloria dared to say "Dannie's jealous aunt."

Standing at the public phone, Dannie felt exposed. He shook

when his wild aunt relayed that the pests—Tony-boy and Little Mike—had spoken to her. Apparently her lucky nephew had been down south. Gretti and the others were still planning to have that little talk with him! Dannie begged Eleanor to take his mother and move the hell away from her apartment on McDonald. He was "a no-good vagabond," she scolded him, who "would be the death of all of them." This time around she slammed down the telephone!

Dannie was hurt, scared, guilt-ridden as he sat in the Kit Kat Kafe downing tequilas, thinking, and getting drunk to quell his damn thoughts. He knew he had to return.

By midnight he had hazily, spitefully decided to push on. He'd try for another kind of luck by quelling, eradicating the damn itch that he still had in his blood for his devilishly lovely aunt. He'd take a Mexican hooker if it cost every nickel he had—for as long as it took to get that elusive erection.

He pushed his green-tint eyeglasses up the bridge of his nose, sat erect at the bar of the Kit Kat Kafe, and, blurry-eyed, studied the splendid, strutting beauties.

The one that caught his eye had on a white dress which looked close to being glued on. She was statuesque, with patrician features and was about Eleanor's age.

He grabbed her hand as she was passing. On eye contact, they both lit up with smiles.

She guided him to a door that led to a shabby, makeshift dispensary, with a fat old lady sitting in the middle. The old lady gestured to his fly, speaking in Mexican. Quickly, she had his fly open and was milking his penis. He drunkenly gazed, before he completely realized what was happening. She was testing him for any signs of urinary tract disease. He passed the test, and then followed the prostitute up a flight of stairs to a room with a curtained doorway.

She held out her hand for the money. Ten dollars for the night, which in reality meant five hours.

It was great watching her undress. Quickly. Same deliberate motions as Eleanor. Hands upraised behind her, under her long hair, her right hand sliding down the V-cut, slit dress's zipper. She stepped out of the dress, naked.

The next two hours were hard work, for both of them.

The petting, fondling, sucking, fingering, gyrating, panting, and her masturbating.

She tried oral copulation. No champagne in her mouth, but warm water. It felt terrific, zinging, sensational. But to no avail. No erection appeared on the horizon of the bedsheets despite his fantastic thoughts of Gloria Bruzzese's bare legs, short skirtline, and soft panties.

Was it the whore or him? He lay there, reddened, drunk, furious, near tears. Physically, mentally impotent at seventeen.

The hired body stood up, expressionless, and proceeded to wash. Squatting by a basin half full of water, she douched with her hands. The soldiers at Ft. Bliss termed it a "whore's bath."

He wanted, in total disgust at his inability, to be able to sleep. There had been no need for her to clean herself. He had never come close to entering her.

She left him alone, never once smirking or grimacing.

The next thing he felt were two broad-shouldered Mexicans rousing him. "*Ondalay Vayase!*" they ordered roughly.

He dressed in a depleted daze, and zigzagged his way back to El Paso. But before he drunkenly reached his rundown room, anger and renewed determination began replacing his self-pity. He punched the telephone booth's wood frame before entering it. He'd call his eatable, sour aunt and wish her a freakin' Merry Christmas.

His mother accepted the collect call. He was in ecstasy just speaking to her.

The spell of ecstasy was rudely snapped when she related that Kathleen Mazziotta had . . . died. Two days ago. The booth reeled. Dannie was chilled to the marrow. Sickly, religious, loyal Kathleen . . . his cousin. It was crazy. There had been shots . . . Kathleen killed by Rocco Bruzzese as she was attempting to shield Gloria, thereby saving Gloria's life—she was only grazed in the temple by Rocco's rifle. Eleanor, on the extension, could only think of the probing, fondling, line-ups of young girls' corpses by lust-hungry morticians, limo drivers, embalmers, "bastards!"

His mother, in great sympathy, told him that she had, without her sister's knowledge, visited Kathleen several times over the past month. The poor girl had given her an unopened note for him, and a heartfelt verbal message that "Christ and the good thief were the first two to enter heaven upon Christ's reopening of that gate—a minute apart." Dannie listened, tears welling, and told his Mom how he dearly loved her, before limply hanging up.

Kathleen. Dead. Dannie envisioned the scene . . . spit-lipped Rocco refusing to go to work when ordered by his father Francisco . . . Rocco intending to kill his father in their kitchen . . . Gloria stepping in between them . . . Kathleen in front of Gloria, a split-second before Rocco's rifle fired . . . a .22 caliber gunshot wound under her left eye. Kathleen died four hours and fifteen minutes later in the Israel Zion Division of Maimonides Hospital in Borough Park, Brooklyn. Rocco was charged with homicide and the Sullivan Law violation.

Dannie's mouth was like gauze as he thought of the damn waste and confusion of it all. So far, life's minutes were filled with gunfire.

But would this bring John out in the open?

How many bullets were waiting for him?

Dannie trembled, trying to muster his courage. He wanted to know more.

His mother again gladly accepted the charge call. They both were hard pressed to believe that Kathleen had entered her heaven. At his urging, she read him Kathleen's last note.

Dannie excitedly told his mother he worshiped her and she responded by telling him that the one and only thing she wanted for Christmas was to squeeze so much love into him. He ran from the booth.

He'd pick up the airplane fare his mother would send to Western Union, and would surreptitiously attend Kathleen's funeral. After digesting dear Kathleen's message, he knew he'd meet an angel, in the unlikely form of Frederick J. Tenuto. Alias St. John, a.k.a. "Angel," also known to him as Augie. Johnny's partner!

Then Johnny!

1953

From his United Airlines window seat the following day, Dannie could see the borough of Queens, New York as the plane came in for a landing.

He saw decorated, lit-up Christmas trees. Santa Clauses and reindeer on the wintry lawns. But where were the shrouded, snow-covered cemeteries in nearby Brooklyn? One certainly had a plot in it waiting for peace-loving Kathleen. The plane's gigantic wheels touched the strip at Idlewild International Airport, bouncing, bounding, screeching.

Queens, Dannie looked out the cabin window of the taxiing plane. The borough where Willie "The Actor" Sutton had partly left his mark—bank-robbed his way to international fame. Dannie unhooked his safety belt. Would the wake in Brooklyn bring Johnny Squint out in the open?

How long would it take Gretti, Little Mike, and Tony-boy to mark a stone for him amidst this never-ending slaughter? Dannie wondered as he walked slowly, warily into the terminal, valise in hand. An almond-eyed vision decked in fire-red velvet jacket jumped out of the crowd toward him.

His mother squeezed the northeastern chill out of him with part of that love she had fervently promised, despite the deplaning flyers scampering about them in the busy terminal.

She clung to him in the face of the customary catcalls and whistles coming from the men passing by.

He was home.

Eve had reserved a room for him at the International Hotel on the outskirts of the airport. It was the same hotel they had stayed in on the night of fungus-faced Al Rispone's demise.

Dannie protested cabbing it the short distance to the hotel. It was too expensive. But his ardent mother won out. Dannie needed an out-of-the-way place to stay, to gather his thoughts and make his plans. And to hide. She knew it was dangerous for him to come.

"I got some from Ru- from Eleanor," she said as she underhanded a packet of money to him. Dannie hadn't missed her saying "Ru . . ." What did it mean, and where was his wacky aunt? he wondered. The car pulled up to the hotel. He paid the cabbie and got out into the New York wind-gusted, near-frigid weather. It was a far cry from the sunny beach and sultry Juarez.

The room was spacious, modern, plush, especially compared to the cut-rate one he had in El Paso.

He plopped down comfortably into the armchair by the big, blue draped window and closed his eyes a second, before Eve, snuggling on his lap, startled him.

"Mom," he stammered, "I . . ." He couldn't finish what he didn't exactly know he was going to say to begin with. She hit him with a barrage of questions and observations, ranging from his missing so much school to his being over six feet tall.

"My good looking six-footer. So handsome." Her *bellezza* green eyes sparked like green flames. She was fondling him, her perfume and body contact causing him to shake. She was teasing him. Nothing had changed, except she seemed devoid of her usual repressed hysteria. He found a way out by pleading to see Kathleen's note.

He read it repeatedly, pacing the room.

Kathleen wrote that she had heard her father whispering to Hugo Duce about her uncle Johnny and Augie. Augie, apparently, was in Brooklyn, hiding, travelling back and forth to Scranton, Pennsylvania. Her father and Hugo had discussed, in hushed tones, how suicidal it would be for John to attempt a get-together. Kathleen felt her death was imminent and that Dannie might get a chance to see her uncle, *his father*, at her wake. Her dying would bring the living together. He was stung by Kathleen's premonition.

She sobbed, in a postscript, that maybe it was better she should face her judgment now, rather than later, to avoid the joy of secretly sinning with him. Dannie cried audibly in the heated room, his sturdy chin quaking uncontrollably.

Drowsy, shaken, a thin line of sleep and wakefulness filtered across his mind like a fog. The next thing he felt was his mother, kneeling beside him, holding his arms, trying to soothe him.

He had been having a nightmare. Of Kathleen cruelly shot in the face. Of Arnold Schuster being viciously blown away before his eyes. Eve had him now in a fierce embrace, her tears mingling with his. She had an intimate knowledge of agonizing dreams. Mother and son. So much in common now. He held her for dear life, for sanity's sake. They quieted each other until the room grew dark. Dark enough outside to travel. Dannie stirred.

He thought of all the dire, respectful reasons he had to go by the wake tonight. The stylish figure of the body next to him was the best reason. He tried to pry himself from her, but she was holding fast.

"Shower . . . eat . . ." he mumbled, easing from her languorous hold. He twisted off the chair to his feet, setting her steady on the chair.

He stepped away, flicking on a table lamp as he headed for the bathroom.

Within twenty minutes he was shaven, showered, groomed and dressed.

Eve had ordered savory lamb chops and pink champagne from room service. They ate, drank in silence. Her eyes, across the table, were daring, haunting. He tried to keep his head down as much as possible, chewing.

He had to say something to break the tension. "Have you heard from . . . Johnny?" he asked, half looking at her. He got no reply. She was gazing green-eyed, intently at him without any movement. Their eyes began to lock. Dannie thought of Roscoe's torture, of how badly Johnny had wanted her.

Her eyes were irresistible, drawing him, enveloping him, and he felt himself leaning imperceptibly forward. Then he caught himself and sat up straight, fidgeting with the stem of the champagne glass, his eyes following the bubbles.

"Are you in love with Eleanor?" his mother finally asked, the words hanging in the air between them.

If he dared drink, he'd have to raise his eyes while raising his glass. So he sat out the question. After a while she rose, stepping barefoot over to the bed, bending tight-skirted and opening the gift-wrapped boxes that had lain there when he had returned from his shower.

She displayed Florsheim black patent leather shoes, English rib wool hose, and a heavy, black leather three-quarter dress jacket with zippered liner. She hoped they'd fit him. He was a nomad for so long she had guessed the sizes.

She wanted her "stranger" to look sharp.

Dannie tried on his new clothes while she stood, hands akimbo, admiring him. He smiled, blushing, as they clinked their champagne glasses in celebration of his return. He'd need the extra drink, he figured, for tonight.

No words would come to him as he set down the glass. He looked at her a moment, then turned hesitantly for the door.

He was by the sixth-floor elevator when he heard his door reopening. Out of the corner of his eye he saw his mother. She was holding something in her right hand. He stepped forward along the royal blue carpeted hall, peering, making out his green-tint, pre-scription eyeglasses.

"We're on the sixth floor," she said, handing him the sunglasses. "You can reach the first quickly by using the elevator." She held the lapels of his new leather jacket. "I can reach the bottom faster than that!" She was on tiptoe, her hands around his neck. "Via the win-dow, if you're not careful in Borough Park tonight." At first she pecked his lips, toes straining upward, her skirted thighs rubbing against him. Out of control, he had slid his hands down, around, and just under her velveted buttocks, swearing to himself that this would be a goodbye and not a goodnight kiss.

Within thirty minutes, Dannie was back in his old neighbor-hood—Borough Park, still gagging from that last kiss!

Snow flurries whipped his face in the night wind as he stood on the corner of 43rd Street and Tenth Avenue. He was now both the hunter and the hunted.

He squinted in the dark, through the cheek-lashing flakes, at Generellie's Funeral Parlor, a half a block away. Kathleen's killing filled him with rage. She was gunned down by a mad animal harbor-ing demented cravings. Dannie felt his own emotions twisted around hatred, fear, loss and terror. If Little Mike or Gretti ever found him, they would certainly try to "clean up" the Schuster death, and Dannie would be lying where Kathleen was now. He felt gnawed at, eaten alive by all the harsh confusion. It was like the child in him needed that reassuring, powerful father-image in the flesh. All his desire to be a "man," all his illusions about Johnny had led him here. To the edge of his own death. Yet, he had been irresistibly drawn to Kathleen's wake.

The whirling snow slapped at Dannie's face as he walked toward the overcrowded Generellie's, only too conscious that he was only a hairsbreadth from Israel Zion Hospital, where Kathleen had been pronounced dead, and three blocks from where Arnold had suddenly got it.

Outside the funeral parlor the enormous crowd consisted mostly of Kathleen's former parochial schoolmates, the north Brooklyn boys. Over a hundred of them were paying homage, dressed like street sheiks.

Dannie blended in among them, an eye out for beaver-tooth Hugo Duce.

9:30, Dannie read the face of the Bulova wristwatch that John had given him over twenty-one months ago to help "clock" Arnold. Lines began forming now. It was the last night of the wake—last long view of Kathleen.

He joined the solemn mourners, reassured that with his taller, older appearance and shaded glasses, he'd be hard to recognize, especially among so many who were his own age.

The three-deep line snaked into the closet-sized vestibule of the funeral parlor. His sunglasses fogged up. Flakes of snow turned to water, running down and smearing them. But he kept them on as the line shuffled into the parlor proper. Short, fedoraless Hugo Duce stood by the "book" angled on the wooden lectern.

None of the north Brooklyners signed in, a signal that they wouldn't attend the actual funeral the following morning. But a tubby, ruddy-faced boy, who Dannie remembered as Firestone, handed the *triste* Hugo an envelope. It was a "boost," a money donation of respect toward burial expenses. No doubt a return gift that Kathleen's clan—mostly Johnny—had given to others in the past.

He now found himself six feet from Kathleen's bronze casket, either side of it lined with flowers.

Two by two, the Boys had been kneeling on the cushioned knee rest by the coffin, making the sign of the cross and bowing their heads. Some even touched Kathleen's arm. Dannie wondered if retribution was on their mind—getting the incarcerated, institutionalized Rocco—or would Johnny reach out and have that attended to?

Dannie's turn came. He knelt, transfixed, his hands clasped by his midsection, the cloying aura of floral rot all but stinging his face.

Kathleen's face resembled bloated, beige chalk. Too many moments were going by. Somewhere in his mind he knew he was being foolhardy as the Boys knelt beside him, paying their last respects, and left, others taking their place.

"Kathleen," Dannie whispered. "You're in your heaven now." He gripped the cold edge of the open coffin for support.

"You believed that," he quaked. "I shouldn't feel sorry for you now. That's what you'd tell me. I should feel that you've won out over death."

"But . . . Kathleen," Dannie half stood, and leaned toward her, "I'm scared now of life. Help me now like you helped me before." He kissed her freezing, rock-lips, his teardrops falling on her bullet-scarred, olive-skinned face.

He stood up, her patched-up, embalmed face glaring before him. He pleaded silently that she somehow lead him to Johnny. Suddenly, he felt hands on his arms, shoulders, turning him, leading him slowly to the side aisle of the overly crowded, flower-filled room. He blinked, trying to clear his vision, and realized that he was looking straight into the creased, bereaved face of Jamesie Mazziotta.

Bulb-nosed Pietro M. quickly hugged him at the parlor's rear, thanking him, in heartbreaking murmurs, that his niece Kathleen would lie more peacefully now, knowing that her first and only boyfriend had kissed her once more.

Kathleen's other uncle, wiry Phil, shook his hand. As did stolid Mush. Hugo Duce remained by the "book" as Dannie squinted through his streaked glasses at Christie, the glinting north Brooklyn chieftain, signing in.

Dannie's fa- stand-in father, Roscoe, held him, weeping. He warned Dannie that local cops and Federal agents were not only outside in the hope that Johnny Squint would foolishly show, but that he'd bet the bulls themselves were planted in the parlour itself.

Roscoe's wife Rosa, trembling and weeping, pecked his cheek for coming to see her poor, darling niece.

Hugo Duce finally took Dannie aside for a moment. He began speaking without directly facing him, his lips barely moving. "Some of the Schuster family had been here turnin' the other cheek. Holy fuckin' Christ, they made the place a built-in precinct 'cause sweet Kathleen visited them. At any rate, I set you up with Christie. His gutsy, connected Boys'll cover. No sweat. Be careful of Gretti. If it's known he knew about that night, known publicly through you, Albert'll take him out. He's also smokin' with fuckin' fury over just missing you in Miami Beach. And *stick around*, or your pretty mother and aunt may be piled up on top of Kathleen. Got it?"

Dannie's mind hazed at the wealth of information. He tried to leave, get outside to clear his head.

Dannie burrowed his way past the crowd blocking the main entrance. Stuck, he inched, excusing his way forward. Suddenly he came jaw to jaw with the penciled mustachioed, sleek Tony-boy— Little Mike and Gretti's prime huntsman. He glared at Dannie, his prey finally cornered.

"Don't even think of cuttin' out this time around," Tony-boy gritted, a showy half-smile on his face. He held his left hand down, pressed against the right, squashing a wide-brimmed fedora into Dannie's crotch.

Dannie's legs trembled, the pointed, hard object hidden under the hat pressed into him.

"Smile a friendly hello, kid," Tony-boy, fighting the press of people, spat out in cold breaths, his lips near biting into Dannie's left ear. "This .45's got a fuckin' mind of its own. The cocked hammer goes off and your fuckin' balls go with it. *Fistace*? Fine. Now keep movin'!"

Dannie was nudged, pushed, prodded until Tony-boy had him outside on the snow-laden, mourner-crushed sidewalk.

Would he shoot? Dannie's brain sparked, the wind-swept snow pelting his glasses that hadn't helped to disguise him.

"You heard and saw too much," Tony-boy now had a tighter grip on him with his free left hand. "And you lived too fuckin' long to tell it." They were by the curbside. "Al-bert or Gret wouldn't appreciate a conspiracy to murder charge over that *serpente* Arnold through you and your snoopin', now would they, kid?" Tony-boy forced Dannie a step into the slushy street. The heavy pistol under the hat dug into Dannie's groin. Twisting his head in quick motions, Tony-boy scanned the parked and passing cars.

"Hey, *friend*," Dannie heard a confident, meaningful voice. "The one with the greasy fuckin' mustache. You, you leavin' so soon?"

Dannie knew the voice, and blessed Kathleen for it. The street was filled with toughened North Brooklyners, the same ones that Kathleen had tried to talk him into helping when he was about to fight Scap in Prospect Park. Glinting Christie. Nervy Dapper, sandy-haired Sailor in the forefront. The cocksure voice belonged to Dapper.

Tony-boy's neck twisted toward the Boys, his eyes alert, alarmed, his face blanching, blending with the sticky "packard" snow. The stunned look rested on Christie.

"Tony," Christie said, his eyes seemingly blank, expressionless.

"Kathleen and I began grammar school together. Her prayers were mine then. Her wake will not be blemished now. Put on your hat. You'll catch your death of cold. Goodnight."

Dannie was saved. Not only was Christie deadly swift with a stiletto, but members of his *famiglia* were on a par with Al-bert's and Don Vito's themselves.

Tony-boy screwed up his face in calculation. Lousy odds. His left hand pulled his right one from Dannie's body. "Cops around," he murmured. That was his "out," his face-saving imperative. He faked a half-smile, the bulky .45 slipping inside his overcoat, the crumpled fedora going up on top of his head. "See ya," he pinched Dannie's right cheek, grinning, before turning to Dapper. "You got no manners, pal," he said. "You shouldn't use 'greasy fuckin' mustache' to 'nice people.' Especially out in the freezin' snow. Could be you'll catch your *death* of cold." Finally, he turned and began sauntering through the array of Boys.

"And fuck you where you breathe," Dapper hissed at the slim figure disappearing into the mob of bodies.

Dannie's hand faltered as he took off his fogged dark glasses, putting them in his leather coat's right side pocket. He kept his head imperceptibly downward.

How could he face these Boys his own age, some two or three years older, who had saved him. All the praises about them from the corner hoodlums on Eighth Avenue were coming true. They were surely tomorrow's Dunskys. He felt like a real Mama's boy among them, sweating, scared, chilled. Firestone had his arm around his shoulders leading him back to the sidewalk.

He spoke to Christie, Dapper, Sailor in turn, stammering ashamedly his "thank you's." They talked about Kathleen, how she often spoke of him, but didn't utter a word about the incident with Tony-boy. Firestone reminded Dannie that Hugo Duce and Mush wanted to see him in ten minutes, when the parlor began closing its doors and the Boys began to drift away in packs.

Time, Dannie stood rigid.

Tony-boy's words "See ya" clanged in his ears, streaking with sharp pain inside his head.

Time to get out of here, his head near burst. The cheek-pinched promise signaled where Tony-boy and God knew who else were heading.

Dannie fled, rounding the darkened 42nd Street corner, and took off up the stormy street.

From behind him, a girl's voice called his name. Fran? About

Sutton's money? He automatically spun halfway around, his right ankle suddenly giving way. He wound up on the glassy-wet tar of the street, his right elbow bruised, burning beneath the leather jacket. He thought he saw a dim silhouette of a girl by the corner. Grieving Gloria?

He rose, slap-brushing his soaked pants, the heavy snow practically blinding him. He couldn't figure out who she was as he kept backing up the street, spinning, sprinting forward. Kathleen's younger sister? He raced. Antoinette? He reached the near-deserted 12th Avenue, turned left and headed for Church Avenue.

Maybe it was the miracle of Kathleen. Maybe she came back to urge him on, or halt him? He slowed down, catching his breath, his head drenched, matted from the thick falling snow.

He shook off the eerie thought. Kathleen had already aided him in death through the N.B. Boys. But he was dealing with earthly *life* now. He reached Church Avenue, where it began by the cobbled, winding trolley tracks, a burnished DeSoto, tires caught, dexterously riding the silvery, slippery tracks. Dannie saw a figure behind the wheel, struggling to control his steering, and paused cautiously, until the automobile skidded safely free.

He ran down Church to McDonald Avenue, slowing up slightly as he passed an all-night newspaper stand/candy store on McDonald Avenue.

His aunt's house—426—loomed through the hectic snowfall—50 feet ahead. A car was double parked by it, amber dimmers on, spotlighting the whirling flakes.

He narrowed his eyes, but couldn't make out if anybody was in the car. Sidling into a front alleyway courtyard, he made it to the rear, hopping a low wire fence, and circling behind the back yards of the row of two-storied apartment buildings.

When he reached Eleanor's building he furtively peeked around the edge into the narrow side alleyway where her front entrance was. He made out two garbage pails, a three-step cement stoop, and an inclined railing.

No sound, no movement, no figures.

He took a quivering breath, feeling feverish, before inching his way half around the corner edge of the red brick building. He looked up, the snow flakes cold, damp against his burning forehead. His aunt's lights were on.

He couldn't see any way to climb to her bedroom window and he was about to turn directly into the alleyway when he heard the slam! He froze, peered, spying a short figure and a taller one coming into the alleyway from the double-parked car in front.

Shit! He stood hidden, weakened, powerless, his lower intestines about to bust. The two men were checking the four separate entrances, going briskly from one to the next.

Suddenly, the two men ceased checking the doors, alarmed by a car pulling up directly behind theirs. They skirted up the nearest stoop well into the wrong doorway—adjacent to Eleanor's. Now was his chance. Summoning all his bravado, he edged along the side of the building, ducking under the railing, and noiselessly opening the foyer door. Inside.

Whew, he mouthed silently, taking the flight of steep steps two at a time.

He knocked as softly as he could on his aunt's apartment door and waited, positioning his left ear against the chipped wood. He heard nothing.

He knocked again, slightly harder this time, listening, hearing. . . movement, rustling sounds from within. "Eleanor. Open up. It's me, Dannie," he urged, his voice a hoarse hair above a whisper.

"What . . . is it?" he heard her silky voice, faltering, through the door.

"What is it?" Dannie was perplexed. "Open up," he had the left side of his face pressed against the crude wood.

"What's the matter with you? Are you all right?" He heard stirring sounds, like she had hesitantly backed away from the door.

If it wasn't for the two men next door, he would have pounded on her door demanding she open it or he'd kick the damn thing in.

The sudden slamming of the foyer door directly downstairs caused him to freeze on the stair landing.

"Hey, kid. Dannie?" he heard a man's urgent voice from below, all but mesmerized by the unmistakable accent.

He knew that his Christmas "Angel" had finally appeared.

"WHEN WILL I SEE JOHNNY?" DANNIE SAT BESIDE "Augie" Tenuto in the burnished-colored, grave damp DeSoto now parked curbside, midway on the wide thoroughfare of McDonald Avenue. They were adjacent to Eleanor's darkened apartment building.

"You'll see John shortly," Augie tensed, short-fused. "By the New Year." He turned, his right arm sliding along the seat's top edge, the vivid scar over his right eye flaring. "Right now, give me a recap, kid."

Dannie didn't quite understand, the puzzlement showing on his face. He knew now that it had been Augie who had traced him through Hugo Duce to his aunt's house. The two men in the alley had been Little Mike and Tony-boy. It was Augie who had audaciously bumped their double-parked car, causing them to scamper to their own vehicle, before double-clutching their way toward the intersection of Church Avenue, barely bothering to glance behind them.

But Augie's question *bothered* Dannie. Did he want to know how he had managed to *stay alive* since that March night, or did Augie want to hear his rundown, his version of that *same infamous night*. Dannie tried a sincere evasion.

"Augie," his throat was parched. "I should telephone my aunt," he stammered, trying to regain his composure. He could hardly look at the explosive man beside him. "She has to be told whether to call"—he abruptly refrained from saying "the police"—"a neighbor for holiday 'company,' or to get the hell out of there. For good. I gotta call her."

"Call *her*? Where's your mother?" Augie's tone bordered between amusement and curiosity.

"I . . ." Dannie was about to lie outright and say he didn't know, but checked himself. Augie had always been ferociously loyal to Johnny and even tender to him the time John had decked Little Mike and Co. over the way Mike had spoken about his mother. ". . . I know she's O.K.," Dannie said, trusting the temperamental Augie.

"Then sit back," Augie said. "Hugo'll be coming soon and your aunt'll be just fine. In the meantime, take it from that night last March '52. From the minute you were by the Ninth Avenue subway station. Go ahead."

Augie had seen him? The words caught in confusion in Dannie's throat.

Did Augie want him to . . . incriminate himself? Dannie felt heady with fever.

Was he becoming too paranoid? Just what had Hugo meant at the wake, when he said "or your mother and aunt may be piled up on top of Kathleen"?

Augie clicked on the car's radio, settling back, then fidgeted, waiting. The news broadcaster was blaring about Vice President Nixon urging arms for Pakistan. Dannie was preparing to relate his story, wondering if his physical delirium was causing this fear of everything around him, including his suspicious, subtle aunt. He had to open up to someone. He clung to Kathleen's advice: "to have *faith*."

"I ran to my house," he began, hot sweaty flashes shuddering through his body. "I couldn't get in. I had no key," his skittish recollection continued.

"There was a pay phone in the Ninth Avenue Station. I tried to get John at Pete's Radio Store, but had no luck. I walked outside the train station and saw the blue Lincoln Capri. And I thought I saw Johnny's red Rocket Olds again. I didn't go near it." Dannie stopped to wipe the steamy, sticky perspiration from his face with the backside of his left hand.

"I know you didn't," Augie's tone was soft, contrasting with his high level of intensity. "Go on," he said, leaning toward Dannie, like he was waiting for a fresh water trout to bite on a quiet, clear lake. Augie was fishing for some kind of answer from him, Dannie realized. He dropped his head, faking a cough, his eyes on Augie's brown weal Bostonian shoes.

"You went back to the station," Augie prodded. "Did you see John? Did you take one of the trains with him? Which train? Which direction?"

Holy Christ on HIS cross, Dannie was breathless, neck twisting toward Augie. His eyes, ears were suddenly alerted at the same time. A Nash had pulled broadside the DeSoto. Dannie yanked Augie's jacket collar, jerking him swiftly down. Augie twisted on the front seat, coming up with a black .38 revolver as the Nash eased five yards forward.

"Al-bert's flunkies," Augie gritted, his back against Dannie. His eyes riveted on the Nash, Augie slipped a dull-bronze automatic to Dannie. "Take it! And use the fuckin' thing!" Another Nash, this one a Statesman four-door sedan, pulled up from behind, hemming them into their parking spot.

Dannie held the automatic's handle, Augie practically on top of him.

Boom! A gunshot. Dannie expected to have his face ripped apart like Arnold's had been. He stiffened, shook, held Augie, heard car motors being gunned, raced, as they roared close by. Dannie felt a needle's heated pricking in his right earlobe, indenting the nape of his neck. The front windshield had shattered, the side driver's window exploding thick glass. Screeching tires slush-skidding along with gunfire and the mesh of gears all added to the deadly night sounds.

Augie shot up, gun in hand, the stink of gunpowder diffused throughout the car. He gazed straight ahead through the blown-out side window. "Winged big mouth Little Mike. 'Sit down' time," he said evenly. "Hugo, the ox Mush, the classy advisor Mike Miranda, five in all," he turned his neck from side to side. "Mother fuckin' Gretti. Tony-boy. Clipped Little Mike. And Johnny Roberts. Four of *them*. Don Vito or Uncle Frank *of our Friendship* versus Al-bert and Co. soon.

"Over a 'table'. Over you and me, kid. I probably signed my own death certificate by shooting that fuckin' Mike. Fuck 'em all from here to Santa Claus. Let them have their stand-off now in the street. Cause we ain't gonna be here later to see who wins the 'sit.'" Augie started the DeSoto. Dannie, going on pure adrenalin, sat upright, seeing the men outside.

They were huddled mid-avenue, puffs of cold air shooting from their mouths, speaking, arguing, gesticulating, sparse holiday traffic halting, circling.

Augie rammed the Ford now parked in front. Clutching into reverse, he then slammed the parked Studebaker in the rear, before right-turning the steering wheel and quickly repeating the crashing process. Finally, he was clear of his slot and up on the curb as the gang of men scurried toward the DeSoto. Augie ran the car along the wide sidewalk, bouncing back onto McDonald Avenue in a sharp, screeching U-turn, and racing, swerving toward the Western boundary of Greenwood Cemetery.

"They hit you, kid?" Augie fumed, as he drove wildly around the winding cemetery. "I got that scumbag Little Mike right by his gizzard. He'll have a hard time digestin' shit from here on in."

There was no tail in sight. Augie had lost the Button Men from two Crews, if they had even attempted to follow. "How many slugs did you catch?"

Augie drove, cursing, griping about his partner, Willie Sutton, being only fifty-two years young when shut-in upstate.

Dannie sat, amazed. Why did Augie keep asking if he was shot? Dannie felt his chest. It was O.K. Checking his wobbly legs, he found that they were bloodless on the outside, but as he sat back up straight to double-check his own butt, he could have popped through the car roof from the *stinging* pain in his . . . right earlobe!

Dannie nearly passed out as he retrieved a minute piece of his lobe between his fingers.

Shit! He stifled the puke in his throat.

Dannie felt the blood oozing along his right shoulder, down his back, feeling more blood with his left hand along the aching, burning nape of his neck. He almost pitched forward from sheer fright.

Don't whimper, don't cry, he told himself, again and again. Be A Man, he begged himself. Don't cringe, cry or pass out in front of Augie.

"My ear lobe," Dannie strained. "And the back of my neck." He sat in disbelief, unable to fathom that he had been *shot* without knowing it. The pain now was surging to his throbbing head. Did Arnold *feel it*? Was Kathleen watching him? Would he die of blood loss? From gangrene?

"Put a hankie around your neck," Augie barked as he drove on madly. "Here's my scarf." He undid it from around his own neck. "Wrap it around your lower face. It'll cover your ear. And don't worry. The two bullets grazed you. So ya got a piece of ear missin'. You're still a good looker, kid," Augie laughed, warmly. "And ya took those two shots like a man."

Dannie bundled up where the bullets had nicked him.

A Man, he sat dazed. Tough Augie had called him a man. He blanched instead of beamed, thinking that he was alive by an inch. Was this the price to pay for his ever-elusive manhood? What would the price be next time around? He prayed that he'd live to find out.

Augie dumped the beat-up car in the parking lot of the Bush Terminal maintenance bus depot. Dannie tagged along to the Fourth Avenue Line's local subway station on 36th and Fourth Avenue, feeling his own blood soaking the handkerchief and the scarf.

They rode the half-deserted subway train, Dannie feeling drained, yet somewhat better than before.

At least he had stopped bleeding, and the tempest was outside while he sat in the heated subway car. Adrenalin alone had kept him going through those touch and go minutes with Augie by the two Nashes, he had his hands deep in his leather jacket pockets, the automatic feeling snug in his right hand.

He'd live, he guessed. Augie told him they were two superficial flesh wounds, as he doused his ear and neck with peroxide and bandaged his aching body with supplies he bought in a Fourth Avenue drugstore before boarding.

When the train trundled into the Pacific and Fourth station, Augie slouched in his seat, sardonically remarking how Willie was spotted on a subway train within spittin' inches from right here and followed by a *gornuda gordenda*. "Now he's monitored in a cell, even when he takes a piss," Augie griped.

Dannie's mind floated to a more pleasant time. He remembered that this was the very station where he had fondled the compact

Antoinette Narghelle. He could have cried rain with the bitter memory of it. Then he thought of his aunt's teasing kissing lessons by another subway station. He knew he had to call her, and told Augie.

They got off the train at the Court Street platform, the downtown Brooklyn City Hall section. Dannie found a pay phone. No answer at Eleanor's.

What the hell was she doing? What was she up to? Dannie sat anxiously on a long wooden bench, his ear beating pain into his head, his neck a raw open scar. He played at "being a man," avoiding complaints as they waited for another train.

Augie bitterly explained why it was best they avoided a "sit." First off, if Johnny didn't appear they stood a good chance of getting killed. John was their only real Dunsky strength. "Al-bert would demand that you and I, kid, were links to putting him in the 'hot seat' over Schuster—that he was in on the kill order. Uncle Frank or Don Vito would declare that we had done our jobs, 'stood up,' stayed away from the Law. But in the end, without John there to take the supreme responsibility, we'd be garroted." The Schuster issue had put too much fuckin' International heat on all the Crews.

"Got it?" Augie concluded succinctly.

Done *"their jobs"*. . . ? Dannie didn't quite get it all. He was having trouble thinking straight, his mind constantly drifting to his quarter-inch piece of ear in the DeSoto. Fragments, words, images creased his skull . . . Gretti . . ."hit" orders . . . loose talk on Eighth Avenue . . . plots. Augie glanced furtively up and down the near-empty platform, and Dannie knew what was coming.

"Which way did John go that night?" Augie was in knots, his voice high-strung and severe.

"I didn't see him," Dannie was shaking his head, feeling mentally drained, questioning himself as to what he originally saw. "I took the West End Line to Stillwell Avenue in Coney Island and got a furnished room. I've been searching for him ever since."

Augie sat sulking, pondering.

He pounded his fist into his palm, springing to his feet.

"A fuckin' setup . . . Gret, Tony-boy that fag . . . all there." Augie kept pacing, punching fist into palm, fist into palm. "That's how the higher-ups do it. Others do the killings, then they give commands to low-lifes to squash that killing . . . no traces . . . I told the Squint . . . told him . . . saw the fuckin' Packard going to the bypass on Ninth Avenue . . . then laid in wait. Johnny couldn't believe it. I split straight ahead through Greenwood Cemetery . . . Johnny didn't get

in his Olds. We had a meet at the Lafayette Hotel. He never showed
. . . a stone's throw from here. The kid says he didn't see him at all
. . . I saw the kid . . . where'd John go that night? . . . turned my back
for sixty seconds . . . *what the fuck happened*?" Augie's last cry
echoed along the underground walls, tiles, rails. A burgeoning roar
joined it, as the light shafts streaked the tunnel, a train bombarding
into the station.

Augie sat back down, the train doors opening, fizzing closed. He
hadn't budged. Dannie sat dead tired, weak, mind-boggled beside
him, the pain in his neck surging, building, near-blinding.

Augie rose again as the subway train pulled away, and began
walking in circles, talking in the same desperate manner: "Lone
wolf on an everfreakin' lam. You know the route kid, but Willie left
me a legacy . . . Arthur Murray." Augie laughed. "Gave us the
money in a hurry." He laughed harder this time. "Arranged that
score this month . . . Park Avenue . . . over 30 G's . . . split five ways
. . . extra taken out for the Actor's appeal. Robbin' the two Dance
Kings . . .Willie taught me some of the science of heisting to survive
in style." Dannie tried to absorb, but concern for his aunt catapulted him from his seat. He told the near-lost Augie that he had to
telephone his aunt's place again.

He weak-kneed it to the upstairs public phone, feeling as lost as
psycho Augie, both of them at a real loss as to where Johnny
"Squint" Mazziotta was!

The upstairs phone booth was occupied, a brunette jabbering
away in it. A lean fellow stood by the semi-closed folded doors, a
three-way Emerson portable radio elbowed up on his right shoulder.

Dannie waited, the noel "Silent Night" being sung by a choir
from the Emerson. No use calling Eleanor. When his turn came,
he'd dial Eve. Maybe she'd know where her sister was.

He rested against an iron girder, bewildered, eyelids closing, his
mind's-eye seeing his ugly earlobe, his neck gash.

Hugo Duce would know Johnny's hideaway.

Holiday music. Home permanents with long lasting waves being
touted over the airwaves.

News breaks—gamblers' occupational tax stamps being ignored
in most states, declared the IRS. The professional gamblers weren't
buying them. Dannie, eyes half-open spotted a wiry transit cop
chatting with the pay booth change clerk beyond the turnstiles.

Trying to stand up straight was difficult for Dannie. His legs wob-
bled. The woman on the phone was talking without letup, while the
blue uniformed cop was tapping his bat against his leg. To Dannie,

only too conscious of the pistol's weight in his jacket pocket, the minutes were dragging by like days.

The transit cop waved goodnight with his nightstick to the bald man behind the glass of the change booth and headed Dannie's way.

The woman in the phone booth finally hung up, as the policeman passed Dannie by, sauntering over to the wide steps leading to the underground platform *and Augie.*

Augie's face, livid scar and all, had been plastered over front page newspapers from Salem to Seattle. If the policeman recognized him, challenged him, the shots that would follow would be blasted across the country. Dannie, hands in pockets, stepped forward, ten paces behind the night duty cop.

"Officer," he called on the platform, Augie in sight, sitting straight up.

"Officer," Dannie now blocked the cop's bench view, "I'm just in from Miami Beach and I got lost in this maze. I was going to telephone for directions, but maybe you can help me."

The cop, narrow-eyeing him, said nothing.

"I thought of asking the fellow in the pay booth," Dannie pressed, "but I didn't know if he could hear me from my side of the turnstiles." Dannie was alarmed, wondering if the night's loud events on McDonald Avenue were broadcasted. He realized how absurd he must look in his makeshift bandages—a wounded Santa Claus.

The transit policeman furrowed his forehead, tipping his plastic peaked hat back up a few inches. "Where do you want to go?"

"Pacific Street and Fourth Avenue."

"The other side," the cop gestured across the tracks with his black bat. "A couple of stops in the other direction."

"Thanks, Officer. Happy Holidays," Dannie said, the blessed rumble of an incoming train reverberating through the station. Dannie turned, walking toward the steps, side-eyeing Augie, standing. "Goodnight," Dannie waved to the cop.

The cop batwaved goodnight as Augie stepped into the train, the doors closing behind him. The train pulled out as the transit patrolman swaggered down the bleak, dusty brown platform

Dannie felt it would be unwise to cross over to the other side of the station and wait for a train. At the same time the telephone booth was tied up, this time by the guy with the portable radio.

Either way, Dannie wanted distance between him and the cop. Ultimately, it was the gun in his pocket which dictated the decision to ascend the second flight of narrow steps to the stormy streets of downtown Brooklyn.

He walked, feeling the brunt of whirling snow matting his flushed face, stinging into his soaked bandages and the back of his raw neck.

There were no public phones in sight among the business, court buildings, bail bond store fronts.

He had to get off the deserted streets, he thought as he looked up at the official city sign above him. Schermerhorn Street. It was the infamous corner known by heart by every borough bookmaker, burglar, and murderer from Borough Park to South Brooklyn—the home of the County's Felony Court.

He spotted some neon lights down along Smith Street, which came from a miniature Christmas tree placed in the window of a combination bar-restaurant.

Dannie entered the step-down oasis. The restaurant section was closed, but the bar portion was semi-filled with patrons, mostly men. Dannie shivered.

He stamped his feet, shaking loose the damp snow. Damn it — the pay phone on the wall was being used by a fat, baseball-jacketed guy. Dannie found an opening at the bar and sat on a backless stool.

Augie, he reflected. He was hunted, a lone wolf, stealing to survive the chase.

"What's your pleasure?" Dannie's reflections were broken by a lilting voice. He glanced up and discovered that the voice belonged to an immense-busted, chestnut-eyed barmaid.

"Four Roses."

The "high yellow" barmaid smiled and soft stepped along the duckboards. The bar was filled with speculations, discussions about the New York Yankees, the Giants, the Brooklyn Dodgers—the teams meeting in Atlanta for a minor league draft convention—that there was big bidding for Bobby Thompson. Dannie slugged down the hearty, throat-scorching rye blended whiskey, the barmaid's lovely eyes lighting up even more as she silently lifted Dannie's hundred dollar bill from the bar.

Finally the wall phone was vacant. As the barmaid deposited his change by his empty shot glass, Dannie ordered another and stepped over to the telephone, his earlobe biting with pain. Tracer thoughts of him being disfigured, deformed, an infection setting in, entered his brain. He'd drink both the pain and the thoughts away.

His mother was thanking the Lord that he had called her. She assured him that Eleanor was safe. She also wanted him to return to the airport hotel at once.

He thought he had developed the flu, he told her. To mention his bullet wounds would be unthinkable, so he concentrated on just running a high temperature, and that everything had gone . . . O.K. at the wake—no . . . complications.

He didn't have the strength to cab it to Queens, he went on. He just wanted a warm hotel nearby for the night. Dannie felt that he wasn't even making sense over the phone, he was so drawn, so weak. But a night's rest would find him fit to travel. "Brave the weather," he chuckled to his mom. "In the morning."

Eve didn't go into her usual suicide act, he observed. She just merely took note of his location, telling him to stay comfy. "And I love you, Daniel," she added.

Dannie didn't go back to his stool by the sports buffs. Instead he walked to the rear, standing shoulder against the wall, leaning by the corner of the bar, his eyes on the entrance for a clearer view.

The barmaid brought him his money and refill, while the sporting fans celebrated loudly that the Cuban welterweight champ, Kid Gavilan, had been declared Fighter of the Year.

"Next it will be horseracing," the barmaid smiled, remarking to Dannie. "They can bend your ears off night after night. You familiar with horse action?"

"In a roundabout way," Dannie answered, shades of Eighth and 40th forever with him. The barmaid had it down to a science pouring him a third shot, while the active group now argued about the jockey, Willie Shoemaker, winning three races at Bay Meadows. The seasoned barmaid circled around the bar and dropped coins in the mute jukebox, pressing selections.

June "the Misty Miss" Christy's, or maybe it was Chris Connors' luring version of "My Heart Belongs to Only You" came close to drowning out the heated debate now as to whether Jackie Robinson of the Dodgers should be allowed to buy a house in the all-white residential section of North Stamford, Connecticut. The half-black barmaid, seemingly ignoring the drunks, refilled their drinks, smiling, leaning forward, her gigantic, puffy breasts encased in a white jersey taking many a sodden eye with them. Dannie, polishing off the rye, wondered why Augie didn't know Johnny's whereabouts. If he did, he certainly would have known exactly what John had done that *entire* night by the station.

Then it hit him. Hugo Duce was the key. He knew, he had to. But why hadn't he told Augie? Or was John dead? "Hit" by Al-bert and Company to quell the furor over the Schuster killing?

"On me," the barmaid offered as she filled Dannie's glass. The jukebox's lyrics "you are the song within my soul" made Dannie think of his mother's unanswered question—"Are you *in love* with Eleanor?" Dannie's icy tremors were melting under the warmth of the whiskey, and he began to marvel at the little island of freedom around him, which the barroom's verbally brawling customers were oblivious to.

Their freedom to light up a Chesterfield, blow out smoke rings, cloud the barroom without fear of some subcultured *dundeech* coming up from behind. Strangling you because you *saw too much.* Freedom. To bullshit all night about the Trots, harness racing, parimutuel betting, unaware of the racketeers that corrupted jockeys, trainers, commissioners; exercising cruelty, distorting priorities, mutilating any "lucky outcome."

Unfettered freedom to tell a transit cop that the *Wanted* Angel Tenuto was about to board a subway train without shitting in your pants every day that a twisted Tony-boy would splatter your balls on the sidewalk like Arnold Schuster's.

Freaking Freedom, Dannie knew he was getting more than high from the straight whiskey, real freakin' freedom to make love to a high yellow doll without the shackles of a temptress tormenting him since he was six.

The elderly couple now next to him left a dollar tip on the bar, and weaved their way out of the place. Free to go *home.* True freedom to go out into the Brooklyn nighttime street without the certain, vomit-inducing fear of Madhatters.

"Midnight," he heard the sultry spoken word and the intimate breath in his ear. "Time flies. Mind if I intrude?"

Dannie, taken aback, blinked to clear his vision.

"No . . . not at all," he said to the barmaid. "Sit. It's my pleasure." He was glad to have her company, glad to shake off his hypocritical self-pity.

The torrid bar maid smelled good enough to lick. Now he knew he was really drunk, feeling no pain, just freakish in his grotesque wound dressings.

Her fragrance came from dabs of the jaunty My Audacious Fancy duo. Her name was Jubilee, and she liked drinking cognac, stating merrily that the Archbishop of the Gauls was the Patron Saint of Cognac.

The cigar-smoking proprietor, Herb, had taken over the bartending chores. He backed up Dannie and Jubilee's drinks, cashing Dannie's twenty, and Jubilee became more appealing with each drink he had.

Jubilee toasted Dannie's "terrific looks," and he clinked glasses to her "lavish sweater-front."

She never asked or remarked about his bandages.

As the rounds came and went, her left hand drifted lazily to his right thigh. He pushed the change from the twenty over to her. Her tip.

He drank. And he waited. To get hard. Her warm hand, fingers circling his thigh. Her comely, attractive face was just inches from his and he all but prayed for the grand gift of an *erection*. What he got instead was nitroglycerin.

Cabochon emerald earrings. Sparkling, matching flaming emerald eyes. His *mother's*—the breathless combination directly before him, combining, explosive.

In his intoxicated state he foresaw a scene like the one in Florida when his crusty aunt had swung at the redhead, Betty Allen. But Eve just pierced him with her exquisite eyes. She strolled easily through the bar, her hips engraving a show-off invitation as she bent, scanning the jukebox selections.

This "new" mother of his was far from the one in the past. She'd gone from dependent, sister-reliant to self-assured and deadset.

"Is that knockout a friend of yours?"

Dannie half laughed, knowing how ludicrous it would sound.

"She's my mother."

Jubilee nearly choked on her cognac. Clearing her throat, she laughed goodnaturedly.

Eve Crosscavale stepped easily between the two. Jubilee had been hesitant at first, but had shifted over as the strikingly beguiling woman had approached.

Eve undid her jet-buttoned, French-crafted left glove, peeling it off fingertip by fingertip. Her cool, bare palm pressed lightly against Dannie's steaming forehead, her long fingernails tracing the damp, dangerous heat of his face. Her eyes took in his bandaged ear, neck, but somehow managed to suppress the alarm in them with a glimmering calm.

She didn't say a word. There was "company" present. But the song she had selected spoke for her. Velma Rae's heart-throbbing "Jealousy" —

"Why am I so jealous, darling —
"Just the thought of you dear with somebody new
"Consumes me with pain —"

Eve softly traced Dannie's lips with her fingertips.

"There's a cab waiting outside for us," she said, pausing. "Or shall we continue our hotel doorway goodnight right here?"

She was leaning forward, so close that as she spoke their lips touched at intervals. Dannie didn't think for a minute she was bluffing.

She remained poised like a falcon for several moments. "You proved your point," he finally said. Then, she turned and walked over to an empty barstool. A wine-colored, belted raincoat lay freely over it, snowball, satin-handled handbag nestled on top.

Dannie now realized that not only had she entered the bar without his noticing, she had taken off her wet coat not ten feet from him.

She stood perfectly poised in curvy angora-on-wool cardigan sweater. Waiting. Her black hair, way past shoulder length, glistening in the bar's burlesque lighting.

If only he had the moxie to shove his hand in his jacket pocket, point the automatic toward his testicles and shoot. *That* would kill the bastard response in him. Shrugging off the momentary impulse, he rocked off the stool, Jubilee silently handing him the remainder of his bar cash.

His mother had the immediate class to slip into her own coat, her left hand smoothing her gleaming raven hair. She partly flipped up the buttoned, matching detachable hood.

Dannie all but begged himself to stand pat.

But he was too tipsy, too feverish to exercise any other options, except staggering out of the place, Eve holding him, her trim-waisted, flair bottom coat a true thrill to the bibulous sports freaks that had seen her mouth-watering frame inside. The patrons parted, allowing Dannie and his *mother* to pass, Dannie feeling like the biggest freak they'd ever see.

Outside, Dannie viewed the cab with stacked luggage rack on top through the torrent of swirling snow.

Inside the taxi his mother again felt his forehead, the sides of his neck. Her hands trembled as she adjusted his helterskelter bandages, her eyes emerald tear glows. "The Lafayette Hotel," she said to the cabbie. Dannie picked up the word *Lafayette*. It was the hotel Augie had mentioned in reference to John. He felt a strange quiver just before he faded.

Dannie awoke at slight intervals. He was exhausted, at a low ebb, burning with a virus, on the verge of hallucinating. Somehow he ended up in a room, his mother nursing him, in the shabby, downtown Brooklyn Hotel—the old known hangout of *Johnny's*.

He woke up feeling as if his body were a Korean battlefield.

He was drenched, debilitated. His mother, sitting at his bedside, related to him that they had cabbed it to the Lafayette Hotel not yesterday but *three days ago*. He had a severe virus, and a doctor had administered shots of Penicillin into his rump.

As for his bullet wounds, she hushed Dannie, her fingertips to his lips . . . the one behind the neck, although superficial, had needed six stitches. The earlobe, it seems, was nicked, the barest of pieces missing. Eve faltered momentarily, but bared her chin up.

The doctor was from Borough Park. It was O.K. He was paid handsomely. A doctor making a house call, probably a pal of Johnny Squint's.

Eleanor had also heard . . . Shots!

Was it all to protect her sister? Did it all stem from Arnold Schuster? Who did the actual shooting? Was it Johnny? Eve hit him with a barrage of unanswered questions.

She composed herself sharply, making him sip room temperature orange juice before giving him the antibiotic tablets with water.

Dannie was glad he was spared the grueling answer session. He'd look at his ear sooner or later in a mirror. Right now, he was just happy to be alive. Or was he? He felt like a garbage truck had run him over and was backing up now to complete the job. The never-ending trail of hostility had rotted the very structure of his life, or maybe it had grown wretchedly out of it.

He lay still that afternoon. Thinking of Hugo Duce. Of places inside and out of the country where gambling flourished. Both were ties to where John might be.

"Is that young man, Arnold Schuster, on your mind?" His mother, clad in low-cut, pink proportioned slip, sat on the sagging bed beside him.

"Put on a robe," he said.

"Close your eyes," she countered. "And don't avoid the subject. Arnold Schuster."

He remained silent, turning his head away from her on the pillow.

"You spoke of him these past three days and nights. Howled is more like it," she pushed on. "Besides your scattered recounting of your latest bullet escapades, you said Arnold at least three times while the Doctor was here. I had to stop you before you said his last name in your delirium by wiping your mouth with a cool compress. I explained to the Doctor that 'Arnie' was your brother who died at birth."

Dannie and Arnie, he thought. Brothers. It wasn't funny.

Eve would let the two topics of his dream menaces go for the time being. What he needed now was rest, warmth, liquids and fever-reducing aspirins and medication.

He had been awfully close to having a case of walking pneumonia, and the friendly doctor had ordered her to administer alcohol rubs.

"And now it's temperature time," she half laughed, patting the side of his buttock below the blanket.

"Like hell it is," he turned full on his back.

"My, my," she smiled. "So shy. But how shy would you have been with that bawdy baboon?" Her smile vanished. "The one in the bar with her hand between your legs." Her fingernails dug into him through the blanket.

He lay there, shallow breaths escaping from his lungs. The last thing he needed was for her to get witchy like his aunt. His eyes closed. The doctor was right. He needed rest.

He began falling into an exhausted sleep, his strength sapped. But there was one thing he had to ask before he conked out.

"What made you choose this hotel? The Lafayette." He was drifting helplessly into dreaded dreamland.

Her quiet kitten-pause was too long before she answered. "Oh, I don't know," she shifted her bare knees on the bed, covering, tucking him in. "I passed it in the taxi rushing to get you," she two-finger touched his seared lips. "It's only a short run from that bar you were in. That's all."

Mistily, he felt her weight lifting off the bed, his head dropping, falling to the side of the feathered pillow, his lips not moving but his mind groggily saying, "I don't believe you."

After two more days, he was up and around, shuffling about in the confines of the drab hotel room.

He sat on the divan, clothed in his robe. His thoughts focusing on Eve, Eleanor and Johnny Squint. The former was out buying food. Eleanor was somewhere safe, he didn't know exactly where. But she had telephoned him yesterday evening saying that the New Year would be *theirs*. He had wryly said, "Who gave it to *us*? Father Time?"

As for his demonic search for Johnny, Dannie was losing heart for the hunt. Shadow boxing was what he had been doing all this time. Traveling in circles then, disgusted now.

Yet his "training" in determination when he had been out on the nearby streets seeking his first girlfriend, Antoinette, helped him to fight the impulse to give up. It had been Johnny himself who had told him to have "staying power," and he admired him for developing it.

He tossed aside a bunch of his mother's fashion magazines, stretching out on the plaid divan, and pondered two clues.

One was money. His aunt had said that her sister had taken nearly six hundred dollars from her. For him. But the grand-spending Eve was shopping these days like she was the Gold Queen of America. Peaked lapels, lustrous rayon robes for him. Not to mention his deerskin gloves. And for her, linen string strapped shoes, LaValle, Bally colored hearts, divine fit silk slips. Her wardrobe alone could well fill one complete fashion magazine.

Money. A wad of it. From someone whose name started with "Ru . . ."? No! Gamblers got it like that. Bookmakers. Policy number controllers. *Johnny Mazziotta.*

Now for the second, a thin shred of a clue that could lead to John. The Lafayette. Dannie recalled the rumors printed in the newspapers last summer. The Lafayette Hotel in downtown Brooklyn was one of the spots where John had supposedly been sighted. Combining that with Augie's statement about this same Lafayette, and his mother saying she "just happened to see it," while the beckoning lit sign of the higher class Granada Hotel flashed right across the street.

New Year's Eve, Dannie wondered with new hope. Augie had said he'd see Johnny by the New Year.

"You may be right," Dan mused aloud. But not through you or Hugo Duce, Dannie's eyes narrowed, but through the brand new Eve.

She came in before dark. Package laden.

He greeted her with a rare generous hug. Told her there had been no true excuse for him not buying her a Christmas present, or sending her a card.

She was thrilled to hear it, eyes dazzling.

He helped her off with her Alpaca pile short coat, after relieving her of the take home Chinese food and the bags from her downtown Fulton Street shopping spree.

She was vivacious, talkative while they ate.

The CinemaScope movie *The Robe* with Burton, Mature and Jean Simmons was playing at the Albee. But he couldn't go out.

"Too cold and rainy, brrrr," she shivered, demonstrating the inclement weather.

They'd ring in the "bells" at midnight listening, via radio, to Guy Lombardo from the Roosevelt Grill on Madison Avenue.

"Okay?" she asked, captivating in her elbow-length-sleeve dress, all-the-way button front.

"Okay," he smiled, feeling like a rat for what he was doing, but he had to know what he thought *she knew.*

After eating, she wanted to show off her purchases.

"No modeling." He frowned.

"Oh, you're blind without your glasses on." She grinned, then checked herself, momentarily afraid that maybe she had hurt his feelings. He laughed, assuring her that he couldn't tell Adam from the original Eve on a rainy night in Havana without them. Her face brightened, and she twirled around to run herself a hot bubble bath.

"The Trapp Family Singers may be on the radio. A Yuletime concert from Town Hall." Her buoyant voice filtered through the bathroom door.

She had bought some Calvert Reserve, a mellow whiskey. But not for him. She didn't want him to have a relapse mixing liquor and antibiotics. She would do the celebrating, welcoming in 1954.

He turned the stations of the wood-frame Philco radio. All he had heard most of the week was about "Reds" under every bed. Senator McCarthy's spy peril alerts. President Eisenhower was also feuding with Senator J.R. McCarthy. Dannie tried clearing a station through the wheezing static. Finally, he clicked it off, but he remembered something said about a Carlos Prio . . . a former Cuban President being arrested in Miami. Dannie wondered if there was an association between Johnny Squint and the wide open hotel casino gambling in Havana, Cuba. The two "Good Fellows" that he liked from the Costello People, Sally "Burns" Granello and Pedro Di Pietro, whom he had met at the Five O' Clock Club, were skimming millions down there. His mother's volatile voice called out again, "There's also some magazines in the paper bag."

He flipped through the pages of the sordid *Detective* and *Mystery* magazines. Two of them had articles on the widely hunted John "Chappy" Mazziotta. One included a mug shot of "Angel St. John" Tenuto.

Twins, Dannie mused, his eyes suddenly glued to a photograph of a body lying on its back on a sidewalk. The form of a blood-soaked face with no eyes. Arnold Schuster. He wanted to fling the cheap weekly across the room. Instead, it fell limply from his grip.

"Well?" his mother said. He looked up. She was posing by the bathroom door, hair upswept, hands on hips, wearing a white petit-slip. "Filmy, modern living," she described the attire. He smiled, averting his eyes, but clapped his hands three times. Satisfied, she darted back into her "dressing room."

It gave him time to mull over one of the *True Detective* features, which had speculated that Johnny Squint was dead! Silenced by the Mob.

Dannie turned that over and over in his mind. John and Augie pulling up on the Ninth Avenue freight-subway bypass-bridge. Was the simple plan to switch to Johnny's red Oldsmobile? But Augie had said he had seen a waiting Packard. Gretti, Tony-boy and clan? A set-up within a set-up? Immediately hit the killers of Schuster, and thereby kill the Anastasia tie-in?

But was it John and Augie who did the actual killing? Where was Hugo Duce? Had the scornful Little Mike played a major part in the murder?

Augie had told John to make it with him to the Greenwood Cemetery main entrance not more than 50 yards away. But Johnny had gone in the other direction. To the subway station? They were supposed to meet at the Lafayette Hotel, though John never showed. Augie had seen Dannie, then had grappled his way over the high, spiked fence to get lost among the mausoleums and tomb-stones, rather than unwisely shoot it out just five blocks from where an ambush shooting had just taken place. Had Johnny and Augie gone there to eliminate Gretti and friend, and protect the Costello Crew?

"Like this one?" his mother interrupted, beaming, in black silk, pointing out with the slow sweep of her right hand, "the exciting swish, swoop of lace." Her hair was naturally long now, the signature of her ultimate sexuality. He let out a low, unrehearsed whistle.

"You always make me feel like a prima donna," she blushed.

He scratched his head, creasing his brow.

"Don't you remember," she continued, "the way you bragged so proudly to the Sesqu family how 'beautiful' your mother is. And to your teachers at school. You were so young," her voice trailed off, "we were so close. My life was worth living." She seemed about to cry.

"On with the vogue-march," he snapped his fingers, ending her slide into melancholy memories. "Go," he pointed, and she dashed cheerily out of sight, first commenting that the room was much too warm in there to parade in outdoor winter outfits. Dannie contin-ued his speculations on the possible fate of John.

If Gretti and Little Mike were there waiting, they never could have gotten Johnny into their Packard. He didn't trust them. Simple as that, and he was too powerful for them to try to strong-arm out in the open—even if Tony-boy and the late Al Rispone had been there also.

But maybe there was a way it could have been done. If they'd used a gun with a silencer. Or, if they had someone present who John truly trusted. Benny Napanack, Mush, or *Hugo Duce*?

Dannie knuckle-rubbed his jaw, weighty with thoughts. Kill Johnny, and dump him over the bypass wall. Bury him among old Pop's, the watchman's, domain. A minute after Arnold had been slaughtered. They entered heaven a minute apart. But then his search would be all for what? His own life, maybe. His aunt's, mother's. Then he clicked with a hope-catching thought. Augie was still *alive*.

"Ready?" His mother was several feet in front of him, half sitting, right hand flat on the carpet, bare legs partially bent, her left hand resting between her lower thighs.

He swallowed, thinking he was in a French designer's studio where outlandish daydreams of consecrated porno came true.

"Now, sir," she was modest, professional, "this is not cheesecake. This happens to be one of the *faite ciel*," she winked, "of our Baby Doll line."

Dannie sat, soaking up her presentation, her expert descriptions; vivid gestures outlining varied nightwear. And she had the "equipment," the contours, to fill them all. He was thoroughly enjoying her show.

Smooth fitting beauty peek-a-boo accents. Sheer Sorcery nylon net by Luxite. Spreading neckline, nude nylon tricot lace.

He closed his eyes, relaxing. It was as if Eleanor were also in the room. Same voice. Long eyelashes. Uncanny. Miraculous, he listened.

"As for our shoe line, we have the backless flat, slim pump on thin heel, printed swiss chintz. For sunnier climes, the alluring opened-toed, slim-strapped Southern Belles."

He felt he knew now where his detailed attention to shoes came from.

"Great," he had his eyes opened. "Let's talk about . . . go into . . . travel now. Hotter weather. Say the Bahamas. Maybe Cuba."

"Right," she said. "Around the Monopoly board." She hadn't "bitten," Dannie let it go for the moment, and she blithely reminded him how she used to beat him at the game.

They started playing Monopoly on the floor. Each one, in turn, shot the white-black dice, high number would be the banker.

Eve won, thrilled.

Inside of an hour she had him on the verge of entering the poor-house.

She drank the Calvert as they played. He the club soda.

She was getting the giggles from the fun she was having whipping him, from the mellow rye, and from controlling the fake money.

Each time he went to the bathroom from steadily drinking club soda or just stood up to stretch, he'd find that she was richer by about a thousand or so.

When he asked her to turn on the radio and get a good or better station, he'd enrich his bankroll with a handful of fifty and hundred dollar bills.

Cheating her as they played, vied for precious property holdings, caused him to laugh more heartily.

But she was laughing fit to tears, holding her sides. Dannie figured that her freer—dishonest—access to the open box of loot was making her laugh more than him. There were times each separately rolled over on the carpet from their own laughter. And each time the other would magically become that much wealthier.

With the help of the radio, Dannie went from Monopoly and toy money to gambling and real, hard cash.

Frank Erickson, the nationally known bookmaker, was jailed again by the Feds. Tax evasion. Six months. He was a good friend of Johnny's. There was lots of money to be made by highly connected gamblers. He tried again to break her silence.

"They advertise a lot of your exquisite perfumes." Eve played, preoccupied. The comments going unheeded.

Dannie passed GO collecting his $200. "Shalimar, My Love, Most Precious. Whew, they must cost a fortune."

She was wrapped in her Calvert and the game.

He'd try something on a more personal level.

"It's good to have enough money after pinching nickels in Juarez, worried to death about my next bite of food. Your sis really came through for me with that packet of cash." He moved, counting five spaces, and landed on Community Chest.

She didn't respond.

"You used to cringe from arguing, Mom. Now you're more flexible, sure of yourself," he watched her hand move her tiny, silver racehorse along the board. She clapped! just missing his Pennsylvania Avenue hoteled property.

Whoaa, he thought. She was either inebriated into oblivion, or more on guard than he had imagined.

"You've really changed. I'm glad," he shook the dice, played the game. "But don't be so quick to break from your Siamese sister. You know. With all your luggage and personal belongings here," he flung the dice on the board, "we'll need her to carry us until I get a job." His number came up seven.

"Carry us," her words merely a reiteration of his own. "You haven't been playing Monopoly, Daniel." She looked at him, misty filament clouding her eyes. She leaned, one hand on the divan, stood, and barefooted her way over the cardboard cartel, toward her make-believe "dressing room."

HE SCANNED THE PAGES OF *REBIRTH AND DESTINY OF Israel* by Ben-Gurion. A book his mother had bought to ease his convalescence.

He stepped to the window. Soon car horns would be honking madly, pots, pans rattling, screams of joy bringing in the New Year.

Maybe he should get warmly dressed, go to that bar where Jubilee worked, and join in some kind of revelry.

He lay on the divan, ashamed, feeling cheap, desolate, thinking of a leashed dog sniffing, lapping Arnold's still-warm, bloody corpse.

He heard the faint swish of a blanket. His mother had slipped into bed.

The telephone shrilled. He counted eleven short drilling rings. Neither one of them so much as stirred to answer it.

Eleanor. Who else could it be. That shrew. She hadn't responded by her door for him, he wouldn't acknowledge her call.

Music, cheers, countdown time bellowed from the Philco. Packed, stuffed, mobbed Times Square flashed in Dannie's head. There was no Happy New Year!

By three in the morning he still hadn't fallen asleep. Mostly it was because his mother had floundered in her bed like a rubber raft caught in a riptide. Then there was his sheer fear of the New Year and what it would bring him. Another two bullets? This time in *his face!*

His mother's cries of "smelly alcohol breath"—"grizzly snakes" holding her, punctured the stillness and caused him to snap up to a sitting position on the divan's edge.

She was a struggling, suffocating contortionist on the bed.

"Slime"—"hands"—"undertakers," she screamed in horror. Swiftly, he knelt beside her.

"Mom," he held her down, trying to prevent her from cracking her head against the night-table's edge.

"Mom, it's me, Dannie," he pressed her down. "Mom, mom," he urged, attempting to soothe her, unravel her. "Wake up. Mom . . . please wake up."

Her body tremors seemed to be settling down. Her hair was ringing wet and he brushed it away from her face.

Her eyes, salty green sparkle, now focused on him.

"Mom, it's all right," he spoke softly. "You had a bad dream. Lay back. Take nice deep breaths."

Instead of lying back, she leaned forward, her cheek on his shoulder. "You're here," she murmured. "No more trips, going away without me. Promise."

He promised. What else could he do? She spoke of nights, of Roscoe. Of her relief when Roscoe had worked nights. Of her fright when they were in the same bedroom together. She would stall, read of the latest styles in lingerie. Nightwear—the irony of it—her dubious armor. She truly hoped that Roscoe's life was now loaded with sex.

Dannie tried to stand.

"Not yet," she held him. "One more minute," she nestled, an urgent note in her voice. "My sex was when I nursed you." Dannie bristled. "Don't tighten up. Please. It was so. You're the only one I trust."

Dannie ran his hand along the bedsheet. It was sopping wet from her nightmare.

He lifted her up in his arms.

"Come on," he carried her to the divan, "get comfortable," he placed her on it. "And . . . Happy New Year," he smiled, "my black-haired Mom."

"Eve," she said.

"Eve?"

"Eve," her green eyes had a girlish glow about them. "We almost began the New Year off the wrong way. Now let's begin it right. Eve."

Dannie shrugged, grinning. "Happy New Year, stylish Eve."

"Happy New Year, Dan." Her almond-shaped eyes blazed despite the dim, lamplit room. She opened her arms.

Because she was in her turquoise, dress-length, sheer robe he felt it safe to lean in for the customary New Year's salutation—the kiss.

But it lasted like the one by the International Hotel room's doorway. After it, she lay her head on his chest, her hand resting above his heartbeats.

"And no more fencing about money. I'll tell you where I got it." Her words were slightly muffled in the fabric of his imported robe. "Johnny telephoned last May, two days after you met with me and Eleanor at Gregnano's restaurant on McDonald Avenue."

At first, she thought the call was a hoax, or a trap set by the police or gangsters. But he had insisted she meet him at a downtown hotel, by the Granada, and the looming Williamsburg Savings Bank. This one. The Lafayette. And he insisted she bring Dannie. That's when she had hung up!

Dannie had his hands resting behind his head on the cushioned arm of the divan, his gut going tight.

"Then?" he said.

"That was the last time I spoke to him," she went on, "if indeed it actually was him on the telephone." She paused to appraise closely his handstitched garment.

"As for the money, it came much later, indirectly by way of that midget hoodlum."

"Hugo Duce?" Dannie asked.

"No. First the other one you know. He dines in Scarola's restaurant on Church Avenue. You saw him there that time in December. He had an entire little army with him then."

"Joe the Blond?"

"Yes. Joe Gallo. That's him." She pushed herself forward, sidling to where her chin met with the groove of his shoulder.

"He was at that same restaurant and somehow recognized me and Eleanor. He asked for you and told us about your *compagno's* niece Kathleen. That she had been shot that very day. I went to the hospital *for you*. It was there that I saw the bucktooth Hugo. Before I left, he gave me an envelope with a note and money in it."

Dannie felt exhilarated. *A step away from Johnny.*

Eve wrestled half out of her robe. The room's two portable oil burners stifling with smoky heat.

Dannie felt frosted black net over a firm thigh.

"*Where is he?*"

"Out West, or so I'm led to believe," she shivered. "But why go? We have enough funds to get us started somewhere else. He's a murderous *diavolo*. An assassin who may be *morto* himself now. Don't you see? I wanted to protect you and not tell you the things I have." She turned fully against him, and her Christmas Angel lingerie's floating-free top strained heartily to hold her sumptuous breasts. She was living a fantasy—being the seventeen-year-old that she had been raped, robbed of.

He stiffened.

"I have the gun well hidden." She was in earnest, her bosom beating quaking heartbeats. "The one I found in your jacket pocket," her dread of his dying, the pure fear of not having him, destroying her *a second time.*

He loosened and turned to face her. Peril, not licentiousness, immobilizing him, he didn't even move his hand to thumb away her teardrops; they rolled to the corners of her mouth, the New Year finally bringing both of them a restful, nightmare-free sleep.

1954

New Year's Day

Willie Sutton's bare, cement steel cell was monitored. *Twenty-four hours a day*. The Warden, Captain (the PK), Administrators, Special Unit Guards watched him read, sleep, excrete in the upstate New York prison. Attica.

And they didn't have to read his mind.

Escape.

"Artistry—vs.—Science."

Willie winked up at the TV screen. His artistry included his experience, imagination, daring, and some assistance from his friends.

The "Science" that he was pitted against was mere electronics—electrons racing madly in patterned directions. Preparation, he thought, groaning audibly as he turned on his side to face Wall One, as he called it.

"Well, Wall One," he spoke to himself. "Maiden Lane will have to wait!" Wall Street area safe deposit boxes. The caper of the century.

Willie's mind zeroed in on Marge, his former park bench companion. She was singing her silly head off to gain citizenship. Willie wondered if she mentioned anything about his '47 escape from

Holmesburg? She could involve sloe-eyed Eve's kid, Dannie, and John himself. No, Willie reflected, she knew nothing of John's indirect part in that. Willie, wincing, turned his body leftward to Wall Two.

"So, Wall Two, do you think John is dead or alive?" Willie grinned sheepishly. He stems from puissant people—musn't forget that. The hope within Willie soared. Preparation.

Wall Two. Maiden Two. Fran. She was searching Staten Island's marshland for his millions.

Willie's blue eyes beamed. Angel had staked the lovely creature. Socializing in his mind, he saw himself taking Fran to a flick tonight. He'd rest his weary head on her shoulder as she stroked his dyed hair.

But she'd have to wait for the key to his greenback farm. He'd need it when he met with the wizard Meyer Lansky, again.

He would talk with Meyer about the unfinished business of upgrading Johnny, in turn contributing a barrel of funds to the Zionist movement.

Now to Wall Three, Willie lay on his stomach. Venuta, of Manufacturer's Hanover fame, is talking his head off, but I'm serving three hundred years, so whatever he adds is all downhill.

Angel, he thought of his trusted friend. Angel, are *you* preparing out there? Willie alighted from the bunk and sifted through his jailhouse papers, law memos. Another way of leaving here? He checked himself against relying on that kind of rectangular folk thinking. Ahh, so many of them out there who don't know what to do with their lives—so they go to work. I'd merely open some money stores.

He looked at the portal of his palace: the front-door wall.

Am I all thought out after twenty-three months? Willie asked the bars. Never happen, he knew as waves of thought swept over the oceans of his mind.

Little Mike winged by Angel.

Al Rispone dying accidentally?

Al-bert incensed by his soldiers' mishaps!

The bereaved Schuster clan forever in mourning.

That butterscotch-appealing broad Eleanor still in John's hair?

Is center-fielder Richie Ashburn still one of Angel's favorites?

Hugo Duce is among us again.

Willie sighed, aloud. Preparation. A feigned trip down to Sing Sing's third floor hospital ward. Detailed, scientific THINKING. Angel would soon be ready.

Willie smiled at his T.V. monitor. No more groans for now. No use over-acting. He found his mental pun not too funny, but remained smiling—as gracious as always to his Public. What a joke.

What a real joke. But Johnny Squint didn't exactly laugh on January 1, 1954. New Year's Day. He was just self-amused, a twisted grin crossing his mouth.

You get embroiled in the shooting of a *schmuck* on a Brooklyn sidewalk and wind up in the swank, garden setting Parklabrea Towers, three thousand miles away. Los Angeles, California.

What a fitting way to cap off nearly two years of making The Most Wanted list. And to top that, he'd be making his Las Vegas debut within a week!

But right now instead of gloating in his nifty apartment, he had details to wrap up on the Rose Bowl game.

After that he'd get down to the news about Eve, Augie, Eleanor and the growing kid, Dannie, from his partner, Hugo Duce, who was back on the east coast.

Johnny sunk his front teeth into the yellow lead pencil. The Michigan Spartans kicked the football shit out of U.C.L.A. today in Pasadena. Johnny's eyes squinted at the bare statistics. Michigan State was a six-and-a-half point favorite over the Bruins. Score 28 to 20. Uncle Frank, the nation's odds maker, going nine points . . . point spread perfect, Johnny tabulated in his mind, tongue wetting the pencil's lead, jotting figures on the tab sheet.

All tolled, it was one sweet month.

The "nags," his intense brown eyes narrowed. Santa Anita, first race. Mercenary paying $7.00 to win. A "boat" race. Hugo bet heavily on it through good old Borough Park "stooge" bettors. The competition—bookmakers from the other four Crews.

Miss Revoked, the five-year-old mare, was a twelve-to-one shot at New Orleans Fair Grounds. Paying $25.90.

Boxing. Paddy De Marco, the Brooklyn lightweight, had won an "upset" down under in Louisiana. Johnny had to truly smile at that one. Smiling wider at the easy money made on the bout.

The wire service . . . Johnny glanced around for the figures he wanted, which lay scattered on bits of Hollywood trades on top of his cocktail table. He reached for them, spotting another figure in a movie ad.

Jeszoo Christ—Esther Williams, wholesome, in a one piece bathing suit, was pushing the film *Easy to Love*. Johnny's light brown eyes sparked.

Esther Williams . . . Eve . . . shit! Johnny flung the fuckin' pencil side-handed across the living room. One was a photo eye-delight, the other real in his head—with nipple-nectared, bigger tits, fuller hips, and a much shapelier ass. She was, quite possibly, on her way out West, the thought of corrupting her still exciting him. Johnny thought of his mentor, Uncle Frank's, raspy words ringing now: "It's always the one you can't get that you want the most."

"Tell that to my prick, 'Uncle,' " Johnny, sotto-voce, was getting heated, his twisted temper flaring.

Lentamente, he told himself. Go slowly. He leaned forward, picking up another sharpened pencil from the table, and sat back.

Back to business. Without Hugo out here now, he had a lot of wrapping up to do himself. Coral Gables, Florida. The Harinero Purse at Tropical Park. Press winning in another fixed upset. Paid $31.90. He took in all the cross country favorites—service edgeoff bets, and cleaned up from Chicago to Philadelphia.

Philly, Angel's glorified city, his mind wandered. Johnny knew that this wasn't going to be one of his most productive days. He sighed, trying to relax.

My pal, Angel Tenuto. He drove through two Crews' Reps along a Brooklyn sidewalk, wounding Little Mike; the kid, Dannie, getting shot in the process.

Al-bert was pissed off that Augie was even still alive. Johnny had to laugh at how Al-bert also felt about lucky Dannie, getting caught on the Miami Beach sand with his pants down and that banana-nosed niece of his with her head even further down. He had to hand it to Dannie V. Johnny abruptly ended his amusement, thoughts of another of Dannie's girlfriend's entering his mind. His own dear niece, Kathleen. Dead.

That was no joke at all, Johnny flared. That spit-drippin' Rocco Brusezze. In a mental institution. Unfortunately it wasn't the same one that whacko Benny had been in recently, or else Benny would have iced that bastard for good!

All in good time. The chance would eventually come to exterminate Rocco. Johnny had badly wanted to take another daring chance and see sweet Kathleen at her wake. Uncle Frank had strictly, astutely, forbidden it.

Killed a virgin. No evil had lived in her. And she died before she learned any. Johnny rose from the sofa, digging his hands in his slacks pockets. There was plenty of life in *them*. *Money*. He walked to his terrace, stepping out onto it.

L.A. Beverly Hills straight up Wilshire Boulevard. But there was no "star gazing" for him. Just an occasional jaunt to closeby Silverwoods. But no driving, no car—that's a cop-stop—when he went to buy the Hart Schaffner & Marx sport slacks, or some convertible sports shirts. There would be no more dapper, flashy needle point suits, nor hand-blocked silk ties to go with them. That fancy stuff was out the window, part of the "yesterday" Johnny Mazziotta image, though he'd keep the Brito brown-on-brown shoes that he was partial to. He turned his head toward nearby Hollywood.

Jane Russell town. The church said it would be a sin to see her newest movie. If the church ever saw Eve on a theater marquee, they'd burn her at the stake for sucking you off with her seducing-green eyes, Johnny grinned, patting his solid gut. He had lost weight and could no longer be tagged as "squat." It had been another of his sage's—Frank "Uncle Frank" Costello—suggestions.

Gotta listen to the Boss, Johnny continued soaking in the 80 degree Southern California sunshine. Why not? A man that had sent Texas Gynen and Mae West to the top, nightclubbed with the likes of Howard Hughes and sported with the venerated Babe Ruth, dirty-dealt with that New York Mayor O'Dwyer, controlled an international gaming arena and distributed nationwide illegal slot machines couldn't be all that wrong. Johnny left the pressing work of the ledgers, tally sheets, sports action—lofty gambling profits—behind and thought of seven days from now.

Vegas. Working, skimming, overseeing with the genius likes of Lansky, and most of all, waiting. For Eve.

She'd come, he knew. Johnny eased back into his living room, the hypnotic strains to "Green Eyes" searing his brain—"To hold you, find you and enfold you." She'll have to. For he was the only one that could save her own personal resurrection—the life of her son, Dannie V. Johnny furrowed his brow at the red ruby ring on his pinky.

She'd come all right. In more ways than one. In the kitchen, Johnny poured himself a cup of Chase & Sanborn, spiking it with a jigger of the Justerini & Brooks rare scotch.

She'd come because he had gone through the bother of getting entangled in the shooting of the curly-haired punk, Schuster. He recalled the instinctive decision to split from Angel by the Ninth Avenue Station. It had been safer for both of them. Then there was the labyrinthian maze of hideouts, in Miami, Detroit, Mexico City, Spain, Bermuda, all cleverly masterminded by the great grafter, Uncle Frank, via De Sapio's Tammany Hall and the Feds of Foley Square.

He was sorry he didn't keep his meet that Sunday with Eve and the boy. She'd have to understand the heat generated by that one crummy death. Johnny, for the life of him, couldn't understand it. Why so much fuss over one killing when people were always shooting each other in Brooklyn? Why *international* heat? Was it because the magnetic Sutton was involved? Did the damn newspapers create the furor? What was so important about one guy dying? *Why single out Arnold Schuster?* He wasn't rich, or famous. He didn't hold any high post where the world would fall apart if he left the earth.

Johnny shrugged, his frustration easing momentarily under the soothing sounds of the melody . . .

"A thirst for love divine . . ."

Eve. She'd better come! His beast-lust for her tore through him. Johnny went berserk, wrist-snapping the coffee cup from his hand. The dry white wall smattered brown as the cup shattered into chunks. He wanted to deck somebody, but settled instead for the counter clock beside him. He smashed through it with his right fist, the pieces flying everywhere. He'd get her through the Badge and the Boy!

He tried to contain his rage. If he wrecked his own apartment, the damned nosy neighbors'd have the LAPD here.

His mind flared from Eve to the cat and mouse game Al-bert and the decrepit arbitrator, Gretti, were playing. He'd kill his fence-jumping ex-friends, Gret and Little Mike, with his bare hands for damaging the kid Dannie. It was a vow.

Next, his mind jumped to the aborted waylay by the station *that night.* All to satisfy the Madhatter. Augie was *living* for the day he'd exterminate that "motherfuckin', face slappin' *animale.*" Anastasia. His rage mounting, Johnny thought of another one who had it coming. That *strega*, spitfire bitch. Eleanor.

The one Hugo reported as being on the move.

The one who had pulled her sister away from him!

The one who had accused him of violating Eve in her hospital "death" bed. She had ruined his shot at possessing the *angelo* he wanted.

Johnny's *pazienza* had finally run out. He smouldered, barely managing to control his rage.

Eve's awakening to her bewitching sister's manipulative games was long overdue.

Dannie, too, would be dexterously enlightened about two particular nights that had determined, recharted his life.

And the blow-torch body Eleanor Cross—the iniquitous joker in the deck of Eve's life—would be promptly visited by Hugo on the other coast to settle the score on a game that she had surely over-played. Johnny would make a no-joke book on that.

HUGO DUCE PLAYED GIN RUMMY WITH JOHNNY Squint's ex-brother-in-law, Benny Napanack—Rosa's brother.

They played in the rear of Pete's Radio Store on the corner of 40th and Eighth, in Borough Park, Brooklyn.

"I'm gonna fuck her between the teeth," Ben's swarthy face was contorted with saliva-dripping delight. "She lied about Johnny. She's no fuckin' good. No fuckin' good."

Hugo paid hardly any attention to his hand, and even less to Benny, a revolving criminal mental institution case fresh out of Pilgrim State.

"I gotta kick her in the cunt," Benny was shifting cards in his upraised hands. "That's only right we do that. Right, Hugo?"

"Play cards," Hugo said, glancing up at the big, black-rimmed clock on the wall. Five p.m. New Year's Day.

Hugo reminisced about other, younger days with his partner, Johnny. There was the hit on "The Shadow" here in their neighbor-hood—an informant. That kill saved Don Vito Genovese from the hot seat. It also paved the way for both of them to be "sponsored," "groomed" and eventually "badged."

Hugo vividly remembered the day before that shooting. John had asked him if he were sure he wanted to tag along. Hugo had replied instantly—"We're partners, John. Never ask me, query me, or tell me. Thy will be *done*." They had smiled, locked eyes, and heartily embraced.

"Used to sway saucy down 38th and think I was a drooling piece a shit," Benny was still shifting his cards. "That's what she used to do. That ain't right, Hugo. That ain't right."

Hugo laid down his cards. "Gin." The clock above read 5:15.

FROM HER RECLINING POSITION ON THE SHOCKING-pink love seat, Eleanor Cross watched the rain intermittently pelt against her finished basement window.

Packing last week, arranging for a moving van and setting up her new apartment had proven to be no great trauma. She slid her hand along the seat's fabric, bouclé matelasse.

Ummm, so comfy.

She thought of Daniel knocking on her former apartment door on McDonald Avenue last week, urging her to open it. The fact that she hadn't opened it didn't disturb her now. She wondered if she should rise and seek a time-killing radio show. Perhaps "The Great Gildersleeve" or "Dr. Christian" with Jean Hersholt. She didn't stir, not knowing for sure if this were their prescribed make-believe evenings.

The one reality that had upset her was not the break with Eve. It was the extra money she had taken from her secret provider, Ruby's, packet. But Daniel would rectify it. And justly so, she thought, now polishing her toenails.

She flexed one shoulder, then the other, the flimsy Grecian melon nightgown's straps floating freely to her bare arms. A New Year, she inhaled, her breasts heaved, braless. "The stealth of a salty wildcat with jasper-like eyes," Daniel had been naughty to her again on the telephone from the Lafayette Hotel. That statement had been mixed in with other snide remarks.

Theirs—The New Year—she had previously *promised* him. But she wondered now if gangland and the gutter would get him first, like the "Arnold" of his howling plagued nights.

Or perhaps the police would furtively appear in his shadowy life. She tugged gently on the double set of quilt cuddlers for better protection against any damp draft.

Or maybe it would be her sister Eve who would wind up on this side of the libidinous bed. Eleanor fluttered her long lashes at the framed five-by-seven photo tacked on her wall paneling. It was high time for Dan and Eve, she fluttered away at the unfading snapshot.

High Time.

THREE HOURS BEFORE ARNOLD SCHUSTER HAD BEEN murdered, Hugo Duce knew that he had to get an alibi.

"Be with people all evening and all night, Hugo. Make 'em strangers. A couple of priests in a rectory if you have to. But stay out of the actual picture," Johnny had told him.

Hugo had taken the "advice."

Last month, when the union boss of Yonkers Raceway in the Bronx, Tommy Lewis, had to be silenced for the sake of Don Vito and Uncle Frank, Hugo had amiably chided John: "This time around, I'll lead the move. And you don't need an alibi. You're a ghost as it is."

"I did it. I did it. Nailed you," Benny chortled as he laid his cards on the table. His charcoal-shaded pigskin palm gloves momentarily covered the cards before he swept them aside and pronounced his victory. "Gin!"

Hugo's buckteeth protruded more than normal as he bent his neck to scan Benny's winning hand. A simpleton was beating him at cards. Hugo knew his mind had really been drifting for the past half hour. Why did he have to bring this sickie along tonight? "For *effect!*" John had said, curtly.

Pietro M. shuffled into the rear of the store, his Arnold Constable overcoat near waterlogged.

"Sal Nap is at Dutchie T's Lafayette," he reported to Hugo. The eavesdropping switchboard desk clerk would buzz Sal if Eve or the tall kid called for a cab. Sal would be the cabbie.

"The deer season's open in New Jersey," Benny spittled. "I'm allowed," he sneered, patting a scoped rifle by his side. "Get that Rocco who blasted *santo* Kathleen. And shoot that other pretty snob *strega* in the tongue while she licks my dick. Good idea, Hugo? Good idea?"

The only really good idea was to shoot Benny himself with the rifle, Hugo smirked. But Benny was a diehard fan of John's. He should be. It had been Johnny who had covered, paid, bribed, and bailed on Benny's behalf—to keep the mental case out of most of the funny farms from Islip to Matawan. Not to mention the fact that Johnny staked him bread and butter cash for over fifteen years.

"Stow the rifle, Benny," Hugo said dryly, looking up at the clock. They'd leave soon. Pietro M. would drive. Mush would come along, lay directly outside.

A New Year, that's the way John figured it.

Hugo sat calmly, resigned. He felt the curved-blade carving knife inside his tan raincoat while ever-ready Mush indulged Benny in a game of Hearts.

He had made a statement when John and he had begun those many years ago, and it would hold true until the moment of his last breath. "THY will be *done.*"

"NOW TAKE THE KID'S HEIGHT," HUGO SAID TO Eleanor Cross. "He stands over six-foot-one. Your sister Eve goes about five-foot-seven. John, five-six."

"How tall was Arnold Schuster?" Eleanor snapped defiantly. She was lying on the love seat, the two thick quilts held up to her neck with her right hand while her left held the hot-water-soaked white towel to her left earlobe.

Hugo didn't flinch at her Schuster remark. He was sitting several feet from her, straddling a folding chair.

He knew now that putting a tail on her after the night Augie had bounded away with the bleeding kid, Dannie, had been the right move. Surveillance courtesy of Sal Nap. He had also been right when he'd ordered Pietro M. to jimmy her outside lock and gain a covert entrance, and even righter still when he had deftly pierced her ear, while drooling Benny savagely held her down and squeezed her mouth shut with his bent forearm.

The "piercing" had been an opening gambit. The fine-honed carver was still in view on the far arm of the love seat adjacent to Hugo. It was a dried blood reminder that she had two ears to hold the matching set of Vitage earrings he had given her a glimpse of.

"Your sister's eyes are green," Hugo said. "Johnny's brown. Dannie's are blue."

"The word is that Schuster died *without any*," Eleanor glared, coy, her blood flow slowing to a trickle now.

Hugo stared at her. "Ever hear of the Place Pigalle in Miami Beach?"

That kindled the barest of detectable lights in Eleanor's eyes. She haughtily turned away from him, wincing from the movement.

"I don't *hear* too well as of these last few minutes." She double-checked the compress that the *cane* Benny had supplied her with and pressed it back against her lobe.

Hugo's patience barometer was registering an even keel. "Your nephew was a bouncer there. Got chummy with the joint's owner. Not to mention the bartender, an old-time doorman. And a stacked redhead hustler."

Eleanor didn't stir, her face in the direction of the darkened kitchen where haywire-head Benny was voraciously wolfing down cold chicken from her refrigerator. The carnivorous geek was on guard by her apartment entrance, and she knew there was at least one other outside her door. Even with the distractions, she paid strict attention to Dannie and *Miami Beach*.

"An astigmatism," Hugo pursued. "That's what he told them. The eye doctor said he was born with it. Heredity. That's why he wears the tinted specs."

"You should have been a policeman," Eleanor observed sarcastically. "Maybe you could even solve the Sutton-Schuster case by giving yourself up."

"A policeman?" Hugo was also observant. "Like the uniformed one framed on your wall here?"

Eleanor turned trance-like to Hugo.

"It was Johnny that night in the hospital," her voice a far-off echo. "He made a *plotz* of the place. He punched people in the room. Defiled my sister in death." Her words were coming from a distance—a bridge to the past—her eyes, face that of a magnificent, enchanted spellbinder.

"Now he's killed an everyday, innocent person. Fooled half the world by evading justice, and brought horrid visions to the soul of his own son, Daniel." She looked Hugo dead in the face. "For God's sake can't you see that right now he's using *you*."

"It ain't true. It ain't true," Benny was by the living room's archway.

"She's lyin' through her blowjob fuckin' teeth about John. Tryin' to set you against him, Hugo," Benny foamed, waving a half-eaten chicken leg in his right hand. He was weaving excitedly, not knowing exactly what to do with himself.

"She . . . named the kid. Kathleen said it," Benny made a short cut Sign of the Cross, the greasy chicken leg gripped in his Cross-signing right hand.

"My sister's niece in heaven said that the kid, Dannie, told her so. Daniel's his damn name. Not John. It's Dannie. I'm right, Hugo. Ask Roscoe, too. He'll tell you," Benny's facial, eye expressions were going maniacal. He spied the glinting carver on the sofa's arm and his eyes became eager, glazed, magnetized on it. The long, curvy knife would speak for him.

Hugo sat tight. His face a mask, void of any emotion.

Eleanor blanched, froze.

Benny dashed maladroitly for the keen blade. "No use fuckin' with her other ear," he spat, food particles slobbering from his mouth.

"The fuckin' *La bonz*. Rip her the fuck open. Get the lies out!" He had the knife's handle crushed beside the chewed chicken leg in his right hand.

"Her tongue. Her tongue. Right, Hugo? Go for the mother fuckin' squealers . . ." Benny spun, lunging epileptic, tearing with his free hand at the quilts. Suddenly he stopped, gaping, gazing at her creamy shoulders. Sensing her advantage, Eleanor fixed her starlit, exotic blue eyes on him.

"Kathleen," she seized the moment of *two lives*, her voice rhapsodic. "Kathleen. God lets her enter Heaven above only when HE sends somebody to replace . . ." She had him mystified and knew it as she braided a melody of words, her right hand gliding slowly through the shreds of the quilt and her scanty gown. Benny's eyes followed fascinated, as her hand came to rest on the swelling expanse of her belly.

"What's up?" Mush stood ominous in the archway, his tone non-plussed at the sight before him.

A communion of crackpots, Hugo nearly uttered. Eleanor was rambling, singsonging to the blade-holding, dumbfounded Benny.

"A different kind of leverage," Hugo said to Mush. A pregnant state of affairs, he said whistling to himself. "Mush. Which one's coming with the cash? Benny, go back in the kitchen. John'll be proud of you. Take the carver and go to work on some chicken breasts."

Taking Hugo aside, Mush related that it was the twin—the sister—who would arrive in about 25 to 35 minutes. Sal Nap had just two-way radioed Pietro M.; Sal would cab her at a snail's pace because of the rainy weather. While Mush was slow-talking, Benny had been entranced by Eleanor's paradoxical earthy sexual arousal and her sainted words "God . . . children . . . Kathleen . . . Heaven . . ."

Hugo jerked his neck to the left side. Mush got the message, and stepping forward, he led Benny away.

Hugo sat. Just him and Eleanor. She flinched, holding her belly, and laughed. *Their* son had kicked. She glued her luxuriant blue eyes on the rookie policeman's walled picture.

Hugo Duce rested his arms on the top edge of the folding chair.

He didn't have to be a super sleuth to track down Eve and Dannie. Augie had telephoned in, saying the kid had been on Court Street, looking peaked, pale. Johnny had once telephoned Eve mentioning the Lafayette regarding a rendezvous, and Hugo, on a first hunch, had checked the downtown hotels where the two might have been holed up. Sal Nap had noted that Eleanor moved about alone.

Hugo had described Eve as "delectable" to bellhops and desk clerks he knew at several of the spots, including the Lafayette. How could they miss spotting her? Willie Sutton himself had been caught off guard on 39th and Eighth by her drive-you-to-drink measure-ments when he had surreptitiously visited John the night Al-bert walloped him.

Looking at Eleanor, Hugo thought it was uncanny. Sisters above their skins. Eleanor was willful, but wasn't fighting ferociously tonight. She was protecting the *baby she was carrying in her womb.*

Hugo thought of the long-ago night when Eve had conceived, Johnny coming to him and Gret to drink the night away. Hugo stood and went to the glassed liquor cabinet. He poured a glass of *vino*, and then sat closer to Eleanor, giving her the burgundy wine.

"When your sister arrives," he said, "I won't be here. I was *never* here."

"You don't even exist," Eleanor inched her back up against the love seat's wood-topped arm. Sipping the red wine, she covered herself up to her shoulders with the salvaged remains of the tufted blankets, the blood-stained towel-compress lying on the rug.

Hugo had the set of earrings in his right hand, shaking them as if they were a pair of dice. "You've been at the helm long enough," he said. "Time to draw life's line. Change is afoot. So far you've admitted nothing. *Now* you will tell the story, Miss Guile. Begin with your sister's shock *before* John came to pick her up." He tossed one earring onto her quilt covers. "We'll keep the other one. For the one *inside* you. Just in case your tale, either way, proves a lie."

Eleanor drank, the wine trickling from the corners of her mouth. She spoke slowly, hauntingly, the anguish in her voice obvious as she spoke to the sacred photo on the wall.

She'd tell it all—in detail.

She had what she wanted now.

For she was dealing with *assassinares* who had beastly taken a young man's decent life from him. And if they killed a helpless man and got away with it, they'd kill a helpless . . . child and care less.

But as she swore to tell her story, she also swore under her breath that the killers of this young, innocent Arnold Schuster would see that they were also at the helm long enough, that the line in *their* lives had been drawn tonight. And she vowed it would be done through the father of her child!

Finally she told Hugo the story.

And Hugo told her to tell it to Eve!

"PAYBACK." THAT'S WHAT SEXY-STEAM-ENGINE ELEAnor Cross was looking in the face of tonight. Augie Tenuto knew it, but had payment of his own in mind.

Before he could leave for the West Coast with Dannie, Angel had a public payback of his own to make.

It had nothing to do with dames and babies: He wanted to give Mr. Albert a manly going-away message.

The great untouchable Albert was gonna pay for that slap to Willie Sutton!

Sharply flapping a cork-colored pair of gloves from his right hand into his left palm, Augie briskly paced downtown Brooklyn's Smith Street, a stone's throw from Albert's South Brooklyn.

Tony-boy was cruising around the Lafayette Hotel in a white Caddy. The nattily attired pimp had tried to bury him on McDonald Avenue.

Amastaso's man. Badged. This section was their backyard, and Tony-boy circled around it like he owned the milkman, mailman, and of course the cop on the ever-lovin' beat. Augie stretched on the fur-lined, whip-stitched gloves.

The bitter gripes were coming faster than he could mouth them to the night's winter wind. How much Godawful power did that madhatter Al-bert want? With the help of his "front" of a brother Tough Tony he had the I.L.A sewed up, beating the attempts at harbor reform. Through muscle-rigged voting, which allowed them to break from the A.F.L., the waterfront had become his racket, not his brother's union. Now he was laying for the *kills.*

Augie plotted as he walked along the deserted street, the windy night wind whipping his eyes. Mr. Al-bert was going to get a goin'-away message!

He fingered a hand-sized compact. Putty. Make-up used to "reconstruct" his broken nose. "Willie, thanks for teachin' me the fine art of disguise," Augie muttered to the wind.

He kneaded the clay, eyeing himself carefully in the compact's mirror, his only light emanating from a shut-tight bail bondsman's office front.

"I oughta be in pictures," he sang, reshaping his nose . . . "I'm really a sight to see . . ."

He improvised on the song's original words, noting to himself how useful this trick would have been in 1940, when he was in his twenties on his own first kill. Jimmy Dee. In South Philly. He also plugged the son, Dom. He had survived that favor, though the shootings had gotten him a second degree murder conviction.

Five years after that, he had escaped from the state pen. But they had captured him a lousy month later, mainly through the identifying eyesore of the broken nose.

Then in '47 he met the Master. The rest was history until that fuckin' Joe Blow Schuster had ratted on Willie from outta nowhere. Augie completed his handmade nose job, cleaned up, paced, and planned.

He had a small tin of plastic explosives in his kit stowed in the stolen Buick, parked nearby on Atlantic Avenue. An old flame of his from Scranton was standing by the car. The chunky, auburn haired, stand-up "skirt" was his sometime traveling companion.

Virginia was her proper name, Gingerbread and Gingersnap her stage names. She was an ex-stripper chum of Baltimore's Blaze Starr and that Pride of the South, Georgia Southern.

A helluva hump, that Ginger. Augie did a lively thirty-second jig on the sidewalk, thinking about her. She had fucked 90 percent of his brains out when John had sent her over to his mole hole in Boro Park. She would come in handy this night, too.

No doubt about it, Albert was gonna *pay* for that slap to the Actor! Augie's mind jigged another minute away.

Thanks for the education, Willie—thanks for everything. He clutched the butt of the .45 caliber automatic inside his waistband. He'd show how grateful he was to sly Sutton. Augie all but danced his way to Gingerbread and the Buick.

"Where to?" Gingersnap asked merrily from the front passenger seat.

"We're gonna decoy a mustachioed creep named Tony-boy this time around," Augie snickered as the car purred to life. "He's a stone sucker for pussy."

Ginger merely shrugged as Augie drove, bumping parked cars along the way as if they were all Anastasia tin soldiers.

Determined to get revenge, Augie laid out for Ginger the part she was to play in the neat job he had planned.

She acquiesced by saying nothing.

Within four minutes Tony-boy was on Augie's tail. Ginger, slouching down in her seat, had on a crumpled fedora.

Let him think it's Dannie, Augie thought as he swung left off the Flatbush Avenue Extension, racing madly, until he screeched to a stop by the Park Terrace Bar & Grill.

Ginger alighted minus her hat, Augie lying on the floor of the car, covered by a blanket.

Tony-boy would soon see it—not him—and then, hopefully, scout the busy bar.

And *wham!* Ginger would snare him with oversized titties, auburn hair and a ream-it-at-will ass. She'd lead him to Pier 22 for a quick, hot lay in the back of the Cadillac.

But Tony-boy was gonna get something up *his* ass. Augie heard a car door slam and felt the presence of someone peering in the darkened, locked Buick. He held the .45 tighter than his breath. Twenty-five minutes, Augie gauged, lying flat on the floor. Fortunately, he was nice and warm under the army blanket. Finally, he heard Ginger's squeals of delight—the signal. She had him inside his Caddy now.

"My pranks would slay a nation . . ." Augie sang, climbing into the front seat. "I'd be a great sensation . . ."

Take that pee, baby, Augie urged silently as he cruised to the South Brooklyn pier. Stopping, he was ready behind the Buick's wheel, the expressway overhead and the choppy Narrows's black water before him.

Gingersnap exited the white Caddy giggling, she was making it to a rusty girder, her hands down by her crotch, wiggling as if holding fast the urine.

"My star of stars . . ." Augie whispered the tune. Then she disappeared in the dark.

After a few minutes, Tony-boy would be out looking for her.

Come to Papa, come to Papa, Augie beckoned. This was certainly better than shooting a Doberman by a Queens bank. He saw snazzy Tony-boy getting out of the Cadillac. The cat has caught the *rat*! Augie eased out of the Buick.

It took three whacks against Tony-boy's *duro testa* with the .45's handle to cold-conk him. Augie would have smashed it in if he had to.

Augie let Tony-boy lie on the wasteland of a pier as he switched the Buick's stolen Pennsylvania plates with the Caddy's. Mr. Al-bert executioner would get the "calling card," as a down payment.

He'd leave the Caddy on the Atlantic Avenue dock right by Pier 22, where the original Schuster guns came from. But there'd be nary a trace of Soldier Tony-boy.

Now for the dock explosion. Looking around quickly, Augie dragged Tony-boy to the edge of the pier, draping him half over it.

Tony-boy was still out cold, his head battered, but alive. Angel Tenuto congratulated himself.

Augie fetched a crate with two one-gallon gas cans, three-quarters filled, from the Buick's trunk and lugged them carefully over to the knocked-out weasel, Tony-boy, wondering all the while if the creep had fucked freckled Ginger or not. Tony-boy's arms dangled down toward the scummy water, and Augie propped his legs over the orange crate. Augie had soaked rags popping up through the crate's slats as wicks.

Now to pull the pimp's pants and shorts down.

Bare ass.

Now the fuse. He shoved the plastic explosive half up his victim's "keester."

Two books of matches and two lit cigarettes.

Handmade, timed detonators. Lucky Strikes and unstruck matches.

"When this fire bomb goes off, it'll topple you, Tony," Augie spoke low, not wanting the Statue of Liberty, his old flame, to hear as she stood holding her torch in the harbor. Tony-boy grunted, faintly.

The explosion will fragment you into the fuckin' Hudson River, Augie beamed. Setting the fuse, Augie felt proud that he had the vault safe-blowing know-how to send Tony-boy to hell while he was half a mile away crossing the ignition wires on a Chevy convertible. The steady, slow burning cigarettes would do their timely work in setting the matchbooks aflame.

Augie steered the Buick through South Brooklyn. Then he heard it!

It was like an avalanche—an exploding, thundering earthquake, which scattered myriad bits of the Anastasia henchman all over Albert's domain!

DANNIE HAD BEGUN PACKING MINUTES AFTER HIS mo— Eve had left the Lafayette Hotel room to taxi it to her loony sister, Eleanor's.

Eve . . . he threw the hand-sewn, kick seam moccasins into the Pullman luggage.

She now had him calling her by her first name.

Well, *Eve*, he stacked the magnificent Sulka ties into the weekender valise, this was going to be the *longest* courtship in history. He stuffed the D.C. initialed, imported linen handkerchiefs on top of the ties, thinking how *close* it had been between them not nineteen hours ago. Dannie's train of thought was almost thrown off the track by an . . . explosion? He stepped to the window, looking out on downtown Brooklyn and beyond that, South Brooklyn. Squinting into the night, he thought he saw some kind of ship's flare. Shifting back into his former thinking, he stepped away from the curtained window.

She wanted to be *courted*. Before falling into a deep sleep, she had been dreamy, ingenuous beside him, taking her own trip back through the furrowed nave of time.

But he had gotten the information he wanted.

Johnny was in Los Angeles.

Now Dannie was on his way to California! He zippered up the rugged leather wardrobe.

Next, Dannie ransacked his room.

For traveling money, Johnny's note given to Eve by Hugo in the hospital, and the automatic.

After three grueling quarters of an hour, he found none of the three.

Where did she hide them? Had she taken them with her? She had threatened suicide if her girlhood phantasms weren't pursued. But that didn't seem too likely after the courtship remark. Damn it!

He should have held on to some of that cash she had given him. Why did she take it back while he was laid up? Maybe she had checked the stuff downstairs in the hotel safe in her kingsized pocketbook? What name had she registered them under? Would they give them to him? He was bombarded with questions, exhausted, sweating.

She had gone out to give his aunt $1,800. Fine. He couldn't go, he was still in need of a rest.

But what would he do now? Hitchhike to the coast? Wait till morning, go out while she was out, hock the expensive clothes she had bought him and bus it to L.A.? Sell the Bulova wrist watch Johnny had given him to wear?

He remembered that pawn shop by Pacific and Fourth not far from here. Antoinette's gift bracelet to him? He tried to think. It was a holiday. The shop would be closed. He had to come up with something before she returned, or face another day of sublimated motherly love.

"Run, Arnie, *run!*" That's how he had awakened this morning. He was infected with a Kathleen-instilled conscience, brought on by the awful memory of murder and the knowledge that one fragile life is all we have!

He all but fell onto the divan. All his other clothes were in Miami, not to mention the precious postcards he had wanted to compare with the recent note, in case L.A. proved to be another blind alley.

Miami. It made him think of lustful Eleanor with her long, tapered, curvaceous legs. The crankcase. She turned it on and off like a light switch. Mostly on. What was she up to now? He was getting dizzy, wondering if God was going to strike him dead for dallying in Eve's schizoid behavior game. That was damnation knocking at his doorway.

He bolted upright at the faint sound of an actual knock. The knock became louder, more urgent against his tinplated hotel room door. Eve? He grasped for hope. No. She'd use the key.

The police? Could they have pieced together the Sutton-Schuster case? He shook, wondering if he would be better off in a damn jail, safe from . . . the third double short knockings came.

"It's John," the muffled voice came from beyond the door.

John? Dannie felt the life go from his cheeks. His hands started to tremble as he inched towards the door.

John? He stood on his shaky legs, reaching the door's thick glass peephole.

The convex magnified face he saw had a broken nose. The hat on the distorted image was a Tyrolean sport, crown down, feather up, the hat tilted down so that the eyes were shrouded.

"Kid, open up. It's St. John," the urgent, hushed voice in the hall lacked the gruff Bronx or Brooklyn emphasis—"*St.* John?" Was he hallucinating? His head began clearing, zeroing in on Frederick *J.* Tenuto—alias "Angel"—alias "*St. John.*" Dannie unlocked the door, but kept the chain lock above the door knob intact.

He stared a moment through the two-inch opening, thinking that his heart would burst, because Johnny and Augie resembled each other so much. His mind raced back to another confusing time. March 8, 1952. Was it Augie, Gretti, Johnny, or Hugo driving the Lincoln Capri? He'd never know for sure.

He let Augie in, then rechained and relocked the door.

Augie immediately took in the pile of suitcases. "It's true," he said, shaking his head up and down. "Hugo felt you'd be hitting the road again. Time the three of us had a reunion. Me, you, and Johnny Squint."

Dannie stood silently. There'd only be one person missing.

The citizen—Arnold Schuster.

"No luggage," Augie instructed. They'd travel light, inconspicuously. Augie began "mending" his nose.

As Dannie watched the astounding clay modeling, he wondered why Hugo had chosen now as the time to set Augie on the road to Johnny's path and conveniently reunite the *three* of them.

"Fuckin' thing half fell off," Augie, standing by the vanity mirror, rambled on. "I always had a stand-out broken nose. Yeah, then The Actor in the Holmesburg jail taught me to set it right by sleight of hand. Remember that escape seven years ago, kid? From Pennsylvania?" Augie kneaded. "Everything's goin' great now. Hear any fireworks tonight?" Augie let out a burst of his madcap laughter. "And everything was goin' great 'till that joker salesman squealed on Wily Willie the Gentleman."

Dannie was dumbfounded at the powder keg of *insanity* before him. He didn't comment on the escape remark, or the warped, zealot interpretation of the careless fall of Willie "The Actor" Sutton.

Augie completed his nose fixing. "World Alarm out for me, uumph!" He seemed like a lynx ready to spring. "Maybe we'll bring Tony-boy to Hollywood with us. He'll be a BIT actor," Augie roared, holding his gut.

Dannie stood as stiff as the Washington Monument until Augie settled down and instructed him to wait diagonally across the street, by the fashionable Gondola restaurant. "If I don't return in twenty, twenty-five minutes, start roaming on down to Pacific and Fourth. I'll pick you up at either spot, or somewhere in between."

"Keep the room lights on," Augie snapped on their way out.

They headed downstairs via the back stairway. At first Augie was tense, explaining that he had to pick up a stray—Ginger. Then he laughed abruptly.

"I sent a fuckin' message
"To Albert on the dock . . ."

He sang the twisted lyrics to the tune of "You Ought to Be in Pictures."

Dannie followed, listening like a zombie.

He waited ten minutes by the rear exit until Augie had clandestinely disappeared into the cold, clouded Brooklyn night, the sky windy rags of cloud, a chilling tomb.

Dannie felt sapped, and in spite of the cold he began sweating as he sought elusive composure. Slowly he headed straight for Pacific Street and Fourth Avenue. He flipped up his leather coat collar, walking partially sideways at intervals as he tried to fight the oncoming wind, which bit at his body and stung his eyes.

It must have been a busy night, Dannie thought, as he saw green-white Plymouth police cars racing here and there, others parked in endless rows. He stopped and stood still, recalling Augie's words, "somewhere in between" the Gondola and Pacific Street and Fourth Avenue. It was then that he realized he was smack outside Bergen Street's Police Headquarters.

The steep concrete steps, the high, iron stem globes of light, and the uniformed patrolmen ascending, descending sporadically two by two made him stop and think. Once again he saw Arnold's face—blood red holes where his eyes had been.

Should he go inside? Tell it? Give the Schuster family their due?

Bergen Street Headquarters. The place Willie the Actor had been "protected" from and then imprisoned in.

It was the official building where Arnold claimed, demanded his title as "The man who spotted Sutton." Dannie inched forward, his mind a primal, raging war-zone.

What could the police do? Lock him up as a material witness? Hail him as a true-blue taxpayer?

Eve and Eleanor. Would they ever be *safe*? He had visions of the two women, mother and aunt, hung up on meat hooks by rulers like the Madhatter, the women's limbs blue from the butcher shop's freezer.

And what of his *father* in Los Angeles, California! He saw him with a shaven head, strapped to the electric chair in Sing Sing.

The ramifications clawed him, ripping his brain.

The sky. Kathleen's sky above would help him. He strained his neck upward. Jigsaw clouds cut the moon. An image. He tried this time to conceive an image, a Being up there that he could talk to.

He tried to remember lessons from Sunday School; his mother taking him to High Mass; a Cross with Christ on it. He envisioned compassionate, blood-tearing, pious eyes. HE would hear him, listen, guide, understand. "God," he gulped, "I didn't mean to ... push Arnold here ... by ... goading him that night in the clothing store. I swear ... I didn't walk him to his last minute ... *knowingly*."

GOD! Dannie implored as the eyetearing wind tore into him. LORD. . .make me brave enough to do what is right in YOUR sight. GOD, Dannie's tears flowed icily down his cheeks, I'll never have that eternal minute before YOU if I don't love YOUR images, all Your children, my life would be WASTED. Dannie was getting confused, feeling desolate, his tears blurring his conception of Above. The pictures in his head were hazy, his words along with them.

"That's why I can hardly wait ... ."

The Jolson lyrics were a near-whispered tune right in his ear. He felt the close, sweet breath. "So open up your golden gate ..." He turned to find its source. "Each morning, at dawning, the birdies sing ..." The song came from a woman in tight beige slacks, she was practically leaning on him.

"You got a lot of crust," she said with gusto, laughing. "Right in front of a Police Station. Holy Shit!"

She had a pretty face, racy brown eyes, and auburn hair.

"St. John awaits," she said, hooking her arm into his. "I'm Ginger. And you're either Tyrone Power or Dannie," she gaily

waved forward a Chevy convertible. "Let's get out of this schemin',
God-cold-forsaken town." The convertible pulled curbside. "'Cause
Cal-if-forn-ia here we come," she sang, high-spirited, coaxing him
forward as she warmly pecked his cheek.

"And SON-kissed Mister don't De-lay!"

1954

"Dad." Dannie tried out the sound of it as he rang the downstairs buzzer of Johnny's Parklabrea Towers home.

That seemed more fitting than "pop" or the too-formal "father."

There was no response, but Dannie managed to gain entrance with the friendly help of two sun-bleached blonde teen-age girls. One, who lived there, keyed open the glass door that led into the lobby. The other, seeing him fumbling in his pockets for an invisible key, held the door open for him.

A too-short elevator ride later and he was standing unsteadily by Johnny's apartment door, nervously pressing the white-dotted, chiming bell. No luck.

He'd sit it out under the California sunshine by the landscaped Towers.

Dad, Roscoe—the two words together seemed strange, as if he had never run home from grammar school calling "Dad, Dad," and showing off his 92 grade average report card.

Mom! That word seemed even stranger, because of a . . . mysterious mother who had waited all those years to tell him who his real father was. He thought of John. *Father*. The hospital coma. How he was born of it.

His hands trembled as he reached for a discarded newspaper on the bench. He tried steadying his hands, trying harder not to dwell on the past that had propelled him here. He browsed through the paper.

The L.A. County jail had a riot, and the bedding had been set aflame.

Paul Small, Dore Schary's brother-in-law belts Bogie at a party. Dannie didn't believe that as he flipped through the pages, an eye out for "Mr. Chapman"—Johnny's assumed name.

Dateline Bonn, Germany. $119 a month for Nazi victims. 500 Deutsche Marks. He continued scanning while fighting off thoughts of his untamed aunt and Augie's statement on the trip here that "the Squint, the Angel and the kid—*the three of them*—had helped erase Arnold Schuster. Dannie's head jerked upward, clearly seeing the first name of that trio.

"Dad," he blurted out, feeling like a Goddamned baby as Johnny Mazziotta halted on the winding asphalt path, squinting hard at him under the dazzling sun.

DAD? JOHNNY SCRATCHED HIS HEAD, HOISTED HIS scotch glass, and drank. He sat at the wet bar in his completely darkened apartment.

Dad! The kid had called him that up until exhaustion had set in and he had to practically put him to bed.

Damn Eleanor and her original lie about who the kid's father was. The kid had missed the truth by minutes, leaving the East Coast before his mother had returned to the Lafayette Hotel.

Son of a bitch! Johnny was on the verge of blowing his top. Son of a fuckin' bitch! He tried to compose himself, not wanting to wake up the kid and end up telling him that his father was a fuckin' rookie cop!

Put it aside, Johnny warned himself. He had a Crew "meet" with Don Vitone and Uncle Frank in Vegas bright and early tomorrow.

Let the mother come. Let her tell it to Dannie.

Let him play it the way he had planned it with Hugo. Eve would never know of Hugo's "visit" to Eleanor, so how could he, Johnny, relate something to the kid that he knew *nothing* of. Johnny sat firm, but two things Hugo had imparted diverted him now.

One. Roscoe had never had sexual intercourse with Eve. Well, the guy was getting it now. From Rosa! Johnny all but whistled "Holy *Dio* behind those clouds" at the pretzel-twist irony of it.

Two. Eleanor was unmistakably pregnant. John wondered just who had finally gotten into her scalding, appetizing pants.

"My eyes!" The cry abruptly broke into Johnny's reverie. He perked up.

"My eyes!" It came from the kid. Johnny quickly slid off the stool and rushed into the bedroom.

Johnny watched intently as Dannie thrashed on the bed, as though he were in the throes of exorcism.

"My eyeballs . . ." Dannie wailed, his teeth biting into the edge of the light blanket, tossing, taking the blanket with him "The dog . . . it's licking . . . eating *my eyes!*"

Johnny knelt on one knee, pinning the kid's arms. Dannie jarred out of his spasm from the touch, the power of Johnny's grip.

Johnny Squint stared into Dannie's eyes. That look. That last minute *death-fear* in them—the exact picture of another young guy's set of eyes. Johnny well recalled the time, nearly two years ago, before he had artfully pulled the trigger on Arnold Schuster.

ANGEL TENUTO WAS FED UP WITH RUNNING. HE looked harder into the mirror in his room at the Beverly Hills Hotel on Sunset Boulevard.

A boyish, but tough face. That's what the striptease artist, Gingersnap, had said. He had dumped her in Chicago, given her three G's and told her to make her way back to Scranton, or lose a few pounds and head for strip city Baltimore. Of course he added the footnote not to *shed* anything if she was ever picked up and questioned. She had gotten the message, knowing full well what happens to show-and-*tells.*

"They never reach home nights," she had winked, gladly taking the bankroll.

Angel plopped on the bed in the outdated room, tired of traveling like a nomad, a man without a country, as Willie used to put it.

He was sick of hiding, looking askew at people who could possibly recognize him, going through life glancing over his shoulder, forever on the move. He thought of what Hugo Duce had implied to him. California promised a chance to stay put.

He'd take it. Mix with the luminaries in Beverly Hills. Grinning on the bed, he thought of playing tennis with sizzling Kathryn Grayson. Why not? After all, he was a luminary also—*wanted*, on five continents.

If only the Actor were here, he shook his head.

Angel clung tenaciously to the hope that Willie had the chance to be free again. An appeal. Willie was getting to be one sharp, hard-writing jailhouse lawyer.

Or that *escape*. Get Willie to fake a dire ailment, and when he'd be transferred down state, they could grab him en route. Angel would mention it to Johnny when he saw him in two hours for the first time in twenty-two months. He wondered if John had heard any news about Tony-boy's strewn remains.

Angel kicked off his ox-blood colored slippers. Wearing slippers was Willie's habit, Angel smiled. Willie always said that you live your one life not from day to day, but from minute to minute, never knowing when your time was up, so walk through it as slickly as you can. It was also important to stuff as much loot in your pockets as you could gather, for even the scythe of death can be bought off from the hands of those who wield it.

Angel treasured the Actor's advice, and he guarded every "kited" letter the Actor's daughter, Jean, had gotten to him.

Jean. She was suing to get Willie's '51 Chevrolet that the Bulls had impounded. Plus the ten grand, Angel laughed. The Indemnity Insurance Company wanted it and would probably get it right out of Willie's pockets.

It's all a grand sham. Angel laughed hardily. The two longshore-men who said Johnny bought the thirteen pistols from them had been *confined* all this time. Holed up and guarded by the cops and Feds, constantly switched from downtown Brooklyn hotel to hotel.

Joe Auteri and Noto. They were two links to John. They would croak before an arrest, hearing, or trial even took place and Johnny Squint would easily return to his little kingdom-corner of the world, Borough Park—scot free! If a section of a borough could satisfy him now.

But with all of Angel's bravado, the thought of that one pistol gnawed at him. Found on Ninth Avenue.

It was *Impossible*, Angel knew. As he had driven the '52 Lincoln Capri away from the scene *Johnny did not flip it from the hot car.* There was no way he could have since John had sat in the front passenger seat and the empty lot was way over on the driver's side.

So who came up with the *alleged pistola*? Who put it there nearly *two months later?*

Could John have ditched it there later on? Angel tried sorting it out. Couldn't be. Did the kid, Dannie, have anything to do with it? There was no sense to that.

The *polizia* might have planted a phony to appease the outraged public.

Gretti, that pus-infected cocksucker could easily have planted one from the same pier to keep Johnny on the everlasting lam, to keep him from striking back.

Angel alighted from the bed and slipped into his luxurious Brooks Brothers cashmere sweater. He'd see John in less than an hour and they'd figure it out. And he'd also see about enhancing his chances of staying in Beverly Hills—a gunshot away from Hollywood.

There was plenty of safety among the stars who lived in tinsel worlds of their own. They avoided any negative publicity which might blow their sacred careers.

Augie glowed as he ambled through the room. Him, a labeled psychopath, an "unstable personality" out in the open with worldwide known Personalities.

The glee on his face died suddenly as the psychopath tag got to him! "The cuntlappin' press oughta be outlawed," he raged.

"The penitentiary shrinks should be lined up and shot. 'Psychopath,' " he mimicked, Willie's definition clear in his ears: "Citizens who beat their kids when broke." Or, "Someone who sees a 'lovely' on the street and instantly she's sucking them—in *their* daydream."

Angel's tide of rage was assuaged by the memory of the Actor's offhanded, jailhouse philosophy. His mind flitted to 1953, his two-month stint in Marseilles, his overseas roaming days hopefully at an end.

He locked his Lon Chaney walking-arsenal kit tightly. Time to see John, though one reservation kept tugging at him: the tall kid, Dannie. It wasn't the sex bit with Gingerbread, or rather the lack of it, but the blood curdling screams of *Arnold*.

Angel sat down on the sagging chair by the bed. Ginger was game for most anybody. She'd swallow a load as if it were her last meal and was even gang-bang ready three-quarters of the time. That didn't bother Angel at all. After all, what else are *cunts* for? But when she made the play for the handsome kid, the youngster just shrunk with shame. There was no way she could get him stiff.

It was disturbing, but hardly worth repeating.

But those wolf-like death-dreams were. The kid had gone to the same school as Schuster. John J. Pershing Junior High on Ninth Avenue. Sure, it had been years later, but still, it was at the same time as the kid brother.

Maybe Dannie felt guilty, maybe he even felt that the stool pigeon's life was precious.

That was worth repeating to John—Angel's loyalty dictated!

DANNIE READ THE HANDS OF THE END TABLE'S ALARM clock. 6:00 a.m. He'd been reading them every fifteen minutes since John . . . his father had left the bedroom.

What had he yelled in his sleep that had caused his father to awaken him, hold him steady?

It had to be the same haunting Schuster memory. He sat up on the edge of the bed and intuitively felt that if he wasn't Johnny's son, he probably would never have awakened at all. Or Eve's son!

His thoughts were interrupted by the sound of *two* voices filtering from the dinette. John and St. John were going to switch places. They were only six months apart in age, the same height and, now that Johnny had trimmed his rock-body, the same weight.

Any lingering illusions that Dannie might have had about the glory of being Johnny Mazziotta's son were crumbling to ash. Especially during the hours he and Johnny . . . his dad . . . had met face to face for the first time in two years.

Johnny had started in right away on Rocco Bruzzese, and Dannie was struck by the fact that he was more bent on wreaking revenge than mourning dearest Kathleen.

Somehow, he had changed. Or Dannie had. He was a strutting, selfish man, who resembled the killer, Angel Tenuto, more than the God that Dannie had once thought him to be.

Almost immediately, Dannie had painfully realized that Johnny's "exuberant" emotions on seeing him again were feigned. He was maintaining appearances, exploiting the past. Dannie didn't even know why Johnny wanted him here.

Then, he had begun bragging about his awesome power in the West—about the wire service empire. Dannie hardly had time to get a word in edgewise, until he had finally managed to broach the topic of *his birth* when John had asked, "How's your mother, kid?"

Dannie had been uncomfortable, but had looked at Johnny with unblinking eyes.

"She told me, Johnny. She told me what happened. She told me that you're my father."

Johnny hadn't missed a beat, his face had become an inscrutable mask.

"That story, you mean," he had said.

"It's not a story, Johnny." For the first time in his life Dannie was contradicting the God.

"I've got a Group meet with Don Vitone and Uncle Frank in Vegas," John had abruptly changed the subject. Bigger fish to fry. "When I get back, you, me, and Angel have to clear up the mess of the past once and for all."

Dannie now heard Johnny and Angel's voices filtering from the dinette more distinctly. Angel would change his hair style to a more prominent left side part—no more fluffed up front. He'd give it a wavy, thicker appearance, brilliantine it, and even thicken the eyebrows. Johnny knew a make-up artist at Paramount Studios on Melrose Avenue in Hollywood, and Angel knew plenty tricks of the trade he had learned from the Actor.

As for a voice change—diction, pronunciation, and "all that crap" would be taken care of by a vocal coach who worked out of Twentieth-Century Fox on Pico Boulevard. "The whore claims she knows all about the South Philly syllable dip, and the Brooklyn vowel slur," Johnny informed his partner.

The two men's voices faded to near silence. Dannie stood up in the bedroom, knowing that they were secretly discussing *him*. He began trembling as he slipped into his slacks.

He walked into the living room barefoot and barechested, and crossed into the dinette.

Now, it was the three of them, truly together again.

Angel, eager to settle out West, was already practicing his New York accent.

The three chatted about Borough Park and the old crew. Wounded Little Mike, the bull-neck bastard, Gretti, whose time was just around the corner, and Al Rispone. "The kid did a nice piece of work on him on the snowy Belt Parkway," Johnny relayed to Angel as Dannie had relayed it to him. And of course, Tony-boy—so much for scattered puppet shit.

There was no mention of Dannie's raw neck scar, or his quarter-inch piece of ear lobe that was gone forever.

As for Al-bert, death personified, Don Vitone was surely stalking him.

Then, naturally, the conversation turned to Willie Sutton, the grand Irishman, for whom a possible escape "that would set the country on its ear" was in the works.

Dannie rose. Entered the bathroom to brush up, shave and shower. The one great difference between Johnny and Angel, he observed, was the red ruby *ring* Dannie had given Johnny Squint as a peace offering in Brooklyn. Johnny must have had it sized, for it fit snugly now on his *father's* left pinky. Johnny wearing it to this day was proof. Proof of the blood-tie!

Refreshed, but still a little weakened from the cross-country trip so soon after his flu, he sat at the round, glass top table. Augie had made him steak and eggs for breakfast.

Dannie dug gratefully into the porterhouse, as the conversation touched upon Hugo Duce. He was running the show now in Borough Park and had been the one to get rid of the Lincoln and the red Olds. He'd been left there on purpose, to do just those things in case something had gone amiss.

The talk then flowed directly into the topic of the Schuster killing. Dannie chewed slowly on the white bread and the eggs, studying the situation carefully. There had been a lot of confusion afterward, and then the enigma of the "discovered" murder weapon. The gun.

Johnny had ditched it when he had bounded over the cuts wall. At that point, he had quickly decided not to follow Angel toward Greenwood Cemetery and had called for a safety separation. Gretti and company had been there waiting for Al-bert's orders on the link-kill. He was at first going to make it to the train station entrance, but had decided not to—the pay booth jerk might someday be summoned to a line-up. So, he had slid down the hilly cuts to the freight rails and had followed them conveniently to the 38th street clearing.

"Dannie," Johnny Squint said at the table. "You know that old beachcomber watchman at the Cuts? The one with the tire-tread face?"

"Yes, Dad," Dannie instinctively shot a shy look at Augie when he had answered. Augie hadn't blinked at the epithet, Dad.

Johnny wanted a storehouse of information about the old guy. Apparently, the case that the cops now had wasn't a case at all. There was no real substantiation for the actual kill, according to Brodsky and Aidelbaum, their top notch Brooklyn shysters, and Johnny wanted to see if it was possible that the old city watchman was the authorities unreleased ace in the hole.

"Pops is . . . wizened . . . friendly enough," Dannie related. "He lives in a shack in the freight yards by the open subway station and collects trash, garbage, discarded bicycles, stuff like that."

It was decided—by Johnny—that Dannie would, after he regained his strength, take a trip back to Brooklyn and interview this Pops. But it had to be when things were right. Timing was the key. "The two longshoremen may well have to be gotten to first. *And Gretti,*" Johnny hissed.

Dannie sat uneasily between the two men, not daring to show *his fear.*

John would be leaving for Las Vegas in half an hour.

In the meantime, he outlined the job for Angel. And the job for Dannie. Dannie was going to be a lot more than the spotter he had once been for Johnny. He would help run the Western telephone gambling operation with Midwestern tie-ins.

Angel would oversee, as Mr. Chapman's stand-in, thus confusing the hell out of anybody seeking the reward money. Dan would only leave when he got the word, whenever that may be.

The mere mention of the reward got Angel ranting again. "We should've finished Little Mike and pals at Pete's Store that night, when Mike mouthed off about the kid's mother."

Dannie didn't even flinch at the mention of his mother. Angel and John just went on rapping, this time about how the bartender in Bushwick, Brooklyn, through the persuasive powers of Hugo and omnivorous Benny Napanack, was made to alter his story about Angel not being far from Borough Park during the weekend of the killing.

Angel, it seemed, strongly regretted that *he* hadn't personally snuffed out "that Coast Guard punk citizen Schuster." Though he was glad that his idea about the eyes and the balls had been followed to a "T."

Dannie felt his breakfast about to come up, he was drowning inside the counterfeit walls of his crumbling identity. Kathleen, his human life preserver, was gone now, and Dannie was left floating adrift. Johnny cut the reunion rap session short.

"When will I see you?" Dannie cried out, now sitting on the living room sofa beside his father.

Johnny stood up and ruffled Dannie's rich black hair.

"Kid," he said, "I had an appointment on a Sunday in March with you and your mother. I was never able to keep it. Al-bert's stooges got in the way. I never expected all the publicity that would follow, either. Well, I'll use that to my advantage. Propaganda. All the CLAN's will know who I am when I, in time, 'surrender' to the law *and beat this rap!*" Johnny stood firm. "I never even made it to my place in Bath Beach, Brooklyn. But when and how soon I see you again depends solely on your mother. *Comprende Lei?*"

"*Io pensaro così,*" Dannie said.

"*Eccelente,*" John winked his right eye. "And I'll send you that message about the watchman trip." Johnny paused by the door, one light valise in hand, wondering if there was anything left to be said. "There's no need to clean up the mess in the dinette. The teenage blonde who lives in the building will do it. Name's Dawn." Halfway out the door, he turned again and added, "The revolver I left is a .38 Smith and Wesson Chief's Special. Four-digit serial number. *Buona fortuna!*" Then he and Angel were gone.

Dannie eased onto a stool at the apartment's padded bar and contemplated drinking, but knew the alcohol would interfere with his fight for *clarity*.

He thought of his mother. Was she on her way out west? He wondered what the real deep-rooted reason was why the two sisters had at first parted. He saw flashes of that March '52 *clarity*.

That night, his father had dashed to 38th Street, secreting himself, contacting Hugo and consulting with the hierarchy of his sworn-in-blood-honor Group.

The decision had come down to lie low—wait and see what Albert's move would be.

Then there was the never-before-heard-of public notoriety. The stink over Schuster!

The revolver had implicated John. In reality in April '52. About the same time that Augie was "dropped" from the suspect rolls. In *May* John was publicly "announced." They were given a chance to disappear, a head start to go on the "lam." The tremendous pay-offs to key law enforcement figures had kept him safe through the hideouts in Miami, Detroit, Spain, a stint on the Italian Riviera, and a sail to Bermuda, where he dipped his hands in the Bahamas' gambling profits. Now he ran a nation-wide wire service from Los Angeles.

With a jolt, the complete clarity of the night of March 8, 1952, jumped into Dannie's mind.

Augie driving the Capri . . . Johnny in the passenger seat . . . Dannie and Arnold Schuster on the corner of 45th and Ninth.

Augie pulled to 44th and Ninth, Johnny alighting from the Capri, his Smith and Wesson ready to do its dirty work.

Dannie had missed Johnny exiting the car, but the deadly premonition had made him tell Arnold to run, run home!

Arnold had been hesitant, or afraid, as Johnny slithered through the back alleyways from 44th to 45th, and hid in the shadows by Arnold's home. Finally Arnold had gone to his house—941 45th, but only got as far as 913 45th!

The final, haunting vision was crystal clear: Johnny firing four well-placed bullets. Arnold crumpling like a rag doll.

Dannie's breakfast erupted from his stomach, mixing with his tears as he knelt over the toilet bowl. Kathleen's biblical words— "the sins of the fathers"—wrenched his nerves.

Emotionally exhausted, Dannie collapsed for sixteen hours. He awoke at two a.m. the following morning.

Once again, his sleep was plagued with his and Arnold's nightmare—along with every murdered person's since the devil-Cain began it all. It was a testament to the strength of his guilt, his damning shame.

He tried to think of the consolations.

At least he could earn a living for himself here while simultaneously steering clear of ever-coaxing Eleanor—that half a twin who had twisted his genitals since age seven.

The elusive manhood he'd been chasing now seemed a lost horizon. If it was hailstoning sex, he wouldn't get hit.

The good. Look for the good, his mind searched in vain.

The hours dragged by while Dannie tossed and turned, and slowly, the room brightened until the sun was streaming through the breaks in the curtains. It took the shrill ringing of the telephone extension by the bed to slice through his gloomy string of thoughts.

At first he hesitated, then spontaneously answered it.

It was a woman's voice. Eve? Eleanor's? His heart raced. Fortunately, it was neither.

Dawn, the teenage neighbor, wanted to know if it was OK to come up and clean.

"I'll do it," Dannie told her tersely.

"But I've already been paid," her voice faltered. Dannie couldn't understand the urgency in her voice. "The extra money I earn cleaning for Mr. Chapman helps me to pay for school," she explained, her disappointment clear.

Dannie gave her the go-ahead and hung up.

It turned out that Dawn was the blonde who had held the downstairs lobby door open for him two mornings ago. She was seventeen. As she stacked the dishwasher and brillo-scrubbed the frying pan, she tried to make conversation with him.

Dawn was entering U.C.L.A., in Westwood, as an undergraduate. Drama was her goal, and she adored the cinema. She asked innocent questions of him in her halter and shorts as she bent, swept.

Great, Dannie felt the pain, she was a prime example of the formal education—and normal youth—he had missed.

"I'm Mr. Chapman's son," he tried to sound casual, wryly thinking that he was surely following in his father's footsteps—well on his way to being a "bookmaker." Johnny had had two dozen arrests for just that—bookmaking.

"I'm eighteen," he went on, though in reality, he wouldn't be eighteen until December. Thinking about it, he decided that he felt closer to forty.

She polished the glass table. "You want to go see *From Here to Eternity*? she asked offhandedly. It was directed by the highly praised Fred Zinnemann, she went on to tell him. A *"casu belli"* sort of film.

Dannie told her he would consult his dictionary, stretched, yawned, and left her to domestic chores, closing the bedroom door behind him.

He lay on the bed wallowing in a mire of sorrowful self-indulgence. He had missed so much schooling, receiving instead a different sort of sordid "education."

He had tried to get girlfriends his age.

He was barred from seeing Antoinette, prayer-book Kathleen had been gunned down, Gloria and . . . what was the point. He rolled over on his stomach, letting the regrets go.

He was *home*, he had a real *father*, and he'd try to make the best of it. He began falling asleep, hoping he wouldn't scare Dawn's shorts off with any of his hellish howls. Drowsily, he wondered if Max Schuster had "turned the other cheek" as Kathleen's poem, "In Imitation," had sermonized—

The launched elongated mass of lead
That hummed with force along its fired flight
Blurred the path so dim by which it sped
Missing me—
As I marked the fleeing figure in my sight
—But the bullet he had earned
Was trigger held and not returned
IN IMITATION

He slept another day away.

The next morning the stand-in Mr. Chapman telephoned him. He was to meet him in an hour on North Beverly Drive off Wilshire

Boulevard in Beverly Hills.

"Take the bus," Angel hung up.

Take a bus? Dannie dressed in his one and only outfit and nearly laughed. He didn't have a nickel to his name, much less bus fare.

He walked Wilshire Boulevard, past the "Miracle Mile," into Beverly Hills.

Angel was surprised the kid was late. Dannie—embarrassed—had to admit he was penniless. "Before the day's up, kid, you'll more than earn your keep," Angel informed him.

"Manna," Angel smiled. "As Willie used to call it."

In the Beverly Drive deli, Dannie was introduced to two men. A bookie, Anton Ben, and a high command *amico* of Vito Genovese by the name of Frank DeSimone—the Frank Dee Johnny had alluded to as a "friend of a friend."

Frank Dee was a temperamental west coast chief of the Costello Group, and made no bones about his sworn loyalty to Don Vitone Genovese, the Underboss.

Frank personally took Fred Astaire's bets and Jimmy Durante's daily long shots. Frank was also an attorney from Downey, and it was through him that Johnny Squint had secured an insulated "cover."

"You know Uncle Frank?" he quizzed Dannie.

"Yes, I met him in Brooklyn."

"Don Vito?"

"I never had the pleasure." Dannie knew the respectful vernacular well. He was impressed by Frank Dee's Janus-like role—a legitimate education and a mob chieftain.

He received his briefing and then made the rounds with Frank Dee's closest man, Anton Ben, dropping in on various cash "drops," betting parlors, and telephone "spots" where out-of-work stunt men and actresses "between engagements" manned the country-wide telephone wagering network.

Their tour seemed endless as they went from Hollywood Boulevard and Vine in Hollywood, Pico Boulevard in L.A., Brand Boulevard in Glendale, stopping off at a country club on Santa Monica Boulevard, a faro game in Brentwood, and floating crap game in Pasadena.

By evening Dannie was drained, his head a collage of names, faces, and places, and he passed on going to the steam baths with Angel when he hooked up again with him at the Brown Derby Restaurant.

Dannie wished Angel luck in running into Robert Wagner, or the round-faced actress, Terry Moore, who was a rumored paramour of the brainy Uncle Frank's one-time associate, Howard Hughes. Dannie wasn't in his apartment ten minutes when the phone rang. It was Dawn. She was ready to tidy up for the day. He wasn't. She sweetly inquired if he were going to the movies with her, "just on a platonic basis."

He was disgusted with himself for not knowing what she was talking about, but managed to counter with the poet Kipling's words that he had been made to study at Fort Hamilton High School:

"Gentlemen rankers off on the spree
"Damned From Here to Eternity
"God have mercy on such as we
"Ba. Ya. Ba."

He paraphrased the last part, not being exactly sure how it went.

Dawn hadn't known where the movie's title had stemmed from, and was impressed.

Well what do you know, Dannie grinned, he scored an academic point with the girl genius.

DURING THE FOLLOWING THREE WEEKS, HE TRIED TO get as much rest as possible, eat as heartily as he could, and exercise faithfully—mostly chins on a bar he set up in an archway between the bedroom and living room.

By February he had erased his pasty-faced look brought about by his virus in New York, and the tedious trip.

He also tried to erase the memory of appealing Ginger's off-target "passes" and his humiliating failure to at least get a hard-on as she had teasingly unzipped herself, hip grinding to the strains of a hummed strip tune, while in the back seat of the car heading toward Chicago.

Don't think about your aborted sex life, he warned himself. It could lead to thoughts of the exuding heat of Eleanor who had put saltpeter in his pecker—an old Borough Park expression.

It was time for Dannie to start adapting to his new arrangement, and Augie told him to dress California-casual. As had been forecasted, Dannie now had an ample pocketful of money, and he bought plenty of short-sleeved pullovers and lightweight slacks.

Dannie's L.A. territory was so spread out that it was decided he would have to learn how to drive. Also, he'd have to learn to be quick with figures: odds, fractions, division, decimal points, percent-ages, and point spread calculations.

Dannie mulled over his two new requirements. The answer he came up with was Dawn. She was educated, smart, and drove her own car.

They went to see *From Here to Eternity*, both spotting "Superman" playing an army sergeant who tells Burt Lancaster that Deborah Kerr is a whore.

By March he proposed she teach him to drive. He'd pay for the full gas tank, "topping it off" as she termed it.

She was more than willing, and he'd slip her a ten spot for each lesson in her stick-shift Pontiac. "Once you master the clutch, the rest'll be downhill," she assured him.

And that's where he nearly took the car on his first attempt behind the wheel—downhill on a dirt road in Malibu, heading all but smack into the roaring Pacific Ocean.

On Saturday nights in April, Dawn tutored Dannie in math, and by mid-May she was teaching him memory devices. If the Win, Place, and Show horses of a certain race were, say, named Bet-It-All, Romancer, and Lindyhop, he could remember them by just memorizing the first letters of their names, or B-R-L. Most surpris-ing to Dannie was that her tutoring was working.

At the end of May, the talk in the string of kosher Delis along Beverly Drive was of Jackie Robinson, Carl Furillo, Gil Hodges, and Duke Snider—the "Bums" murderer's row line-up. Dannie knew he had some fast work to do, and he decided to lay off $60,000 of Mr. Chapman & Company's money to other bookies throughout the country. The Dodgers were too strong a team to handle all the favored Brooklyn betting.

On an early Sunday morn, Dawn took him to church. A Protestant one. She told him she was Presbyterian and they'd sing "Rock of Ages."

He stood beside her, trying to think saintly, Kathleen thoughts. Instead, Angel's curt pointers came to mind: "Come on New York-style when you have to with Anton Ben. Sure-footed and gruff. Talk low and throw blows. Throw a punch at a lesser bookie when called for. Don't give any of these sunshine worshippers too much *con-fee-dence*. If they tell you it's Monday, check your calendar. Be cocky in the way you carry yourself, but don't talk much. As for the major complaint department," Angel had patted his bulky left hip, "I'll attend to it."

Dannie wasn't sure if Angel was embittered or just plain insane.

His errant thoughts forced Dannie to lower his head in the church. He couldn't face the altar. But he trusted Dawn, though it bothered him when she had once asked about his ear and the scar on his neck. "I used to be a teller in a piggy bank, but three little pigs jumped me," he told her. She smiled, letting it go at that.

Dannie escorted Dawn down the church's marble steps. She was all golden hair and long legs, revealed under a sun-catching wonder dress.

In late June, on a rare afternoon of taking time off, he sat out on the apartment's terrace, comfortable on a webbed chair.

Dawn, in-between exams, was in the kitchen making lemonade. Funny, he thought. He was so often abrupt with her, but she still remained sweet.

It was also funny that she had met the second Mr. Chapman (who had moved temporarily to Beverly Hills) and not batted a golden eyelash. The switch must have been working.

His mind moved to his own work. Seven hours a day, every day, on the streets. Spot-checking tallies, huge bets, race track odds, and supervising the men and women who handled the rotating telephone locations.

Then he spent an average of four hours every night tabulating, counting cash, and figuring point spreads.

Every other night he'd meet Augie at one opulent hotel or another, deciding on what bettors got just how much credit, and what tactics to employ on deadbeat payers. They also made sure that the winners were properly paid, and doubly sure that the employees were kept honest in their turn-ins.

Dannie stretched his arms, rubbed his eyes, and looked down at the Tower's grassy lawns. His heart missed a beat when, below, he spotted a wanton walk that could only belong to one of two women that he knew of!

The staccato farewell words of Johnny stabbed him—"when and how soon I see you again depends solely on your mother." Dannie stood up, shading his eyes, and squinted down at Eve . . . his mother.

He rushed to greet her by the downstairs lobby door.

She seemed somehow different than he had ever seen her before. There was a strange light in her eyes. The word that kept coming to mind was carefree.

She looked chic in her Mme. Lily Daché hat with front net mesh gold veiling and a moss green grosgrain ribbon to one side. From the neck down, though, she was sheer wholesome obscenity, smouldering to the naked eyes.

He took her upstairs and introduced her to Dawn, or his "play-mate," as Eve called her.

Dannie only wished that his mother's word had fit the picture.

Dawn sighed, buzzing him that the portcullis between them had appeared. Dawn's words went over Dannie's head, but he had the feeling that jealousy was afoot, like the time with Gloria outside St. Agnes R. C. church.

He couldn't control his blush when he reintroduced "Eve" as his *mother*.

Now it was Dawn's turn to go rosy-cheeked as she re-greeted "Mrs. Chapman," before happily excusing herself, all but dancing from the apartment.

"Dad's in Las Vegas," Dannie said to his mother as she undid her ultra-stylish hat.

"He is?" she said, her green eyes blazing. "Your evil Johnny may be in Las Vegas but your *father* certainly isn't!"

"What . . . what are you talking about?" Dannie stammered, the room beginning to spin.

"I'm talking about a six-footer." Eve's defiance left her, and she seemed ready to collapse as she poured out the truth to Dannie about the night he was conceived—the way Eleanor had finally confessed it to her. "I'm talking about Daniel Huntingdon. His father's name was William. English. His mother, Ruby. Ashkenazi. Eastern European Jewish." Her eyes simmered, but her voice was more like a whimper as she explained what really happened—who her son's real father was.

"I'm talking about a blue-eyed probationary patrolman who, while drinking in celebration of an upcoming marriage to your aunt Eleanor, mistook me for her.

"I'm talking about how, while in the middle of a peaceful sleep, I was attacked—raped into shock! I'm talking about your . . . father." Eve swayed, and she tilted headlong into Dannie's reflexive arms.

Dannie cradled her in his arms as he carried her into the only bedroom. He'd swear she was deranged as he lay her on the bed. His *ragno* of an aunt had made her this way. He touched the sliding zipper of her moss-green zip-up-front sweater, and pulled it half way down, trying to give her airy comfort. He pinched her cheeks, rubbed her wrists.

Slowly, she came to, her green eyes glazed.

He took off her flair sprite shoes.

"Are you . . . all right?" he choked.

She stared up at the ceiling and blinked her eyes.

"It's okay," he said. "Rest. Breathe easy. You'll be just fine." He had two immediate telephone calls to make before he exacerbated her state by churning her mind with a storm of anguish-filled questions.

He stood by the living room telephone, fishing in his wallet for his aunt's number. Butterfingered and nearly blind with frenzy, he couldn't find it. He wasn't even sure he had it to begin with. Losing hope, he spotted his mother's pocketbook on the barstool. Digging through it, he came up with a tiny red address book, and found his aunt's number. The long-distance operator connected them.

"Aunt Eleanor? It's Dannie."

"Yes?"

"Yes my ass," he raged into the mouthpiece. "Is what you told my mother *true*?"

There was a ten-second pause. "Is . . . what true?"

"About my supposed father, you fuckin' nut!"

"Daniel," her voice was velvety, poised now. "It's quite true. And I could do without your vicious tone of voice. And your . . ."

"*You motherfucker*!" he ranted, his words even shocking himself, as he cut her short.

"That's another thing *you* should be doing!" She slammed down the phone, stinging it in his ear.

His hand shook as he held the droning receiver. Her minute was coming, he took a heated oath, her *Dies Irae*, as Kathleen used to put it.

The Flamingo Hotel and Casino, his mind clicked. Vegas— Johnny. He dialed long distance again and asked for Mr. Chapman. They would page him, he hung on.

He shivered, hearing the crack of death if all this madness were true. The Flamingo operator related that Mr. Chapman was not answering the page. Dannie left an emphatic message from his son!

Dannie slumped limp on the swivel barstool. Why had his face-slapping, bastard of an aunt waited all these years to jolt the cells right out of his mother's brain? To stab her through the heart by renewing buried memories—replaying a scene she never knew of. The telephone rang.

"Hello, Jo . . . Mr. Chapman," he checked himself in time.

"Kid?" He heard Johnny's voice. "What's up?"

"My . . . mother's here," he stuttered. "I have to . . . ask . . . you a question."

"Shoot."

"Did you . . . do you know a Daniel Huntingdon?"

"Yeah. From a long time ago. Hunt. Your aunt Eleanor's beau. I'm pretty sure that was his name. An academy cop. Why?"

"Johnny," Oh, shit! Dannie slipped, "Urrr, I thought his first name was that," he tried covering on the phone, before suddenly remembering that an Armand, a private investigator on Little Santa Monica Boulevard, Beverly Hills, used electronic equipment bi-weekly to see if the phones were bugged.

"My question is," Dannie mentally, emotionally *tried* to prepare himself. "Are you my *real* father?"

Johnny was silent for a moment or two. "No, son. Put Mom on the phone."

"She's in . . . like a trance," Dannie seemed to be in one himself.

"When she's fit, tell her to call me. Life's got a way of turning around and kicking us square in the kisser, kid. Chin up," Johnny hung up.

Dannie's tears spilled down his cheeks, to the corners of his lips.

Not only chin up, but *grow up.*

Since that battling night with Roscoe, his mother and aunt on that Borough Park corner he knew he was . . . illegitimate. But he had immediately settled on his secret wish that John was his dad, and it had been confirmed by his mother's revelation in Gregnano's restaurant when he was hiding from the gangsters and the law.

Should he now take Dawn to a synagogue instead of her taking him to Protestant church? He tried to smile at his little joke as he took the pitcher of lemonade she had made to the outside balcony.

Neither the meek breeze under the waning sunshine nor the chilled drink refreshed him. He felt desolate, alone.

Maybe if he had a walkie-talkie tuned in directly to the Skies Above, God would tell him, *"Don't worry, Son. I AM your True Father."*

He still had hope that John and his mother would get together. Or was he *cursed* for daring to enter his diabolical, spiteful aunt? Dusk settled in around him on the lonely terrace.

Poor Roscoe had lived like a zombie. He was promised two for one, but got neither.

Daniel Huntingdon. His alleged real father. *A rapist.* He'd gone after one and violated the other.

Johnny, who had lusted for so long after Eve, was shafted by Eleanor.

He, Daniel . . . Huntingdon had the supreme chance at many a man's fantasy—both of them. The hours slipped by in a maze of confusing contradictions, the minutes adding up to nothing. It was a maze with no exit, and Dannie felt walled in.

Liquor. That might help. Johnny had stocked the bar with everything from Seagrams V.O. Canadian whiskey to the Hungarian Shlivovitz plum brandy. Dannie kept telling himself to move, go get it. Hearing something stirring behind him, he turned and saw his mother by the wet bar, beating him to it. She fixed them both drinks.

She sat at the terrace's table across from him, her cat green eyes seeming even larger than normal. She spoke softly, solemnly, her words like vespers in the unholy night. "You unwittingly witnessed a murder that Rabbi Aaron Wertheim said opened the eyes of the whole country. He was the same Reverend who officiated at the Bar Mitzvah of Arnold's younger brother, Wallace." It was a service Eleanor had urged Dannie to attend.

Dannie listened, sipping his gin.

"At Arnold Schuster's eulogy," she went on plaintively, "the rabbi traced the befallen fate of murderers since the time of Genesis. He said that the young, murdered man lived a full life though the actual span of it was short. Through his death, a turning point may have been reached. Americans were brought to the crossroads of morals, thinking, justice. Your aunt Eleanor herself heard the words by the flag-covered coffin.

"If the truth of your birth had come out when you were eight instead of eighteen," Eve's hand trembled as she drank, "you would never have been subjected to the terror of your dead giveaway dreams. You wouldn't have idolized a street hoodlum, trying to make him a father image—involving yourself with him to the point of becoming the true son of Cain." She raised her gin glass with two hands in an effort to keep it steady by her lips.

"May God and you forgive me for what I just said," she wept freely, the gin glass shaky in her hands.

Dannie waited on his mother, thinking of his bloodhound of an aunt. She had immediately pieced together his being a part of the Schuster killing simply from the timing of his March Saturday-night phone call, his disappearance, and the banner headlines.

He poured the transparent gin, a myriad of perplexing questions flooding him.

Eve seemed composed again. "Mom," he urged, "tell me more of the story. The face-slappings . . . closeness. From Johnny and Daniel Huntingdon to you and Eleanor. Kathleen used to tell me that each minute of our lives is merely a stay of execution. Eve, tell it from that point of view and I know I'll hear the long overdue truth."

"A truth?" Eve fretted, holding the glass close to the generous cleavage of the fantail white shortie nightgown she had hastily pulled from her set of suitcases. "An overdue one," she rose, and caressed her son's abundant black hair.

Now, Dannie truly was the only man, the only person, she could really trust without reservation.

Why shouldn't she act as if she were truly seventeen again. She had been raped of her own youth.

Her poor, poor Dannie, Eve cried. She drew his face tight to her. All those times she had slapped him, it was as if she had been slapping herself for trying to coax him into holding her, giving her warmth and safety amidst the ugly, brutal antagonism of her memories.

She knew she was drawing Dannie close to her bosom, half like a child and half like a woman, but she couldn't help herself. She so badly wanted to be selfishly comforted, though she knew it was Dannie who needed the comforting. She was the one who had led him astray by feeding him the poison that John was his father.

Dannie couldn't help but be moved by her fragrance as she held him, the soft, sweet flesh of her bosom pressed tightly to the side of his face. More than anything in his life, he wanted to hear that somehow, through some miracle, *she was not his mother*. Just . . . a . . . woman . . . *who needed help*!

He moved a hairsbreadth away, as her lips brushed his scarred neck, blemished right ear, the top of his hair. Then she sat again.

"And in the beginning," she said, sighing, tipping the gin glass to her full lips and draining it.

"The beginning of the overdue truth that you want to know. Your truth. Not mine. Lord help me." Her green eyes glistened, and Dannie, struck once again by her beauty, leaned forward. She mixed them both new drinks and sat back in the webbed chair, crossing her long legs. She noticed Dannie's split-second gaze on her bare legs. Was it an alcohol-induced reaction?

When she was fifteen, she had worked part-time at the Pilgrim Launderers, a gigantic, red brick factory.

At sixteen and a half, she began as a stock girl for Worthy Women's Wear, an elegant fashion store. At seventeen, she became their top sales girl. In time, John had sponsored her to fashion design school, paying her tuition, unbeknownst to her.

Eleanor had been in high school, also working part-time, for Western Union. She met Daniel Huntingdon at the library where she was cramming for exams. At the time, he was attending the

Police Academy at Seven Hubert Street. She worshipped him, and he adored her from head-to-toe, as he often avidly stated. Despite their individual heavy schedules, they dated six times a week. Their plans were to wed when he became a full-fledged policeman, which couldn't be too soon for either of them.

Eve met Johnny in the neighborhood—Borough Park. He was frantic, chasing, wooing, corralling her into conversation. He was quite dashing, confident, and yet almost timid before her.

He proposed taking the sisters to a movie, and said it was O.K. to take the "cop Hunt along," though he had the notion that Daniel had eyes for both sisters.

Eve and John dated for five months. He was manly, passionate, but she wouldn't let him so much as touch a forbidden spot until she had a wedding ring on her finger. Then she'd show him the real meaning of Scotch-Italian *passion*.

That night, he said he was ready to ask her a big question. As he probably didn't suspect, she couldn't wait to have him, give herself to him.

"What month, what day?" Dannie found himself asking, breaking into her brisk recollections.

"March. As to the day, it was either the seventh or the eighth. I'm not positive. We can verify . . . the hospital records," Eve tilted her head back, draining the glass.

He'd do that, Dannie promised himself, suddenly willing to bet at that moment that it would be the *eighth*, the date of his conception. . . the same date, years later, of *Arnold's demise*. Dannie sat stark still, transfixed.

Early *that evening* Eve had soaked pleasurably in a hot perfumed tub. Her *baignoire*, she continued.

She had worked rather late that day and felt like taking a catnap. John Mazziotta was a late-night person and nightclubs were fast becoming his nocturnal habitats. Eleanor would be home soon enough to wake her up in time. They had argued earlier that day over nothing important. But it had a debilitating effect.

The next thing Eve recalled was the oppressive weight on her body—on the bed. Like a boulder the size of a building was smothering, suffocating her. *Anentir*. Her heart, lungs pumped madly for breath, pulse rate soaring her to dizziness.

Her mouth and her eyes were being vised by a cruel inhuman pressure. Her legs went into uncontrollable tremors. Her arms felt stone-numb as she lost motor power to thrash them.

Alcohol. The smelly, stinking, nausea-inducing stench of alcohol filled her senses, her mind, before she blacked out. Died, they later, falsely diagnosed.

Dannie had sat taut, absorbed. Somehow, he managed to hold onto the gossamer thread that this naturally captivating creature across from him was not his natural parent. That, like Moses, he had been found on the proverbial doorstep. He had fired more questions at Eve while she paused to refresh her courage—her drink.

"How did Daniel get into the apartment?"

"Eleanor said her boyfriend Daniel had a key made," Eve gripped her thick glass tightly. "She found this out that night."

"Why did he have a key made?" Dannie asked, thinking that maybe Johnny had just lied to please Eve. He fished for some kind of mistake, discrepancy in the narrative.

"He did it in the hope that my sister would give in." Eve uncrossed, then recrossed her legs, carefully watching as Dannie's eyes followed the deliberate movements. "Eleanor and Daniel had been petting heavily in his car, in our downstairs foyer, and at the picture shows. Daniel had wanted her so madly, and we both know how lovely she is." Eve watched Dannie carefully for any telltale sign of admission. Dannie didn't flinch. "He thought that if he walked in on her in our apartment that he'd have a flying start. The exclusive atmosphere of a cozy nest."

Dannie remembered being on the floor with Eleanor after their fight in that same apartment. It had not been his first irrevocable sin, but had come *close to it*. His cringing abject disgust was mercifully diluted by the liquor, and though he felt that his mother's mind wasn't on her painful storytelling, he pushed for more.

"Did this Daniel Huntingdon drink much?" he asked.

"Not much, as I recall."

"Go on."

Eve eyed Dannie coyly, repulsed yet *jealous* of Eleanor, as she had been since New Year's Day when she first heard the whole tale. But she held her emotions at bay, continuing.

What she had recalled first that night was being engulfed in blackness. Flickers of white sheets in a white-walled room . . . white-clad figures beside her, above her . . . a doctor, nurses . . . trying to revive her . . . the weight of a body so close by. Eleanor later reported that it was Johnny.

At one point during the coma-shock, Eve had seen a spiraling hand. That's the best way she could describe it. It kept coming and going. Then a voice spoke to her as if from a million miles behind the hand, telling her she could not follow. There was a task she had to perform.

She awoke prone on a wheeled cart, on her way to the hospital basement freezer, wrapped entirely in a sheet, except for her head. "They were . . . molesting me," Eve faltered. "The sheet was down to my belly." It was the truth, but she'd embellish it to see Dannie's reaction. She told herself that it was because she was tipsy now. She'd follow his actions, reactions. "They had argued on who was going to be first," she told him.

"They were going to play peek-a-boo with my long hair over my naked bosom." She had Dannie entranced, his eyes diverted to her heaving chest. She couldn't go on. It was too downright disgusting and rotten! *More than despicable*!

But she watched as he shifted his body on the webbed chair. God help her, she prayed. She trusted him alone in a world where she had been stripped naked by so many men's eyes. Where another woman might take it as flattery, she saw it as an *invasion—again*!

Dannie sat silent, fighting the feelings she had brought on with her stories. He imagined the horrific sight of strangers ogling her, thinking that she was indeed dead. God, it was even dangerous to be dead.

More questions darted through his mind. When did she find out she was pregnant? When did she discover she had been raped? Had John denied what he was accused of from the beginning? Hadn't she suspected anything when Eleanor had named him Daniel? Had she eventually told anything to the police? Did she now believe Eleanor one hundred percent? Could it really have been John after all? Maybe a demented, freakish hospital attendant, or someone else committed the act?

"What makes you believe it was actually Daniel?" he said.

"You do."

"Me? What, my traits? Did he have a delicate stomach, too? He certainly wasn't too slow 'having' a girl." Dannie didn't add, "Does he have sex-on-the-brain, like I do?"

"Slow having a girl?" Eve seized on that. "The girl from South Brooklyn? Gloria Bruzzese from Boro Park. What of them?" She did not add *Eleanor*.

"Nothing happened. But never mind," he blushed crimson. "I make you believe that it was Daniel?"

"Something else," she thumbed the V-front of her nightgown as she spoke.

"What else?" he pressed. "Does he look like me? In Brooklyn

you were sure it was Johnny. After all, I do squint a lot. Like Johnny *Squint*. Now your sis turns your head and it's suddenly her old steady boyfriend. Is that what you meant by 'something else'?"

"No," Eve slowly shook her head, wisps of her raven hair breezy by her misty green eyes. Her thumb swiftly hooked the low cut gown. The enticement worked. Dannie's blue eyes riveted to her luxuriant bustline.

"Christ," he gaped. "Stop it! So you have . . . more charm than any star out here. *So cut it out!*"

She had made her point.

"Now tell me 'what else.' " He looked beyond her at the L.A. night, the sky above weighty like a tomb.

"The what else I was referring to now is *your* grandmother." She sat up proper, satisfied.

When Eve had at first heard the gruesome details from Eleanor, she had detested her sister and gone directly to the Lafayette Hotel, only to find that her flighty son had left.

She had stayed there for three days, alone, dazed, crushed. Thinking. It was Daniel, not Johnny as she had been led to believe.

She returned to Eleanor's for more proof. Despite her sister's devastation, arrangements were made a day later to meet the matronly, kindly Ruby Huntingdon.

Mrs. Ruby Huntingdon had shamefully corroborated Eleanor's story, and the decision to protect Daniel's career by covering up the dastardly, drunken mishap.

She produced a ledger, check stubs and actual checks—child support payments—from her and her late husband, a high-ranking librarian, for their grandson. That was the extra money Eleanor had flaunted along with her own salary for schooling, clothes, and emergencies.

"You had a slip of the tongue once," Dannie interjected. "In the taxi cab at Idlewild Airport. You said the money you gave me came from a Ru . . ."

"Yes," Eve admitted. "You needed money after returning from your search in Mexico. Eleanor had told me that it came from Ruby, who she was still in contact with. That's the only part of it I knew."

Dannie believed her.

Ruby had related that her son, Daniel, had confessed the truth to her, purging himself.

"Not only that," Eve went on, "but she also had it in writing. In his sordid state, Daniel had penned it for posterity. I read the confession. How, in the grip of his horrid, blinding passion, he had drunkenly, violently mistaken me for Eleanor in the darkened apartment."

Yet rape was rape, and Ruby Huntingdon had wept bitterly, begging Eve's and "the boy's" belated forgiveness.

After that, recently, Eve sought out a doctor for hypnosis, to help clarify the past. The one fact that Eve did recall was that the length of John's body differed vastly from that of Daniel Huntingdon's. She would never forget being blanketed from above the head to much beyond her toes.

"During the second session of psychotherapy the doctor played detective," Eve related, "untangling Eleanor's story that she had caught this first fellow in the apartment itself, and that the second one had arrived approximately fifteen minutes later. He was the one who had brought Eleanor to the hospital—the same one seen uncovering me in the hospital room. Double rape by the same person seemed outlandish." Eve's eyes glazed over, seeking the gin.

The bottle was empty.

Dannie was nearly as numb as she was. From the drinking, and from the tale he had just been told.

One more question stoked life into him. One that his mother seemed to have inadvertently forgotten under the influence, or maybe one she had purposely avoided during her convincing storytelling.

"Where is Daniel Huntingdon?" he said, leaning forward.

"The same place where Arnold Schuster is." Eve's eyes closed as her head fell back.

Dannie bent over, his right-hand fingers kneading his brow.

God, how do you win? Weak light-headedness began engulfing him. He barely had the fortitude to stand, hazy visions of his bedroo . . . no, back to the couch now—compelled him to sleep.

"What I heard tonight were chapters written by Eleanor Cross," he said. "When I get back to Brooklyn I'll read the entire book."

His mother's tears streamed down her lovely, but heartbroken face. "You certainly will."

"ANGEL TENUTO HAS SEEN BETTER DAYS," SAID VITO "Don Vitone" Genovese, as he adjusted his thick-lensed eyeglasses that slid at intervals down his oily nose.

Johnny "Chappy" Mazziotta hunched forward close to the edge

of his armchair. He absorbed what Don Vito was intimating during this third and final meet at the end of July in the growing town of Las Vegas, Nevada.

Frank "Uncle Frank" Costello, the Prime Minister of Crime, losing his edge, attending Democratic conventions, sat placidly, his right hand fingering an empty water glass. The hands and the glass reminded John of Frank's image on national television during the 1951 Senator Estes Kefauver Committee that had brought his Boss contempt of Congress charges for pleading the Fifth Amendment.

"Angel took Tony-boy out," Vito's voice was as slippery as his sliding eyeglasses. They hardly concealed the liquid poison of his eyeballs. "Neat, noisy job. He also winged Little Mike." Vito's eyes shifted almost imperceptibly. "But regardless of the fact that an outsider does not kill a soldier no matter what separate Crew he belongs to, it sets a bad invitational example."

Johnny listened intently in the Flamingo Hotel's guarded suite, his thoughts roaming for an instant to New York's Waldorf Astoria's Blue Room where Arnold Schuster's future had once been debated.

Vito wanted Angel killed. He was the second primary witness that could put Johnny in Sing Sing's hot seat, his organs cut out, pickled, and stored in Albany, the state capital of New York, as proof that a life was lawfully taken.

It made all too much sense, and forced Johnny Squint to pay heed to the Underboss. But other thoughts gnawed at him. Namely, Angel's diehard loyalty to Willie Sutton, and *to him*, Johnny. The guy was playing his double, after all. Poor slob. He was the youngest of ten kids. His mother died when he was four, and afterward he'd been shunted between foster homes and orphanages. Later, he committed burglaries to survive. That, and killing on behalf of a friend led him to the clink. The big question in Johnny's mind, though, was who would be next? Johnny felt it coming. The other main witness—the one that could establish concrete corroboration—was the kid. If he went, Eve would be gone, too!

Angel's lifestyle too closely imitated the Actor's, Don Vito observed. Willie had dwelled by Brooklyn's Main Police Headquarters. A big, if rare, Sutton slip. Now Angel Tenuto was out celebrating. An open cover among Hollywood celebrities seemed dubious. His trying to put the arm on Larry Parks was impetuous; shacking up with Gloria DeHaven, foolish. He was acting like he wasn't on the FBI's Most Wanted List, never stopping to consider that his capture in California could well lead to the loss of a twenty-million-dollar gambling profit. Poof! The West Coast up in smoke.

"Is one life worth that? Anyone's life?"

Uncle Frank, gravel-voiced, always the shrewd politician, paused for some analysis, diverting the confab to Johnny's own situation.

Johnny had catapulted himself from a corner of the world to international notoriety through his own volition, the enormous impulsion of—*Ambition*. True, Al-bert had instigated the Schuster hit himself. Though there had been a round of meets over it, and many were mad over the fall of the gracious Willie Sutton, John had ultimately made his *own* decision.

Afterwards, however, the entire affair had been blown out of proportion. The T.V., rag newspapers, and detective magazines had become a menace. It was a modern day phenomenon going beyond the scope of the once influential radio. "The media created this case, not four bullets on a Brooklyn sidewalk," Uncle Frank summed up.

"But there's nothing as old as yesterday's headlines," he went on.

A young longshoreman had at first pointed the finger to the alleged pistols that connected John to the murder. This one tie to the Schuster gun was now severed. The young fellow's memory— through our *friend,* Tommy Ryan—had since faded, along with the ink on the police records.

"Two of Al-bert's four men gone through no designs of our Group," Frank analyzed the situation. "The second, Al Rispone, from the hand of the standup boy from Borough Park. Gretti and Little Mike are left. They're possible co-conspirators, laying in wait to cover Al-bert's initial tracks."

Their fate? Uncle Frank's throat seemed to be grinding up rocks. He glanced sideways at Don Vito, the look telling Johnny that the titular Boss, the brains, would leave the matter to the Underboss— Don Vitone—the master of treachery—who would arrange for the quelling of this aspect of the pain in the ass Schuster case.

But Johnny picked up on what *wasn't said*. Albert Anastasia had a strangle hold on Frank Costello. Since Lucky Luciano had been deported in 1946, leaving the Group's reins in Frank's hands, Albert knew that Frank was not tough enough to keep control. So with the power of his own solitary Crew behind him, Albert backed Uncle Frank. That would be two sets of people that Albert could manage on his way to becoming the Boss of Bosses. Uncle Frank did not want to buck Albert, so Vito Genovese would see to Albert's men. The knob of the door to a Group takeover was in Don Vito's grasp. Johnny knew that Vito would *open that door*, sooner or later.

Uncle Frank attempted to carefully gauge Johnny's plight. What it would eventually boil down to was the other two pier workers. "They are now not only being shuttled to and from Downtown Brooklyn hotels by a special police task force, but are also well into the furlough stage, providing easy access for Dame Fortune to visit them in the form of sudden riches." Presto. Links no more. Hence, the adage: it is not only dangerous to be poor, it's deadly.

This left only two aspects not discussed. First, the maze of the actual revolver. And second, a *boy* who stood on the corner that night.

"*Questo ragazzo, Italiano?*"

"*Sì*," Johnny answered without thinking, split second pictures of Eve and Huntingdon, not Roscoe *Valencia* making him check himself.

"This *giudeo* matter will be concluded in this fashion," Don Vitone summed up, speaking to Johnny but shooting a near imperceptible look at the Boss—Uncle Frank—whose wife, Bobbi, was herself *giudea*—Jewish.

Vito did not stop to express the formal "nothing personal," but forged ahead, his words as if lubricated pistons, speaking curtly of the various possibilities as to the actual revolver, and Angel's set up by the innocent boy, the slow leaks in the airtight case that could lead to a guilty verdict for all "our Brothers!" Standing resignedly, Vito "solved" his predicament by dumping the whole loose ended mess in Johnny's lap, for clearing up!

Johnny embraced his two superiors knowing it was unwise for all of them to linger in this garden of money. Don Vitone had held him extra hard by the back of his neck, whispering again his gratitude from that same ever-waiting chair, for the old Borough Park "shadow" kill that had saved Vito himself. Then, the two kingpins shuffled out, leaving John alone in the expensive but "comp" suite.

Physically alone, yes. But his mind was immediately invaded by a barrage of thoughts, foremost among them Eve.

She hadn't telephoned him yet. He pictured her in the Towers in L.A., a tight-skirted nymph, and wondered how she stood not being banged daily as she was born to be—not having anyone to hold her, rush to only her.

The kid. The kid had to set up Angel, John mused, the flashscene of him screwing the voluptuous Eve a permanent after thought.

Schuster, John thought angrily. A *matza christo* coming out of nowhere who he had sent to hell on the four-slug express. Johnny knew that deep down no one really cared about this bastard dying, and he took heart.

But it was time to concentrate. Within the hour, he had a sit with the wizard of finance—Meyer Lansky—the best Jew that Christ was ever kin to. He tried readying himself mentally for the talk with Meyer about *inter*national gambling and, more importantly, Willie Sutton's first, original proposal: the upgrading of John Mazziotta. Sutton had given Lansky plenty of aid, American *money*-muscle, to further the *Hagannah* and the Zionist movement. In turn Mr. Lansky would open skimming, gambling, and business doors that would place Johnny Mazziotta in a position of being the Group's Underboss—with Don Vito as King—when Uncle Frank was asked nicely, but firmly, to step down so Mr. Badass Albert could be wiped off the face of the earth!

Not bad, Johnny smiled, trying to formulate a sure plan in his head. To grab Gretti . . . silence the cruddy cough that tore William Alligretti's phlegm chest apart.

More than anything, he sought a sure plan . . . to insure himself a woman straight from Eden, and to make the life of the poor kid secure, thereby gaining his re-entry into the open underworld. Johnny adjusted the flapped pockets of his center-vent suit, grinning. Ironically, it was through Schuster that he had gained his powerful foothold on life's real action. Or rather, through Schuster's murder.

AT THE TAIL END OF JULY, EVE DECIDED TO TELE-phone Johnny. She was going to sail into him about his using Dan in the horrendous 1947 escape. But she decided against it. He'd only deny it.

"Are you the fellow that still owes me money for a Movie Show when the cashier couldn't change your fifty dollar bill?" she asked coyly.

John laughed, exhilarated, remembering the incident well. Eve wanted to know if he had somehow heard the cruel story of her conception. She didn't outwardly mention it, though, and neither did he. They went on chatting pleasantly for twenty minutes. Nevertheless, she knew him to be a true *rogue, using a boy in an iniquitous murder plot.*

However, for a few moments of their long distance chat Eve actually felt like a needy seventeen-year-old, like the girl she was in the days she and Johnny had courted—perhaps even more so since

Eleanor had told her the true story.

He asked about her nightmares, and she stated that she would have to face up to her chronic dreams in order to conquer them. "If a trip with me to Miami would help, be my guest," he offered.

"For a weekend rendezvous?" She was girlish.

"For marriage." He was forceful.

"I'd be dead weight," she teased.

"You wouldn't know how to be." Johnny felt his motor running like old times.

"We'll see," she had hung up, feeling as though she had acted like a smart ass instead of the sweet ass he craved. So what! She'd see him rot on the vine first for polluting his own life and involving her innocent boy. She cringed. For now, though, she would hold him at bay, for he held Dannie's life in his holster.

At the beginning of August, Eve had formulated a plan concerning her and Dannie.

Tranquility would elude her forever if she didn't pursue it. She could no longer suffer the dreams of the past that were eating her alive.

It was because of John that Dannie had an aural impediment and a neck scar—because she had ever known John to begin with.

It was Johnny's fault that Daniel's nights were tormented by his past fears.

It was up to her to find the cure for Dannie, she thought as she busied around the apartment. She'd make Dannie blood pudding that night.

Her thoughts were erratic, and she tightened her canary yellow mantua, trying to get a better grasp of the situation, while his subconscious mind was tearing him apart on the couch. They would have to conquer their fears together.

She was seventeen, or at least she felt like it. He was seventeen and a half, going on fifty. Why shouldn't they help each other?

She felt cheated of her youth. He, on the other hand, felt old, stifled by his boyhood blood-visions. Two young people needing each other. What could be wrong with that in such a short, unrelenting life?

Eve fidgeted about in the kitchen, doing the lively galliard.

Two cures would be forthcoming, soon enough.

BY THE END OF AUGUST, DANNIE HAD STILL NOT heard from Johnny Squint. He attributed it to his mother's refusal to call Las Vegas.

He was feeling so bad, so wrong recently, reflecting upon his intense quizzing of John as to "that story." Had he put him down too harshly? Maybe that was another reason why Johnny hadn't called.

But at the beginning of September, he did hear from his wacky aunt. Over the telephone, she told him she was pantyless, skirt up, lying bare ass on her stomach on her thick living room carpet with only him in mind. He told her to go fuck herself, slamming the phone *in her ear.*

As for his mother, she was demanding he call her *Eve*, and insisted that it would be . . . therapeutic for . . . both of them. She'd pout, go in her room, and give him the silent treatment. Other times, she'd crumple at the breakfast table if he hadn't abided by her ardent wish, or by accident had slipped into "Mom."

She wanted them to sleep together. Not sexually, of course, but just to comfort each other. Maybe they could both conquer their fears and ward off those lonely, dreaded nightmares by having each other as company.

He thought about that. He wasn't prepared to go through a life of sleepless, scary nights. Yet the consequences of accepting her offer—her sinuous toss-rhythm—might prove more frightening. Clarifying his confused thoughts, he decided with certainty that the disease was less evil than the cure.

During the month of November, mother and son came to an agreement. Eve would call Johnny if Dan would contact Eleanor.

Eve's conversation with Johnny lasted four long distance minutes. She spoke of the vast difference between the climates of Southern California and New York. "We'll wait, think on it," was how she ended the phone call. A mention of losing out on Miami was made. Dannie had the suspicion that she had previously telephoned and spoken to him, but he didn't push the point. As long as they were communicating, it could lead to something. What the heck, it wasn't John who had betrayed his mother.

Dannie spent an hour listening to his aunt rave on and on, from her sex insinuations, to needing money, to the saga of David and Goliath.

The sex, he said, he could do without, though their brief, heated exchange had brought him to an erection. The money was no problem. He'd send her three thousand dollars immediately.

As for David and Goliath, he repeated that he had heard of that

"Biblical bullshit."

But she pressed him in earnest. "Be careful, Dannie. Be David . . . an eye for an eye . . . Your heritage, your birthright . . . They killed one of your own."

He chalked up her latter sermon to being a nut. As devious as ever.

In late November he took a rare day off and went to Santa Monica beach. "No sweat," Angel told him. He'd handle things. "Have a ball, Danny-boy." Dannie was saturated with the talk of gambling by Angel, Frank De Simone, Anton Ben. The Department of Justice had a war going on against the sale of illegal slot machines by crime syndicates across the country. Back in the Bronx, New York, Yonkers Racetrack had their expansion plans upset by the city's re-zoning.

Dannie adjusted his green-tint glasses, taking Dawn by the hand and leading her into the bright sunshine.

Driving the length of Wilshire Boulevard West to the beachfront, Dannie had to smile. He had bought a dead-bolt lock and was that close to placing it on the outside of Eve's bedroom door, as part of his efforts to shelter himself from a "teen-age" mother. Night after night, Eve would insist that he re-enact the night of her torment— act it out so she could face her fear, gain an upper hand over it. She in turn would stir him from any death-cries, making him understand that they were only buried thoughts and that he was safe. In time he'd go to sleep confident that she was there to save him from the lies in his dreams.

He hadn't bought it.

On the thick sand Dawn helped him expand his vocabulary. Three words a day. Use them three times in speech and he'd have them for life. Today—his day off—she'd only give him two. *A capella*, and *brassard.*

After the instruction, she frolicked with him, messing his hair and pouring Pepsi Cola down his bathing suit. He chased her into the Pacific, diving headlong into a mountainous surfing wave, and kissed her three feet beneath the briny.

At eventide he made the mistake of falling asleep on the fluffy beach blanket. Dawn woke him up with a hardy stir. Observing several bathers semicircling by him, Dannie knew immediately that he had had a bad dream. Just exactly what he had cried out loud he didn't know.

He squinted up at Dawn's now matted, stringy blond hair. Time now to go. He'd ask her later what he had screamed.

Parked in front of the LaBrea Towers he coaxed her, and he couldn't help but smile as he saw a blush spread across her fair cheeks. He had been yelling that his . . . balls . . . were bleeding on the ground. He had been writhing, covering his crotch with his two hands. Thinking quickly, she had thrown her beach towel over him, thumbing the elastic of his brief beach suit.

With a look, he urged her on. All she had discovered there was that he was circumcised. No blood, but still a surprise, it being a Hebrew must-custom.

Now it was his turn to do the blushing. She was relating that "If you wanted to calm any future horrible dreams," her voice was reassuring, "a little grass may help."

"Grass?" He turned to her from behind the wheel of the Pontiac. Was this one of her high-falutin' words used for another meaning, or did she mean plain lawn-grass?

"Weed," she smiled at his confusion. "A joint. Reefer. You know, marijuana."

In his old neighborhood, that stuff was considered drugs, and he was no "junkie."

"All you'll get is a good 'high,'" she laughed easily. "A little gabby, maybe hungrier than usual . . . hornier than most," she was blushing from ear to ear now, "and a great night's sleep."

The last part was what tempted him.

Climbing in the back seat, she carefully plucked two frail "cigarettes" from under a piece of patchwork beneath a floor mat.

She lit both "poppy paths to bliss," and passed him one, showing him how to delicately puff, hold the smoke till it went hilariously to the brain, and sit back while it washed away life's agitations.

They stripped down to their bathing suits in the dark car.

He was laughing at her only "surprise" on the beach. She was tearing from laughter as she "swam" around the car seat.

She would prove to him that she was a *true* blonde.

He searched for dark roots on the top of her head while she slid her bikini past her *real-gold* mound.

He called her a "pothead." She retorted that they were both virgins.

She exposed her "teats." He said, "Tits," and she corrected, saying, "Teats are the nipples of the tits."

This was cause enough to break into another fit of laughter. Fading in and out, it seemed that time didn't exist. A blink could have lasted minutes. She disappeared, and reappeared as he held onto the seat, trying not to black out to nowhereland. Again.

She had her hand inside his bathing suit, seeking the feast of the circumcision. "Chapman," he told her, "is a part Maccabean name."

He couldn't "get it up" as she probed, cool-handed his penis. So she didn't turn him on. So what? He was floating. Maybe western girls didn't turn him on? No pluck daring-do like Gloria back east, or eye-depth like compact Antoinette.

She was coming out of it. Her tolerance for pot was high. His was low. He'd sleep, forget to Kingdom come.

She helped him safely to his front door. They kissed goodnight, not bad night. Missing the target, his lips settled haplessly on her pug nose. He reared with pleasant laughter, as she wound her way to another part of the building.

Dannie stood, more like wavered, alone, trying to fix a bead on the lock. Every time he thought the key was about to enter its slot, it missed, weaving away, and at times disappearing altogether. He chuckled, telling the key to behave.

Then, as if by magic, his door opened. Eve stood in front of him.

"*You really oughta be in pictures,*" he sang to her way off key. "Your face would thrill a nation."

She led him inside, closing the door behind them.

"Dawn said I should be a screen extra or an actor," he prattled. "She said my father hangs out with, or at least knows all the big stars. Veronica Lake. Faye Emerson. Dane Clark. She still thinks that Augie is Johnny. Baloney. I don't want my picture up on any screen. 'Strangers' in Borough Park may see me again. I'm babbling like a crooked brook."

He blacked out for several moments, but came to.

He was ravenous, devouring a plate of cold meat loaf.

"What did you mean by 'we'll see?'" he rambled. "On the phone to John this month? It's November isn't it?" he asked as he munched an over-ripe banana. "I used to know a girl called this. Anna," he grinned sheepishly at the soggy banana. "So what did you mean by, 'we'll see?'"

"Nothing," she said, amused, sitting beside him at the kitchen table. "Are you . . . drunk?"

"A woman says 'we'll see' and means nothing. Great. And I'm not drunk," he batted his chest, the kitchen blurring.

Eve was astonished. Apparently, he was totally unaware of being clad only in a bathing suit. She could detect no odor of liquor on his breath, but leaned forward to make doubly sure.

"I never asked John about the postcards." He tried to focus on her. "The ones from Miami. Games. Do you think he had really signed them? Why did you have me circumcised?"

"It was your aunt's idea," Eve sat comfy. "At any rate it's now proving to be better for your health. Did you just notice or did Dawn help you?" She watched for a reaction, but he seemed to be riding obliviously on a magic carpet. "Are you sure you haven't been drinking?"

"No. I'm sure. Now tell me again about the slaps to my face. More, more cried the boys in the back. Why was I hit all the time by you and Sis? To punish me for being born? Did you both think I was Daniel H.? Did you both use me to get even with him?" He rocked sideways, nearly falling from his chair. In an instant, she was up, holding him steady.

"And why . . . ?" He lost view of her for several seconds. "Three in a bed? Who . . . made . . . damn sure I would be feeble when it came to . . . someone else?" His eyelids weighed a ton, and his brain felt as smoggy as L.A. "Was keeping me in short pants part of the . . . plan?"

Eve helped him stand and steered him through the living room. She had picked up on his feeble comment, and she wondered if he had taken some sort of pills to make him so spaced out.

He blinked twice in an effort to clear his vision. The blood was rushing wildly to his head. He broke out into uncontrollable laughter, which stopped abruptly as he banged his right knee against the sofa's arm, then plunged forward, landing heavy, half onto it.

She helped him turn on his side.

"We should help each other to understand our dreams," she breathed close to him, kneeling. "Face our fears together, conquering them. We sleep to renew our days. Why spend it in unspeakable terror?"

He heard her voice coming from inside a distant tunnel. "We're two people that tremble in our sleep."

"I've got the sleep secret," the words were wool in his head. "Give me answers. I'll help you."

She lay beside him.

She did slap him too much years ago, but it was never because of Daniel Huntingdon. She hadn't known about Daniel until recently. The slaps were her way of disciplining him. No, it was her way of trying to gain complete control of him—her shameful way of striking out at him for rejecting her closeness, pulling his hand from her lap while riding subway, trolley cars. For he, through the years, was all that she had.

Dannie felt himself go out of his body. He was apart from it, his flesh existing, nonexisting at intervals.

As for contact, the same applied. She had never consciously known a man . . . Dannie tried being attentive but was lapsing into inner space. Snapping out of it, he looked around, wondering where he was, how he got there, and when would he come back.

Eve. Dan . . . he heard the heartthrob of a voice. ". . .We're both scared. Call it psychoanalysis, but don't let that stop us from reaching out to each other. What sin, what crime would it be to hold on to each other? The breath of your life is perched on a cliff. You refuse to see this. Yet without you I have no life . . ." Dannie caught some of the words, knowing that his own dreams would in time get him killed. But he felt comforted by the utter warmth, the firm supple body beside him.

"I can't look in your eyes," her face came and went with the clouded, automatic blinking of his mind in the lamplit living room. "We need *help*. But your green eyes are *breaking laws*."

She laughed, rolling on her stomach. Her laughter was contagious, and he caught the hilarity.

A re-enactment. Smother her. Sure. A test. Live it all over again. Face it, vanquish it. O.K. He kept giggling, sure.

Breathing heavy into her flock of long hair, he knew he was going to conk out any second. He had her smothered from above her head to beyond her toes, at his mercy, lying on her back as she lay on her belly.

She was flailing her arms and legs, her entire body tumultuous, but he had her pinned down. She kept trying ferociously to break free, but he squirmed, holding her firmly.

After a while, he slowly unlocked his ankles. The room was like a steam bath, and the gaseous aphrodisiac *morte* to even breathe. Eve had gone limp, as he sunk in and out of quiet repose. She slept unblemished.

In the late morning Eve had to practically roll off the sofa. She stood up, two-hand-brushing the crinkles from her brown skirt. Dannie shifted, falling into even deeper sleep.

She happily decided to let him be and prayed that he had had a nightmare-free night as she had, before running off to the bathroom, where she soaked wonderfully in her hot milk bath. In her calm-delirium, the tub took on the form of a barge gliding along the Nile.

She could forgive Eleanor for recharting the course of her life, Eve decided as she stood in front of the cabinet mirror fashioning her hair pony-tail style.

In a way she owed her boy, her son, to Eleanor. She slipped into the champagne Miss Swank. She'd make him breakfast first, then wake him up.

Dannie awoke and took in his surroundings. His mo— Eve was dressed like a Roman Goddess he had fleetingly seen in a Victor Mature epic movie.

His head was full of cotton balls.

"What happened?" he asked her, at first quite surprised that he had on a bathing suit.

She explained, while he swallowed his bacon and eggs like Johnny's brother-in-law Benny Napanack gorging calzones outside of Fiola's in Borough Park. He had slept like the blameless dead after they had experimented with "therapy." She had "lived" her ordeal and had survived it—trusting him. She asked as to exactly what *he* recalled.

"I don't know," he said, searching for a tight, orderly spot in his mind's eye. "Both of us on the couch. Laughing . . ." He was mixed up, visibly shaking. "We were only reliving . . ."

The telephone had an acute ring to it, snapping them to attention. Maybe it was Johnny . . .

He quickly answered in the living room.

It was Dawn, he felt relieved, she was asking him how he had slept, and he suddenly recalled the damning reefer. At the same time Eve's voice filtered in from the kitchen. She was making plans. Both of them had to get away. Begin anew. She could begin in the apparel industry, after all she was a fashionmonger. He would return to school. It was never too late. They'd have a future. Their "treatment" of each other, at intervals, would safeguard their nightly sanity. He, not alone, suffering aloud. Her, the re-enactment, compressed, held down on a couch . . . Dannie quickly cupped the phone's mouthpiece . . . too late, he knew by the abrupt silence at the other end.

"Dawn?" he spoke through the spread fingers of his right hand.

"Either you're harboring a starlet," she said, trying to sound lighthearted, "or you have a Gordian knot to untie. Good luck, Dannie." The phone clicked lightly. "Was that Dawn?" Eve asked innocently. "She certainly has eyes for you. But I know you can't reciprocate. You don't have to, hon."

No excuse this morning, Dannie knew, overflowing with disgust at himself. But stupefied, crimson at "intelligent" Dawn's overreaction.

No "drugs" to blame now. The effects of the lowly marijuana had long worn off. Eve stood before him, looking so young in her girlish hairdo, and smiled broadly.

He stood there. Roscoe and Eve's bedroom had always been forbidden terrain . . . *now* after trying to "re-live" on a sofa with her . . . "You know," she remarked, "you should do whatever it was that brought out your—cooperative—theraputic behavior last night, more often."

He took a shower. As the drops pelted him, he contemplated his next step.

He couldn't call a psychiatrist for her, for he was unsure of the factual extent of her reaching backwards. She wanted to eliminate her consummate fear of the three-day meantime of dying. And at the same time dispel his damaging terror of having his . . . testicles torn from him!

He dressed for the late day's travel, calmly making it down to Dawn's car.

What the hell could he do to get away from this pseudo, half-witted "treatment"?

He couldn't go to the police and thereby make his family targets. This was no time to finish what he had nearly done before leaving Brooklyn. He felt . . . like he was going . . . against the ordered ritual and . . . structure of life, like the Devil had him by the throat. He drove toward Augie at the Beverly-Wilshire Hotel.

Dannie flexed the gold plated Bulova wrist watch that John had given him to clock Arnold. 12:15 p.m. Late. But he'd catch up working all night.

This time he'd get the guts to do what he had to do through Dawn's "joint" smoke. He parked by the stately hotel.

He'd get the marijuana and puff, inhaling it deeply, holding it until his head was as foggy as the San Fernando Valley. Then, he'd finally give Eve and himself what they both need, exorcising their ulcerated memories, and he'd chalk it up to devil "drugs." Sitting behind the Pontiac's wheel, he felt like the childish fool he was.

No, he alighted from the car, formulating an . . . escape. He'd go one better. He'd get Eve to smoke the poppy and set her up with *Johnny.*

He felt dizzy under the sun on Wilshire Boulevard's sidewalk.

Christ. He thought he had the answer. Knew, felt, thought it was somewhere clearly in the back of his head. He'd figure it out, grasp it before he went home. Swaying a little, he made it up to Augie's hotel room.

Augie had his hands full living it up in Dream City. He was laughing about the Hollywood star entertaining him. She was bare-assed, but wore a silver blouse.

Dannie squinted at her. Blonde, perky. He'd seen her on the screen during his movie buff Brooklyn days. In a Frank Sinatra movie—*The Kissing Bandit.* "I was the one who gave Sinatra his first screen kiss," she bragged hotly.

After the actress had given him an intimate kiss, Augie pulled Dannie aside. "Gretti," he said, snapping a Florida newspaper with glee, "bought it. Beaten to fuckin' death. If that ain't the Squint's handiwork then I'm a lowdown mother fucker."

Dannie's chin dropped. He wasn't too happy about another death. Carousing Augie saw that the kid was down in the dumps, and invited Dannie to take a "crack" at the blonde, who was bent over on the phone, serenading her agent, her ring-shaped ass high and available.

"She loves to get fucked there," Augie said. "Come on kid, hit 'er in the shitter. She creams over it." Augie had the exaggerated ego now of an ex-recluse.

Dannie nervously backed out of the hotel room, shrugging haplessly.

He stood by the door not knowing whether to burst out crying or laughing. His "relative" impotence was proving itself again, as his limp prick registered zero on the blood escalating scale upon viewing the famous blonde.

Before he could leave altogether, though, Augie filled him in on the heavy betting. The country's racetracks. Dannie was to make his rounds, calculate the action, gauge whether to edge off over the wire service.

TAKING HIS LEAVE, DANNIE HIT THE SHOPS ALONG Rodeo Drive. He spoke with lower bookies in Santa Monica and the San Fernando Valley. Chats of Israel opening up its first papermill. The "City of the Dead" pyramid, emerged in Egypt.

He decided to hold the bulk of the long shot betting. John had always said that when the sucker does win spending money, he comes back betting the rent money as well—and losing.

Dannie thought of Johnny and the old Borough Park gang.

Gretti. Dead. His chest and head bashed in by brute fists. He had heard Eve mention Miami, Florida when she had spoken to John. Did he go there, beat Gretti to death, and then return to Las Vegas?

Little Mike. Al-bert himself, and Johnny and Augie's score would be settled. Dannie tried to picture the broader battlefield around him with generals in civilian suits, soldiers in wide-brimmed fedoras.

At day's end he took a room at the star-studded Beverly Hills Hotel on Sunset Boulevard and North Beverly Drive, palming the desk clerk an extra thirty dollars, as he registered under the name Mr. D. Chapman.

Lying in bed, he thought of his grandmother Ruby. Then his mind shifted to Dawn and the degrading disgust she must feel over sexless him. Finally, the doom shrouded uncertainty of the rest of his life flooded him.

Turning on his side, he took comfort in the fact that at least his perennial fear of death was waning. Maybe they would eventually kill him. So what? He had already *died* at the feel of Eleanor's animal heat, and the sight of Arnold Schuster's eyeless sockets.

The telephone in his choice room rang and rang!

His mother? Augie? He hesitated before answering.

The call provided the answer to his day's dilemma. Johnny Squint had tracked him down. Important business. He was to fly to Las Vegas first thing in the morning!

It was a Godsent call, and Dannie thanked his lucky stars.

1954/1955

To Dannie, Las Vegas was an ulcer, a dot in the desert. At least that was his impression based on an aerial view.

As soon as he had received the summons to come to Nevada, he had telephoned his mother, telling her to pack for both of them.

Eve didn't want him to leave. She didn't trust the fact that he was going to Las Vegas instead of home to New York.

That hadn't dawned on him, but in any event he was grateful to get away.

"Come to Brooklyn afterwards," she insisted. "Promise you'll see me again there."

He had promised, while putting her on a plane heading back east.

"Have a safe flight," Augie told him. "I'm getting help to run the west coast operation. Mush's comin' in to oversee with me."

Stolid Mush. Dannie remembered him well.

The plane landed on the dot.

The Flamingo Hotel on the Strip—Las Vegas Boulevard—was a true oasis. Air conditioned against the Nevada heat, and seemingly sheltered from reality, the casino was an array of legitimate slot machines, crap, card tables thronged by customers in the wide open, free liquor drinking aisles.

He met Salvatore "Sally Burns" Granello again, in an office behind the cashier's cage. He recognized the Costello "Good Fellow" from the private party at the Five O'Clock Club in Miami Beach.

The barrel chested Sally Burns—a keg of dynamic energy—informed Dannie that Johnny Squint had left for Cuba not more than four hours ago. "Sit tight. Wait for further instructions," he told the kid.

That night a dog sunk his carnivorous teeth into Dannie's balls. Trying to force open the dog's mouth before his balls were torn off and swallowed, Dannie screeched to high heaven until he woke up in the Flamingo room, his top sheet shredded.

The dreaded dream, so vivid that he nearly passed out, made him fearful of going back to sleep.

Maybe Eve had a point. Maybe he did need someone to sleep beside for safe company. The rest of the night, he sat up reading a room service menu.

He read tourist magazines, racing guides, sports pages—for a month.

Where was Johnny now? When was he returning? He didn't ask Sally any of these questions. He'd be told what he had to be told when they wanted to tell him. He knew all that from Borough Park.

Between the December holidays, Dannie dined with Sally. They were joined by five other men. Prominent among them was a thin-faced Carlo Gambino who Dannie had spotted at the Miami party as well as Fiola's. *An Al-bert man.*

Sally told Dannie not to fret . . . yet. True, Carlo was a top Anastasia man ir fighting *trattatos* were afoot. True also that the Costello Group and the Anastasia People were separate, as different and as far apart as Russia and America. But once in a holy while they traded treachery for the benefit of all the *alleato con-*federates.

One of the other five men was named Meyer. A mellow man. Dannie knew from overhearing many a conversation that the short man's last name was Lansky.

The talk throughout dinner ranged from Johnny earning big money for the Group, to giving points in casinos to Mickey Rooney, and Tony Martin. It shifted to Bugsy Siegel—who built this gold-mine of a town.

The language also shifted—from English to Italian. By the end of the seafood feast, Lansky, a thin, soulful man, asked Dannie if it was surprising to hear a Polish Jew speaking Italian.

"Not at all, Mr. Lansky," Dannie said respectfully, thinking also of *himself.* "Not at all, Sir."

During the start of the new year, January 1955, Dannie exercised by the Flamingo pool. At night he fantasized. Anything to get his mind off dogs biting him just below the belt. He could spend a long ten minutes on Eleanor's hips alone. The hellfire, wondrous meeting of her thighs. (But he congratulated himself on his admirable will in not seeking her out for that!)

So he indulged himself in his wistful loin yearnings, his sinister, though harmless, reveries, his imagination taking the place of gambling downstairs in the house-stacked casino.

Little Mike had a gun at his head . . . forcing him to make love to her. Punishment before execution.

Eve was kneeling on the floor. He knelt bringing her down with him, her blanket mostly falling free.

He'd manage it. Die unblemished as far as she was concerned.

Betty Allan, the redheaded Mamie Stover from the old Place Pigalle, had imparted to him many a hooker's cheap tricks.

He'd reverse one, rolling her on the sawdust floor, away from gun totin' Little Mike's full view. He hickeyed her neck, which was slightly better than four bullets in his belly first. She was responding, embracing him in a whirlwind, but he kept kissing her eyes till *they closed.*

A soft rapping on his door made Dannie snap out of the time-killing daydream. It was Sally.

"You know a skirt by the name of Fran Rothstein?" Sally, raised to *commita* Captain of Captains by Uncle Frank, asked Dannie.

Dannie was suspicious, like a noose was hanging ready for him, but answered truthfully. No.

"You were never in a Queens courtroom with her?" Sally didn't so much as bat an eyelash.

Oh, yeah. Now Dannie remembered the elegant girl, Fran, from Staten Island. He had never known her last name.

Sally looked convinced. "They put a garden snake up her twat," he said matter-of-factly.

Dannie gagged while Sally explained why Little Mike and a couple of his crumbs nailed Fran. "She was supposed to know where Willie Sutton hid his loot. Before she died she said that you were out on the Island with her talkin' about the marshlands. They never found the stash."

"Watch ya' back, Danny boy," Sally wished him a goodnight.

Dannie had the angel-face of Fran before him. Oh, Jesus Christ on His Cross.

A young woman. What a crime! How could he have just been dallying in daydreams with Little Mike and Eve in them! He didn't have enough time to figure it out. The following afternoon, Sally laid out instructions for him.

He was to ferry skimmed money to Miami. He'd carry it, be the main runner.

Second, he was to contact Angel Tenuto and make arrangements for Angel to escort him, back him up, to protect the cash.

And third, the Brooklyn watchman. Pop. Attend to it!

Miami? Dannie purposely showed no surprise. Training told him not to.

So he took the instructions in stride. He was still too astonished at Fran's fate (he had warned her!) to show any real disappointment over John's abrupt absence.

He left by evening with his "cover," the money, and his escort— all in a supposedly inconspicuous convoy.

His cover was a stout woman, her "daughter," an infant and a forever growling, black and white Great Dane. A "family" all ensconced in a beat-up station wagon.

The precious money was stuffed in pillow cases beneath bathrobes, brassieres, and panty hose. Dannie didn't know the exact amount, but he knew for sure that he was *responsible* for its safe delivery to Shadows Kravitz, a Lansky sidekick, and Genovese liaison.

Augie followed in a dented pick-up truck. The road destination was St. Louis, Missouri. From there the family would part, he and Augie taking the *gelt* via airplane, switching flights together, but not daring to acknowledge each other.

In Missouri, Augie had a run-in with the Great Dane. The smooth-haired dog was chewing, sniffing at the undergarments, and the healthy pillow cases. Augie took him for a short walk, and then Dannie swore he heard a pistol shot.

The stout woman was upset. "What did you do with that fine dog?" she queried Augie.

"He knew too much," Augie winked, his right eye scar visible, blinking along with the rakish eye.

The big lady didn't find it amusing, but she shut up fast when Augie asked if *she* would like to go for a walk in the St. Louis moonlight.

BACK IN MIAMI BEACH, DANNIE ALMOST FELT AT HOME
on Collins Avenue in Bal Harbor. Augie, Dannie beside him, hand-
delivered the cases of cash to Shadows.

Mr. Kravitz then introduced both of them to a baggy-pants fellow
whose eyes were hidden behind rose-tinted eyeglasses. Dannie
noticed several incised scars on his right cheek. Mr. "Don Vitone"
Genovese.

Dannie shook the extended right hand, feeling he never should
have left sunny California.

Vito "suggested" pleasantly that they lay over in Miami for several weeks.

"No?" he proffered. "It's in fact up to the both of you."

Dannie knew that it *wasn't*, and quickly said that would be fine
with them before Angel had a chance to speak, maybe hotheadedly,
and they never got to leave Miami Beach at all.

The layover lasted two and a half months. Dannie filled his time
with one arm pushups, swimming in the salty Atlantic, and minute-
to-minute worry that he'd never leave at all!

Augie spent his waking days at the Dog Tracks.

At the end of March, Shadows Kravitz gave them a suitcase
jammed with old clothing and cash for delivery to Greenwich
Village. "Laundered money," he jovially wisecracked. "Regards to
Al-bert," he laughed again. "That *lump*."

They caravaned it in two cars on the way up north to New York,
and dear ol' son-of-a-bitchin' Aunt Eleanor!

1955

April

Within four days of leaving Florida and delivering the suitcase to lower Manhattan, Dannie waited for Eleanor in Sunset Park, Borough Park/Bay Ridge, Brooklyn.

Their meeting place was surely apropos. It was the spot where he had tried to help that visiting Russian princess, only to be pulled in by the police, and later released to Eleanor. His subsequent fight with her that night on her apartment floor had begun a series of encounters which eventually consummated in his Miami Beach furnished room.

He spotted her sashaying up the park's broad, winding concrete path. The April noon sun seemed to make her strapped braid starlit shoes twinkle.

"You're even taller than your father," she said, sassy as ever.

"I heard that story from Eve," he said. "Now you can tell me about the slaps."

"It's simple. I hated you for not being mine."

Simple? He stood waiting for some spark to ignite his right hand into an overwhelming, backhanded blow to her damned cheek.

"The seductions?" he nearly cried.

"Seduction? Is that what you call it?"

"What do you call it?" he said. "Tying my testicles in a knot since

I was seven."

"I'll tell you what I call it after I tell you who came to call on me on the New Year '54. Your chums. The midget Hugo Duce. And the freakin' *bulvon* Benny. Do you know why they called? Do you know that I'm as dead as you!" Her eyes went from raging rich-blue to an unclouded azure, as she looked up at him and the almighty sun played color tricks with them.

He listened to her tell of being shadowed when she had moved from McDonald Avenue. The dull clunking of horseshoes being pitched by beer drinking men not forty feet from them brought him back to the harsh reality of *the neighborhood.*

Hugo, Benny Napanack, brutish Mush, and at least one other had been present at Eleanor's "interrogation." A carving knife had backed up explicit threats as they grilled her regarding his conception.

Her words, revelations, made him feel even more like the hapless pawn. Why? Was it as Meyer Lansky had said in Hebrew and translated to English that *payback's a motherfucker!*

Payback. He walked, Eleanor's walk more like a sexercise beside him, relating that it had to be Johnny Squint who had sent the mongrels to her home.

Payback. He wasn't far—just four streets—from where Arnold had lived.

He glanced far down the park's hill to the Harbor and the Statue of Liberty.

Kathleen. He chugged downhill, slowly raising his head to her "pie in the sky." From the background he heard Eleanor warning that if John ever found out that she had exposed the raw invasion of the "visit," all four of them would be food for fish.

"Four?" he stopped.

"Yes, *four.*" Eleanor two-stepped away from him. "The 'seduction,' remember?" She kept inching away. "I have my Daniel back all over again. Late 1953. Miami Beach. Recall?"

"Recall what?"

"Recall what I'm telling you now," she sidestepped onto the hilly grass, loads of kids hula hooping in her path. "Recall that you came here to deliver your own death sentence," Her voice had an eerie ring amongst the joyous cheers of hip-swinging youngsters. "But your *ebrea*-killing friends will never touch my son!" Her last words slammed Dannie's ears near shut under the sunlight.

Son, he remained stranded, stunned. She's mad. He squinted feebly into the sun and for a moment saw her fluttering away like a charcoal ash in the breeze.

He inched along with heavy steps, his mind isolating on her. Perhaps strangling the blue-eyed bitch would bring out the truth. He had to find out if the warped nut had plotted this since the beginning. Maybe he could choke her into revealing exactly what happened to his . . . father. Standing by the park's Fifth Avenue exit, clusters of shoppers and strollers in the broad daylight, she was hugging her light, flaring silver-blue jacket to the neckline he so badly wanted to put his hands on. With a show of being unruffled, he strode downhill toward her.

Payback. He was sick to his hypocritical soul.

"You think that Johnny Mazziotta is in Cuba?" she spoke as if she were expelling venomous blow darts. "You fool! He telephoned your mother a month ago. I monitored that call. It came from right here in New York! It's you that should be in Cuba."

"And it's you who've been changing the fucking subject right along. You got a truth to tell, tell it!" Slowly he began realizing why she hadn't let him into her McDonald Avenue apartment at the end of '53. He stood painfully aware of Fifth Avenue, grim now, crowded, Arnold and his father's store a short walk away. Eleanor practiced her seventeenth-century black arts repeating how and where she had met Daniel Huntingdon. It didn't take long to get to the FACT that after his fervent act on the *wrong sister* she had to protect him from his own—the police. He would have been arrested, disgraced; his career, his life a shambles. She produced Daniel Huntingdon's photograph in a rookie police uniform, and along with it, a silver hexagon.

Dannie stared at the photo in his left hand, the six pointed silver star and chain in his right.

"As for the new Daniel," Eleanor snatched back the picture, "you could have refused to zipper *down* the back of my dress in your furnished room that night," she walked the six steps to the corner of 44th and Fifth. "The Star of David," she turned to him, "will remind you of your other heritage. Along with that desecrated young lady, Fran, that makes two of *your own* killed!" She crossed the avenue, her ass swaying in her blue skirt like a built in swing on a plush porch.

Dannie followed her as she paid her way into the Park Theater on the opposite corner. He hadn't yet summoned the courage to ask to see a snapshot of . . . the . . . baby. Shit! She'd had that damned zipper propped in position for sixteen fucking years.

"The New Daniel." Dannie put on his presription sunglasses inside the movie theater, adjusting to the sudden glare of *High*

Noon playing on the screen.

"The New Daniel." He felt more like an OLD puppet. Eleanor sat on a padded bench against the wall by the busy candy counter in the rear of the theater, the screen's light reflecting on her curvy legs.

"Ruby is minding Little Daniel," Eleanor crossed her legs, baring shapely thigh flesh. "She feels as if her own son is born all over again. We have a built-in babysitter, sweetheart."

Ruby knew. Dannie's right eye angled toward the movie screen. *High Noon* starred Gary Cooper, Grace Kelly and a clock. He'd seen it on Staten Island with the *late* Fran.

"What happened to . . . my . . . father?" he felt bitter about the past and repulsed by her "sweethearting" him.

"We were out driving," she had her eyes focused on the two sheriffs, Cooper and Lon Chaney, Jr., fighting the big clock that ticked away. "We had an accident," she seemed lost. "He was then the same age as the young man Schuster was. How could you be a part of that?" She fell into a devastated lull. "I sat *shiva* for him after the Riverside Memorial Chapel services. In my apartment. Your bloodline." Turning to him, she continued, "Your ear, your neck, isn't it High Noon time for you? Time to get out from under the slime you stay with. Come with us. Ruby has a home in northern Florida. You, I, and Eve. We have much rapture to catch up on. After all, Dannie," her hand rested lazily on the side of her exposed thigh, "I more than enjoyed our night and morning together."

It must have been the same phony pitch Roscoe had gotten. He wanted to be a hundred percent free of Eleanor now—even free of Eve. "Wait another sixteen years for that. With your own son," he cried, turning away, feeling able now finally to separate himself from the two sisters. Eleanor's fierce control of Eve, her possessive, enraging obsession with the baby—the new Daniel born through her—was too much for him, and Dannie broke free, trudging along Fifth Avenue through Bay Ridge into Bush Terminal.

But without Johnny, Eve, or Eleanor, Dannie also felt lost. Without father, without mother, without aunt. But he recognized the experience as a rite of passage for him—a chance to take control of his own life and to clutch at that elusive manhood. Yet, while thinking he was on his way to finding himself, he felt so lost. He wound up wandering the streets into South Brooklyn.

The past was coming back to him.

Joey Gallo. The snotnose had jumped on his case on President Street and Fourth. Brooklyn.

Ed Lynch. He was now just a handful of blocks from where he

had seen Mr. Lynch gliding past him in backless bedroom slippers.

Anna Banana. Bucking Joey, she'd come to his rescue when Antoinette's brother had been on a rampage.

Antoinette. Pacific and Fourth. She lived about two hundred yards down from where he now stood. Would she remember him? Would he recognize her?

Luggage.

Furnished rooms.

Eleanor's past lies and calisthenics for company.

All his clothing, personal effects, and even the other pairs of tinted eyeglasses were left behind in Miami.

Suitcases, more expensive clothes, had been ditched at the Lafayette Hotel.

He was losing his soul and becoming a father at the same time. His location reminded Dannie that he was also an *outcast* in South Brooklyn.

Albert, who can make your bones feel like rubber with one *significare* look. The Toughest Man Alive. Dannie wondered why Shadows Kravitz had mentioned Albert, when the cash was being delivered to the Costello Group in lower westside Manhattan. Dannie would ask Angel about that when he'd see him at the midtown Astor.

Angel and Albert. Killers. By his involvement, Dannie felt that the evil of life had indelibly stained him. As if one single human being *wasn't* everything.

Maybe he'd look for Gloria. She'd always had her battery charged. They could reminisce about Kathleen. Yes, he'd try to see her. But first he'd better pay a visit to the Valley of the Cuts.

"WHAT BRINGS YOU HERE, DANNIE LAD?" POP'S COLD blue eyes had a liquid film over them, as he hunched by his fire that licked hungrily up to the April night sky.

Dannie sat on his haunches across from the scary old watchman who had come up on him suddenly by the freight tracks, scrutinizing, recognizing him, leading him up the rock mounds of the cuts and the smoke-choking fire.

"I threw all my . . . relics down here years ago," Dannie's right hand traversed the breadth of the open subway tracks, station platforms. "You told me to keep steady on that ledge then," Dannie pointed up to the Ninth Avenue bypass that was a hundred or so yards distant.

"Did the junk heap getcha, lad?" Pop's face, his cheeks and forehead were lost in a sea of crag lines. "Did you come to reclaim?" he leered, the fire crackling flickers between him and Dannie.

It got me, Pop, he said to himself. He thought of the T.E.H.M.A. inscribed medal from Kathleen, slipping from his hands and sailing to the freight tracks below. "I came to reclaim," Dannie lied. "Anything else of interest hereabouts," Dannie ventured, trying to smile.

Pop laughed his same old eerie laugh, and Dannie knew then that he was playing cat and mouse with a motorman-capped *fox*.

"From gloves to guts to ten pair of dice," Pop's crazed laughter belied the clarity beneath his cunning blue eyes.

"Can I see the treasure chest," Dannie smiled broadly, hoping the alarm in his own eyes did not give him away. "Say like at an . . . auction?"

Pop rubbed his aged hands inches above the fire. "Have to look over my stock, Dannie lad." His weird mirth pealing from the rock mound was swallowed by the thunder of a west end line train roaring into the station below. "Give me time to take stock, my good lad."

DANNIE DRIFTED ALONG THE NARROW HILL THAT paralleled Greenwood Cemetery, following the narrow dirt path that led down to the openness of 38th Street and Gloria's apartment house. Pop knew something, and Dannie would have to take the matter up with Angel. He drifted in front of Gloria's brick building, the former home of Eleanor Cross, his gut fluids all but fermenting.

Gloria Bruzzese was enthusiastic upon seeing him. She had just shampooed her . . . brunette hair. It wasn't frosted blond anymore, but it would be next week. She worked in Manhattan as a beautician. East 34th.

Her father was out drinking after work.

Within five minutes of Dannie's appearance at her door, her happiness turned to sorrow as Kathleen came directly to her mind.

Silence reigned in her four room apartment. The kitchen had been the spot where Kathleen had intervened—been slain.

Dannie rose from his parlor chair not wanting to disturb dormant memories.

Gloria held his arm by the door and spoke of their heavy petting session years ago, that she now wore bras, and of how madly she had wanted to go steady with him.

"You were in California?" her hazel eyes livened.

He smiled. "Yes."

She talked animatedly about her drama lessons, and, blushing slightly, the dirty words she used to whisper to him, like lovebox.

"Do you know any stars?" she said close to him.

Dannie laughed. "Not really," he said. "But I know people who do," he was thinking of Angel palling around with so many of them.

She talked abruptly about her . . . brother, Rocco. One of his eyes was gouged by a North Brooklyn Boy leader—Dapper—in the Brooklyn Raymond Street Jail. Dapper, always the wild one, had said Kathleen believed also in the Old Testament. "An eye for an eye"—Kathleen's eye had been mutilated by the rifle bullet.

Dannie said nothing, but tried to stem his burgeoning tears.

"I've always been outspoken," she grinned. "Can I get any intros if I make it to Hollywood?"

"I guess so," Dannie replied. "When are you going?"

"I don't know," she was squeezing his arm, while Dannie kept thinking of Kathleen. She went to her heaven assuming that they were cousins. Related. That it would have been unnatural to . . . kiss. Eleanor's lie!

"I can make a call now, if you like," the words spilled out of him, her excitement catchy.

She all but dragged him to her black telephone, and her left breast under her robe squeezed against the side of his head as he sat dialing the pompous Astor Hotel.

He was lucky catching Augie in his room. Augie complying, rattled off a Hit Parade of names. But he was in a hurry, had to go down to the lobby and lay in wait to see General MacArthur. He'd tell him he should be President.

Dannie gave four of the names to Gloria. She was . . . astounded. Barbara Payton. Robert Mitchum. Natalie Wood. Janis Page.

"Are you in the . . . movies?" she was awestruck still. "Your . . . ear," she traced it with her fingers. "Are you a part of . . . gangland? Part of those Friendships bound by . . . honor? Can I really use these names?"

"If he says so, *bet on it*," Dannie concluded firmly.

For lack of anything better to do for the rest of the night, Dannie sauntered over to Church and McDonald Avenues. It was a nearby corner and maybe he'd meet Joey Gallo again.

He had left Gloria after ten tongue-kissing minutes. She had filled in several pounds, and was looking *fine*. He'd try to telephone her soon. They'd go out on her one free, dateless night and talk "shop"—Tinsel Town. She must hear all about it!

"Date me or hate me," she had said, live-wire as ever. He had gotten a momentary thrill holding her tight, and his heart raced now on Joe the Blond's corner.

Joe was neither in Scarola's nor Jack's All-Nite Eatery, so Dannie left a message. Included in it was a question: had he ever heard from Antoinette Narghelle?

Dannie taxied it back to his hotel, the St. George on Clark Street, Brooklyn. He and Augie had decided to split up, get the lay of the land, then regroup.

AFTER HEARING NO WORD FROM AUGIE IN TWO DAYS, Dannie decided to taxi it from the St. George to the Astor in Manhattan.

Maybe Augie went on his own to the cuts and the police were there? Dannie sat in the sedate but classy lobby of the Astor. He had knocked on Augie's hotel room door, he had had him paged under Marv Lembeck, and he had waited four hours in the lobby. But still there was no sight of him.

Dannie bought a chinning bar and hooked it up in a door archway in his St. George suite. Exercise had become a tried and true means of passing the time.

Restless, he wondered if Joe Gallo had gotten his message? Should he telephone Gloria? Should he dare leave and miss Angel's call?

He fell into the all-too-comfortable rut of his California daydreaming. No sweat, he didn't plan on seeing Eve while in New York. He thought of how Eleanor had accomplished her latter life mission. One spirit-damning mistake in an eighteen year lifetime was enough.

So he slid into the idle fantasy. Dawn and him. Little Mike aside. Waiting for the double kill. She was in "pot" ecstasy-land, gyrating. But of course he wasn't aroused. Just so much dead "meat," she was bewailing that "love was no one's fault."

Her legs spreading, she was nearly blinded with her own mess of blond hair.

He gripped her buttocks, his fingers by the crack of that wide ass. He cracked, split, and tore the fingernail of his trigger finger with his right thumb, feeling his own trickling blood.

His finger entered her wet vagina (the ruse he had heard about from B-Girl Betty Allan). He pumped and groaned, kissing feverishly, before . . . he found himself fully conscious fingering the . . . hexagon shield in his right pants pocket. The vivid, liquid daydream was evaporating.

He telephoned the Astor and left yet another message for Augie.

Putting aside his cautiousness, he dressed, cabbing it over to Church and McDonald.

Joey was on the busy Brooklyn corner, semi-circled by a dozen of his "men," holding court as usual. Dannie waited for visible recognition.

Joey was notorious, publicized these days. He had been summoned to Senate hearings in Washington, D.C. Senator John Kennedy was investigating juke box union infiltration while his kid brother, Robert, belligerently dogged Joey's criminal tracks.

"Still on the outside, lookin' in, good lookin'," he heard Joey's voice exuding his distinct street charm.

Like old times, Dannie followed Joe around the McDonald Avenue corner, but stayed within immediate sight of Joey's clique.

Joey was the undisputed underworld rising star of the 50's, he bragged on the nighttime street. "Come a long way from a kid who didn't weigh a hundred pounds soaking wet."

They spoke of Scap, who was still incarcerated upstate not far from Willie the Actor. Dannie handed Joey three hundred dollars for Scap. Cigarette money.

Joey didn't miss a trick. He had heard about Dannie getting clipped in the ear right inside his territory, and he had heard that Hugo Duce was in California helping Mush run the show.

Finally, Joey told Dannie about Annette, shortened from Antoinette. She was working in the formica factory on Fifth and 39th. He hadn't been able to get her phone number, yet. "She's still short," Joey mean-eyed smiled. "And still stacked," Joey Gallo winked fondly. He liked this "stand-up" kid, Dannie V.

"Be careful of Al-bert and Little Mike," he cautioned. "It'll be a while before I trigger that Lord High Executioner money grabber." Joey was not smiling, his pale blue eyes bulging menacingly in his taut-skinned skull. "So you're on your own till then," he concluded, his beaming smile returning.

Hailing a cab, Dannie mulled over the possibility of making time to go to the hospital in order to verify the date of his . . . conception?

No, it was too late. He'd return to the St. George, see if he had any messages. If not, he would take a swim in the hotel's indoor pool and try to get some of the drive-you-up-a-wall restlessness out of him.

"MOGEN DAVID. THAT'S THAT PASSOVER WINE THAT'S pissed in once a year."

Dannie lay stretched on his back by the indoor pool, trying to ignore the meaningless conversations around him. Restive, he wondered if he should call Gloria. 8:45 p.m. Kind of late. He lay his Bulova wrist watch down beside him.

"These sheeny bums think they own poolside, among other things, in this city." Dannie didn't know the two bruisers with their girlfriends, who were lying four feet from him around the crowded, heated pool.

Time for a quick swim, Dannie smiled, thinking of poolside Miami Beach and the *lotta* over Anna, Eleanor, and Eve. This wouldn't be kismet.

He dove in, careful not to collide with anyone. He sank lazily underwater and came up for air, clearing his eyes but looking more to refresh, clear his head.

He dried himself and stretched on his former spot, before he noticed that his wrist watch was gone. The two muscle bound guys nearby were smirking, their girlfriends somber.

Stay cool, Danny-my-lad, Dannie begged himself lying quite still, flat on his back. Maybe they took his watch, maybe it was someone else. Could be it was accidentally kicked into the pool.

It would turn up. He decided to concentrate again on his quacky daydreaming. The last thing in the wide world that he wanted was attention in public.

Dawn. Little Mike. Where was he?

Oh yeah, he had just fooled her. And Little Mike.

"You're more than a woman." He knew she had come full cycle, pretending limpness in his arms. "You're the reason why masturbation by men was invented." The blood from his finger would suffice for sperm in her rapt state. He lay on her, fondling tenderly, Mamie Stover—Betty Allan's trick in reverse had worked (she used to slide her hand behind her and let the Johns fuck her fluid palm, most of them being too drunk or too hot to notice). He rolled over beside her, feeling like a creep but *proud* of it, and pressed his bloody finger into the sawdust on the butchershop floor to stop the bleeding, and hide the shame. She had her first taste of conscious, "alive" sexual intercourse, her paradise on a phony island in the universe. The blood, if spied, would be a "hair-cut" from the opening tip of his penis. He would face Mike, the Anastasia henchman, clean. Face his execution purged . . .

"These Christ-killers don't even know what time it is," the deep male voice broke Dannie's melodramatic meandering.

"Get off the case," a female voice castigated lightly. "You're jealous 'cause I said he's so handsome that I'd like to take a bite out of his other ear," she said, trying to subdue her light giggling.

Dannie didn't stir a muscle. How did he rate Christ-killer? But the mention of "his other ear" had hit the mark. He turned on his side, casually, away from the foursome, his silver, six-pointed shield dangling from his neck, and clunking on the red tile.

Oh, God, he had put on David Huntingdon's Star of David before he had gone out tonight. It wasn't meant to remind him of Eleanor's bullshit about "his birthright," "his lineage." Rather, he had been thinking of his . . . father, grandmother, and had, instead of tossing it on the bed in his room, just matter-of-factly put it around his neck. It was better than laying cumbersomely in his pocket.

Screw it. Those guys' remarks had. . .stemmed from jealousy, as the one girl stated. But he was still mad about the watch that John had . . .

"There ain't a kike in the world that's got any balls!" the gruff voice sprang at Dannie from poolside chatter which seemed to echo off the walls.

Dannie took deep breaths, trying to let his mind blank out. But the blood was going to his head, reviving the scene with John and Arnold.

"I'll wager he has a pretty you-know-what minus the foreskin," the second female voice came in earnest.

Time to go, Dannie knew. Without his wrist watch, he was up and out of there heading for the locker room.

He dressed, but before he could completely finish, muscle-bound and his pal were in the locker room. They had mistaken not wanting *disturbo* for weakness. Dannie was trapped.

"Maybe we'll see if the Jew bastard's got any foreskin," musclebound glared. All options closed, Dannie slammed his open locker half-door square into the husky fellow's face. He spun round, the pal's blow missing him, and quick fisted him, crowding him with body blows, and hammering at the solar-plexus—"the blows that take the wind from anyone's sails," as Johnny had taught him.

Muscles, however, was far from backing off and lurched forward. Dannie sidestepped, banging Muscles's temple with a short right for his grandmother! Then he connected with a whammy of a left hook to muscle-bound's jaw for . . . my . . . father, he half-uppercutted the huge guy's jaw again . . . for good measure, Muscles fell limp, and smashed into the metal lockers. An attendant came trotting over, mumbling something about "damn girl trouble." Dannie ran, thinking he should have blasted the pal once more for Arnold. He made it to Clark Street and, flagging a taxicab, he scooted into it.

"Boro Park!" he ordered, hearing sirens at least two blocks behind him, his head a whirling adagio.

"For how much?" the cab driver swung the rig into a tire skidding turn.

"Fifty," Dannie promised.

"You got it," the cabbie sped through downtown Brooklyn. "And ya got company."

Dannie turned, twisted in his back seat, saw another cab on their tail.

"Fifty more when you lose that."

The cab driver floored the gas pedal. "For a hundred dollars I'd even move to Boro Park."

Later, Dannie lurked by Tenth Avenue and 38th, nursing his knuckles. He'd lost whoever it was, but decided against going down onto the cuts anyway.

Determined to see Angel, he took the subway to Manhattan.

The hotel desk clerk had a message for Mr. Cross from Marv Lembeck. Marv was downing a few at the Red Coach Grill. A minute away. Hop over.

Dannie had to smile. Angel was O.K. And he could use a quick drink.

"We'll mingle with the uppercrust swells until this sly watchman is dealt with." Augie Tenuto drank his J&B rare scotch, before setting the glass firmly down on the lustrous wood table. "Then you and I, Dannie, will make it to good ole glamourtown Hollywood, to plot The Master's re-entry into many, *many* fuckin' Money Stores!"

Dannie sat with Augie in the crowded Red Coach Grill, drinking the iodine-tasting scotch that Augie had ordered for him. He noticed Augie's voice inflection, pronunciation from the L.A. coaching diminishing, slipping back to the northeastern speech slur.

Augie couldn't figure who had tailed Dannie from the St. George. But he immediately proposed that the kid not go back there. Instead they'd share the room at the Astor.

Was it Little Mike?

Augie had caught Shadows Kravitz's snide remark "regards to Al-bert." Maybe Shadows had said it in reverse jest, Augie drank, pondering. Well at least they both haven't been hanging around the city like a spare cock, Augie shrugged, then brightened, as he relayed why he had been incommunicado for the past several days.

He'd been out polishing up on his trade. Stealing.

Dannie looked askew at him, wanting to talk more about Pop than "shop."

"I know, I know," Augie caught Dannie's look. "We made a pile of money out west. But that ain't it, kid. You never were a pupil of the Master's. Robbin' was more than going after the shekels. It's excitement. It's a form of being *alive*. It was Willie's way of droppin' a load. Of showing the world that he more than existed. That he was out there *doin' it* while the peasants were singin' paeans over it. Got it?"

Dannie sipped his scotch. He got it, but it still didn't make too much sense. He could see that Augie was drunk.

Augie toasted the Master Willie, relaying to Dannie how he had just scored, taking Bankhead's jewels—the one that played in *Lifeboat.*

How he had mixed with Rockefeller's brother, the banker, representing to him *the fact* that he was in the jewelry business.

Dannie, who had come in down-and-out, now laughed. He could see, in his head, Augie's picture plastered on the cover of *Mad Magazine.* He smiled more to himself, but he knew that they had to get around to the cuts—Pop. That's why they were here.

The more Augie drank, the more he lamented Fran's dying. A sweet skirt.

"Did you hear how she got it?"

Dannie gagged on his drink. He slowly nodded, yes.

"I'm gonna get a cobra. A fuse went up Tony-boy's keister. Now the fuckin' king cobra's going up the bull-neck Mike's lard ass. How's that for payback, kid?"

Dannie couldn't swallow any more liquor.

"Didn't you hear what happened to Marge Moore, The Actor's other paramour?"

Dannie shook his head, no.

"They're gonna deport her Arab ass. That's what she gets for talkin' and trustin' the *bulletzee.* Fuck her where she eats. Did ya ever get a good blow-job, kid?"

Trying to ignore the question, Dannie noticed that Augie's right eye scar was showing. "Let the chumps know it's me," Augie roared, referring to "the actress" and "the millionaire." He'd "make-up" tonight before he went to see wizened Pop, again.

He had seen the old shakedown artist and heard about the upcoming "auction." Maybe he'd take a vicious dog with him to *persuade* this overall-stained Pop—he was good with dogs.

The following morning, 7:00 a.m., Dannie lounged on 39th Street between Sixth and Fifth Avenues. Brooklyn. Fifty feet, on an angle, across from Dominick Formica Factory.

Antoinette worked there.

Adjusting his green-tint prescription sunglasses, he watched the buses unload their passengers, thought of her. Could he trust her if he met her in *South Brooklyn*?

Was she forever close to Anna, "a girlfriend is like a sister among *friends*"—Johnny's warning words—"they take it to heart."

Had Anna told her about the night on the sand in Miami Beach? He saw a short, compact young lady, with a polkadot kerchief. Was it her? His heart ached as she walked toward the factory.

Would her murmurs, her sighs of years ago count now? he wondered as she disappeared into the factory doorway across the street.

He thought of free feels, her moon-eyeing, moaning below ground, the subway trains blocking their erupting passions.

Body pressing, hot kisses, her letter to him. . .Damn! The i.d. bracelet that she had sent him was in the St. George. Yet, perhaps he was making too much of a big deal out of incidents which had happened years ago . . . *damn it.*

He walked away. Thinking. Overthinking.

He could call Gloria tonight.

He could contact Eleanor Cross. The Crosscavale was, no doubt, cut down to Cross because she had borne one for so long.

Stevie Sesqu, what ever happened to him after he had moved away?

After cabbing it back to the Astor Hotel, Dannie sat in his room alone.

Augie. He had been a recluse, under wraps for many years. Now he was out making up for all that.

Roscoe. Where was he now?

He should call Joey Gallo, he thought as he nibbled on room service supper.

He'd be gone in a few days. In the meantime, he'd talk to himself, do his push-ups, sit-ups, and deep knee bends. Tomorrow he'd go out shopping for clothes. He nearly wept. Life in a suitcase with only nightmares for memories.

Nineteen thousand dollars was his "pay" from California, but his only soul was bankrupt. Falling to his knees, he longed to see and speak to Kathleen.

Forgiveness. Could he ever get it? He clasped his hands in prayer, reading the swift record of pain, ugliness that was etched within the core of him.

A weary hour later he fell heavily onto his bed, his right hand in the sweeping fall, knocking the telephone's receiver off the hook. A moment later he heard the switchboard voice asking if he wanted to place a call.

YES, he decided, plopping off the bed to a kneeling position by the end table.

He'd call Joey. To find out if he had Ant . . . Annette's telephone number.

"DANNIE?" HE HEARD HER VOICE. AND LISTENED TO it as if he were still fifteen years old and the demonic nightmare of the past several years had never happened. He listened to Annette for half an hour.

He had never kept their movie date. Never telephoned her after she had written him. She still cried nights over the beating he had suffered on his Ninth Avenue corner. Did he blame her, was that the reason?

Dannie couldn't get a word in edgewise and just loved hearing her speak. He deposited extra coins.

She had walked many a weekend to where he had lived on 39th hoping to glimpse his face.

She had broken her friendship with Josephine—Anna Banana— over him. A lie about Miami Beach.

She had haunted that brave girl Kathleen's wake waiting for him to show. A friend she used to have, who's *persona non grata* now, Elaine Cahill, from Seventh Avenue and 17th Street, advised her of how close he had been to Kathleen. But he had run from her that snowy night. Did he still hate her?

She was shocked at six o'clock this very morning. Three of Joe the Blond's hang-on followers had rung her bell, wanting her telephone number. Was he friendly now with that rebel?

Her own brother turned out to be a mental case. Her father had an accident working down on the docks. Crushed by a Hi/Lo.

He could tell that she kept lighting, puffing, Old Golds—if he remembered correctly—at constant intervals.

She was Annette now, not Antoinette. Shorter, more modern. Her name shorter, not her. She was five-foot-three. She had heard that he was a giant. Was that true?

Did he remember their first meeting? At the Fifth Avenue Playhouse? They hadn't spoken but she had teased him by throwing popcorn in his hair. She couldn't resist it. Their second, on the corner of President and Fourth? Their third, down in the subway?

"Dannie, you're still so quiet." She struck a match, puffing.

Dannie laughed into the mouthpiece of the public telephone. "And you're still a chain smoker. I'm on Pacific and Fourth right now. Our . . . corner. Can you fly?" He let caution go take a great frog leap for itself, along with King Al-burt and his blood-soaked South Brooklyn Badges.

Waiting breathlessly on their fateful corner, Dannie felt it was heaven to trust someone.

She flew at him before he recognized her. His eyes were a mist. Through it he saw her as a bundle. A stacked, packed in skirt and blouse sexpot with black bedroom eyes. Her hair seemed more fluffy brunette than short black as he had surely thought he remembered it.

He lifted her off her feet and looked into her moon-shaped loveliest of faces, as his box, the wrapped robe he had just purchased, tumbled to the sidewalk.

The first gust of their exhilarating meeting over with, they both fell into silence amidst the jeering, cheering throng of afternoon onlookers.

She was looking down at the package. He picked it up, thinking that maybe she thought it was a gift for her.

He felt her keen observations on his suit and realized for the first time how dirt cluttered and wrinkled it was from his Cuts trip.

"Lunch?" she smiled.

He groped to say something, as she led him across Atlantic Avenue to the familiar Bickford's restaurant.

They both had coffee, and she was quick in paying the tab.

He stared across the table at her as she puffed away. "Doll in a teacup" he remembered the phrase from a Kipling poem. At eighteen, she still had a girlish face, and he recalled well that she was— was it four or five months older than him? She'd be nineteen soon.

"I took off from my job today," she sipped her cold coffee.

"I thought as much," he said. "I was at the factory by seven a.m. again this morning."

They walked outside, stood by the towering Williamsburg Savings Bank. Dannie thought he saw two men that he knew in a Hudson Hornet, both wearing dress hats. The car shot by, and he dismissed it. Why should he spoil the day?

"We're going . . . shopping," he was embarrassed, but took her hand in his. "Or would you like to see the movie we never went to?" He was aware that she either hadn't noticed his ear and neck, or had decided not to mention it.

"You name the stars," she said. "I'll name all their movies. That was my get-lost pastime."

"John Garfield," he kidded.

"*Body and Soul. Pride of the Marines*," she shot back. "Clark Gable."

"*Mutiny on the Bounty. It Happened One Night. Gone With the Wind.*" He beamed. "My escape too." He steered her to the cobbled Flatbush Avenue Extension, her hand candescent friction in his. The gangs of people on the sidewalks made it a far cry from the zippered-up streets of Beverly Hills and the San Fernando Valley, L.A. She insisted on carrying his package, and they settled on taking turns.

"Frank Sinatra," he said quickly.

"*From Here to Eternity. It Happened in Brooklyn.*" She was fast. "James Stewart."

"*It's a Wonderful Life. The Philadelphia Story.*" He was having a ball.

At A&S Department Store he bought her seamless bare nylons, dresses that swirled, slip feats with pleats, and silky soft undergarments. Annette blushed from ear to ear, jabbing him kiddingly in his kidneys that he was spending a year's pay on "private garments."

They made the Ladies Shoppes rounds on Fulton Street. Strapless bras—free bust, no under bust wires needed.

"You are definitely going to get it, Dannie," she frowned, teasing. "And I don't mean what you may be thinking. Where in the world did you get this kind of money? Is it *your* year's pay?" She was simultaneously stunned, annoyed, happy, worried.

Shimmers, rippling Bodice-Grecian-peignoir yoke. She kept trying to guess what he did for a living. He kept evading the issue by saying life's a secret. Dannie spied a Hug-me-Tight cape in a store window. "Let's get it. Your reward. You called me a living doll, remember? But you also said: 'Hey, short pants!' "

"Well, your pants now would be short on most anybody else," Annette had her arm around his waist, trying to tug him away from the shopping spree, but he won the battle.

They ate Cantonese food, their table and the extra two chairs, a shower of packages. She delicately asked why he had not shopped for himself. His teeth sunk in a spare rib, he said he would. "Both of us, O.K.?"

She stirred her hot tea replying that if she missed two work days in a row without a doctor's note she'd be fired. Saturday too was out of the question. "My bosses are slave-drivers," she said softly. But Saturday night would be their date night. "O.K. with you?" she leaned forward, going tense.

"I'll show," he assured her, delighted. A momentary glance out of the Chinese restaurant window, however, revealed that same Hudson whizzing by and dampened his mood.

He was about to put his gift-laden princess in a taxi, but the distress, the awful hurt that showed on her face halted him. "I may not have to shop for clothes," he tried, handing her a key. "It's to a suite in the St. George. You wanna go there, hold my baggage for . . . ransom," he tried a feeble smile.

She was perplexed. He wasn't going home with her? With a weak smile, she slowly took the key from him.

He said he'd explain on the phone tonight, gave the waiting cab driver a ten spot, and whisked her away.

He thought of the two fleeting figures in dress hats in the Hornet. Coincidence? Maybe he was seeing things.

He left the nagging suspicions unchallenged.

"Dance
"I want my arms about you
"The charms about you
"Will carry me through
"To Heaven . . ."

He crooned "Cheek to Cheek" to himself as he had done after their hot and heavy pet-session so many years ago. Feeling free, he made the store rounds by himself, buying the clothes, shave cream, and effects that he needed in case she couldn't go to the St. George for him. Better he had new duds. He didn't want to feel ashamed, like a ragpicker, around his new found soul-black-eyed Annette.

He called her from the room at the Astor that evening. Augie was out. Where, Dannie couldn't care less. He only wanted this conversation to be strictly personal and private.

Antoi— Annette was Miss Gabby, more so than this afternoon. In person she was demure, quiet, all eyes and lashes. Over and over they said good night while speaking for over three hours.

He was too strikingly handsome for her, she pouted. She was blue because he had not even attempted to kiss her goodbye.

She Old Gold chain-smoked through the gushing talk telling him that he was the first boy she had ever really kissed, swearing it on her dead father's grave. She asked him if he still thought she had doe-moon eyes, tight hips, some of the things he had whispered to her while down in the subway.

She said she sounded like a flirtations baby, but she loved it. She had missed so much.

"Dannie, are you there?"

"Right here," he laughed. "Heaven, I'm in Heaven . . ." he sang way out of tune. "Keep going."

She was going all right. Back to those stores to exchange those expensive gifts. Get his money back.

"No, you're not," he insisted.

And she . . . had gone to the St. George Hotel. She had the "ransom" plus her I.D. bracelet. *His* I.D. bracelet that she had mailed to him. It was on the glass table by the chaise longue. He was such a *doll* keeping it all this time.

On that memorable note they finally hung up. But only after he had promised four times that he'd see her Saturday.

Dannie bathed, spruced up . . .

"And the cares that hung about me through the week
"Seem to vanish like a gambler's lucky streak . . ."

The song was infectious, and he sang his way out of the Astor.

When he arrived in Borough Park, the 37th Street dead-end walled entrance to the above ground train tracks, freight yards—Pop's Cut's Kingdom—he had a strange premonition that he was being shadowed. Maybe those two men he had seen earlier today were now somewhere in the area. He backed off from climbing over the five-foot cement wall and cutting across the four sets of tracks.

Instead, he walked to Twelfth Avenue, suddenly thinking of Gloria.

He couldn't call her. It wouldn't be right. Anyway, she'd be quite set if she ever did make it to Hollywood.

He walked around Twelfth and cut up the tarred new highway that ran between the cuts and Greenwood Cemetery.

Passing Ninth Avenue, he looked down at the freight cars, and an embarking subway train.

Finally, he made it all the way down to Fourth Avenue and the new highway where the open subway passages loomed, the trains snaking from the 36th Street tunnel.

Dannie stepped into the Duck Inn on Fourth and telephoned the Astor. No answer in the room. Augie had not showed at all last night. Dannie's skin prickled as he walked, scanning the dark, quarter of a mile breadth of the valley of the cuts, Pop's pirate treasures stowed who knew where. Again he reached 37th and Tenth, by the dead end wall. The elevated Culver Local line rumbled above, while cars cruised noisily by on 38th Street.

Something wasn't right. Or was it Annette? Was he losing heart because now he had something . . . someone to lose? His mind was being battered by the double crosses, the merciless killings he had seen around him.

"Fuck it!" he began hightailing it away, before turning, reconsidering, and then turning sharply again leaving with full, determined re-reconsideration.

Augie had still not returned to the room. Even though it was 1:00 a.m., he must be on a jaunt, Dannie figured as he telephoned Annette.

She was home, in bed. Safe. Fine. He was sorry for calling her at such an outrageous hour; he had been . . . overreacting. He was just about to hang up when she asked what number she could reach him at . . . just in case.

He hesitated, giving her the proper number, glad he had needlessly pressed the panic button.

He tried sleeping on one of the single beds, but tossed instead. T.E.H.M.A. The inscription on Kathleen's gift-medal to him. The thief entering her heaven on the heels of God a minute apart from the Messiah, a deliverer of the Jews.

Her other messages. If one life does not mean everything, then life's total means nothing. It was all too complicated, so he shifted his thought to Annette.

Below Fourth Avenue. He had hoped even then that she would be able to dispel the disturbing sexual thoughts of blazing Eleanor, be an answer to her beckoning. Or was it only an intermezzo.

In those days, Annette had been so outspoken for her age. She had so much vitality still.

September eighth was her fifteenth birthday, he remembered her telling him a long time ago. She was only three months older than he. He hoped in vain that he would doze off.

And she spoke Italian. "Creamy looks," her fluttering compliment, though, had been said in plain English. It had made him feel like a giant, giving him confidence, as they had gone hotly down the subway's steep steps.

His telephone shrilled into the silent room. He hoped to God it was her.

It was.

"The man who answered the telephone said he was the desk clerk and that this is the Astor Hotel," she said in disbelief.

"It certainly is." He tried to explain that what he was trying to explain would be unexplainable. She said she had called him back because she was worried about him. She was rambling about the shopping, the money that was in his luggage at the St. George—six hundred dollars—the awful emptiness of no kiss. "I could arrange limousine service and have you safely here in twenty minutes," he cut her short.

Her end of the phone line went silent for too long for comfort. He told her it wasn't what she may be thinking and she cut him short this time.

She never misses Mass on Sundays. She is as she was born, if he got her drift.

He got it, alright. Despondent, he began to lay the phone in its cradle, but the sound of her voice brought him back.

"But make the arrangements, Daniel. I have your baggage, money, and I.D. bracelet. And I'll be darned if I'm going to let another damn three years go by with you going with it!"

Dannie counted each of the twenty-eight minutes it took for her to arrive. He had champagne ready, but they hardly touched it.

She smoked her Old Golds as if her family manufactured them. He groped, trying his darndest to tell her of the St. George, of the past, but it seemed an impossible task.

What he could talk about freely was them. He had considered her his first conquest. Quest. *No*, he had never had a conquest at all. His very first and only girlfriend. He had been anxious to ask her to go "steady" while running home after being together down below on the Pacific Street platform. He recalled the first, fumbling kiss, leading to the kisses that couldn't be counted, "experimenting" together, the blouse front. How he cherished the memories.

"The button on my blouse," she had her *sesso* eyes downward, her head bowed, sitting on the oval chair adjacent to his. "Torn off."

The big event of his life at that juncture, he thought to himself, was not only touching her bare breasts but being *hard* while doing it.

"Why didn't you show for our Tuesday-night date?" She spoke more with the beauty of her troubled eyes than her soft voice.

"I was ordered not to. By Chappy Mazziotta."

"Dannie, I don't know . . . all this seems so . . . confusing." She wiped at her eyes, her right hand shaking, ashes fluttering to the thick rug.

It was a mistake having her here. An uncomfortable, unfair mistake. He rose, not really aware that he was crying.

She lay near, mentally exhausted, fully clothed on the made bed adjacent to the bathroom.

"It's like I . . . flew here," she had her arms up over her eyes. "And landed with a great big thump. Is it the . . . Schuster case? The Mob in Miami Beach? The Gallo brothers? Are we making too much of two kids stumbling in the dark, losing their way?"

"Listen to me, just listen to me," he sat on the edge of the bed. "It's me, not you. All me. I have to know something, prove something. Will you trust me? For just five minutes? That's all I ask. Just five minutes of complete trust. You could say no and go. But I need it to escape a witchcraft that tempted, brought me to purgatory's baited, mortal gate. Just five minutes, Annette."

"The busted bicycle. The awful beating you received. I tried to claw them for it," she was trembling. "The letter I wrote you, saying I wanted you all to myself. I called you God-face. Warned you in a story of Anna's . . . Josephine's uncle. It was our unlucky fifteenth year. I didn't blame you if you'd never see me again. I gave you my address, you lost it. My undying love. I asked your forgiveness . . ." She was weeping, turning over on her side away from him.

"I sealed that letter with a lipstick imprint kiss that I've never really gotten back. Even yesterday you refused to attempt to kiss me. God in your majestic mercy, help me grow up," she lay quaking, her body curled, going limp.

"Let's both grow-up," he lay down beside her, stretched out on his back, letting moments tick by before turning sideways, completely enfolding her.

Within five minutes of two-sided hungry kisses, he had her nipples bared. An imaginary Brooklyn BMT subway sparked, rumble-roared periodically through the Manhattan room. He sucked through her moans, her no's, it's not rights, her ferocious-tender tight neck holding embraces.

He had her skirt, her half-slip up, his penis out between her welcoming burning thighs by her panty crotch—*His erect penis.* He humped, nearly smothered *his doll . . .*

Coming!

"I did it," he was crying, praying, laughing. "We did it," he held her with the hold of a gentle madman. "I . . . DID . . . IT!"

"You darn well did, Daniel," she stroked his hair, his shirted chest. "I feel as sticky as a glue bottle."

He couldn't help breaking out into delightful laughter.

"It's not funny," she said as she lay warm-snug in his arms. "We . . . came. And we almost came close to doing something without benefit of clergy. The pan . . . undergarment you bought me is gooey . . . soaked. So is the slip and skirt. Imagine the bedspread?" She had his medal, chain out from between the buttons of his shirt. "A Star of David?"

"I'm one-quarter a member of the tribe of Judah." He wanted to clean up, but even more so he wanted to hug-sleep peaceful beside her without Arnold bloody between them. She nibbled his earlobe, murmuring she'd bite the rest of it off and swallow it, such was her passion for him. Sliding from the bed, she blushed blooming crimson roses before scampering off to the bathroom. To soak away the stains.

Juarez legal whores, ladies of the night, go to the dickens.

High Yellows in bars go ply your wares. Gingerbread, go find a foreign army to please.

Redheaded, oval-faced, gray-eyed Betty Allen, Mamie Stover in Miami, go be a B-girl with somebody else.

Aunt Eleanor go and fuck yourself!

Dannie sprang from the bed and reached for the champagne, only to be frozen by the sound of a . . . key turning in his room door's lock. It must be Angel. Fortunately, he had double-chain locked it. He'd tell him that this was *his* star-night around. Then, he heard his . . . Aunt Eleanor's voice . . . gritting, demanding to be let in.

Dannie dropped the sparkling bottle, celebration time abruptly ending.

He wouldn't dare let her in. Annette was coming out of the bathroom, clad in blouse, hotel towels.

"Later. Three million years later," Dannie said through the two-inch opening of the door to broom-flying Eleanor.

"Your J.M. is dead," he heard her hushed voice as if it came from a molehole in the ground. "Eve is with me. We did your dirty work." Her tone was witchy, tunnel-hollow.

"Johnny Squint is *dead*!"

Why did they let her out of the sanitarium at this hour? "Go down to the lobby," he whispered through the slight door opening. "And shut up in this hallway. They've got guys with nets on twenty-four-hour call here. Go. I'll be down in ten minutes," he pushed the door closed against her weight.

How in the world did she catch up with him? Dannie wondered, and what in the world was she raving about. He had no clue regarding this latest mad statement of hers.

"Who are you?" he heard Annette's far away sounding voice beside him. "The initials on the back of your Solomon's seal are D.H. I thought your name was Dannie Vale."

"I thought so too, among other names, until recently." He twisted the hexagram seeing for the first time the two letter script. "It's a long story, hon. But isn't everything."

Annette lovingly tried a smile. "Well, at any rate, I'm glad I came."

"*So am I*!" Dannie embraced her, backed off. "Can you trust me one more time. Just one more time right now?"

"One question," Annette held the bath towel to her inverted waist. "Who was at the door? I heard Eve mentioned. But who was the one talking of . . . death, and . . . dirty work?"

"She's my mother's sister," Dannie had to let it go at that. "Now can you dress, pack up everything in the room, check out for me and check in at the Plaza or Waldorf?"

Annette stood in a haze of bewilderment as he gave her rapid instructions and a fistful of twenty and fifty dollar bills.

"Can you do it? Will you do it?" He waited for her reply. None came. She was numb. He stepped, downhearted, into the bathroom, washed up, and hurriedly changed his clothes. When he emerged a few moments later, she was standing, pensively biting her lower lip.

"Shall I . . . call limousine service?" he faltered. "You can be back in Brooklyn . . ."

"I'll do exactly what you told me to do," she bucked up her spirits. "I'm scared silly because I'm . . . confused. But after what just happened on that bed I'm not going to let it stop there," she began dressing.

"Don't peek," she weakly smiled. "And get on your high horse before I get *you* on that bed. Git. Take care of your lobby business."

"I love you," he blurted out, before kissing her. Holding her, feeling her proportioned indentations, he didn't want to leave. "Call me!" he had to all but dash for the door before he decided not to go at all.

"Dannie!" Annette shouted. Dannie spun half-round facing her large, wide-open eyes.

"It's nothing," she said, looking at him intently. "I'll tell you later. Just make sure there is a later. *Promessa*?"

"*Bet your life on it*," he lingered, "this one and the next thrown in. They're both only a minute apart."

Dannie waited for the elevator.

Eleanor's lie, the entire lie of her made him free. There was no longer a sex-bind between them. She was a user in the flesh, as she had often termed Johnny. "Those who take or use a life," Dannie heard the words echo in his brain. Annette had completely sexually untied him from Eleanor. Now he was FREE to be with Annette, free to be his own man. As the door opened, Dannie stepped briskly into the waiting elevator.

Downstairs, he walked determinedly through the spacious, austere lobby. It was going to be a thorny affair handling his "relatives"—nettlesome would be the word that U.C.L.A. Dawn would select. He sat with Eleanor and Eve, a rectangular marble table their mute referee.

Vituperative Eleanor began by inquiring as to "that tramp up in the room." It gave Dannie a near headache, his right hand looking to belt her, but it also gave him an instant idea. He held his temper, excused himself, and walked around to the staid night desk clerk.

For two hundred dollars he and the clerk saw eye to eye.

Money talks and bullshit walks, Dannie thought of *bunamo* little Reb Sica often saying that by Pete's Radio Store. He returned to the two loonies, one feline-eyed, the other blue starlight, sarcasm incarnate.

They had rotated tracking him since the Park Theater. His grandmother Ruby had been minding Daniel, Dannie listened.

His future was theirs. His jeopardy theirs. They had no other choice. And maybe they could all patch things up. Ruby had a home in North Florida.

"Get to how you killed Johnny," he near scoffed, the 2:30 a.m. downstairs lobby, their private "ring."

"You never die for love, you kill for it," Eleanor snapped.

"Like you did my father," Dannie glared.

"I'll get to that," she was haughty, a devil in a smudged blue jump suit, Eve dressed the same way, both uncharacteristically disheveled.

"I took over sixteen thousand dollars from the apartment in Los Angeles," Eve said. "John will *never* miss it. We need it for *your* baby."

Dannie flinched, powerless before the two women who had

wielded so much power through his life, *thus far*.

"Tell me more about the 'other' dirty work." He glanced at his new Picard wrist watch. From rags to riches he mused. Another one of life's quick turnarounds. "How did you do it? Fuck him to death?" he said to Eleanor with as much rancor as he could muster. Immediately he felt surly pangs of guilt for the rotten way he had spoken.

Taking turns, and at times chiming in together, like two harpies, they unraveled their deed, virtually ignoring his derogatory slurs. They had lost him by the St. George Hotel, but had picked him up again by the Cuts.

He sat, quiescent, hearing from them that the two fleeting men in dress hats had been none other than Pietro M. and Benny the neuro vulture.

Leaning forward, he scraped his front teeth with his pointer fingernail.

They saw him back away by the 37th Street Cuts entrance. Johnny Squint had entered that way twenty minutes prior to that. They knew of Pop's shack through watching him, and headed directly for it, via different routes.

They told their story with such verve that Dannie found himself actually getting caught up in it.

Eve found the darkened shack unoccupied.

Dannie asked her to describe it.

She did, right down to the floorboards, make-shift oil burner and chimney. He and Pop had gone to it after leaving the eye-stinging fire on the Cuts high rock mound.

Eve had waited in the beetle-crawling hut for John with the only weapon she possessed, *herself*.

Eleanor had lain in the high grass across from the dilapidated shack. She had the automatic, the one along with his gear from the Lafayette hotel. She was quite accustomed to firearms. On several occasions, Daniel H. had taken her to various firing ranges.

The sisters, upon Eve's return from California, had made peace with one another. Two pregnancies evened the score. Now they were working together for *four* persons—they reminded him.

The simple plan was to wait for Johnny Squint to reappear. Eve had lit the dim lantern inside the shack for just that purpose. When she heard him approaching she would douse the light, entice and bait him while Eleanor stealthily made her way to them, *blowing the back of his freakish gangland head off*.

And that's exactly what transpired.

Dannie found himself perspiring in his lobby chair. Were they for real?

"What about Pop, the watchman," he quizzed. "Where were Pietro M. and Benny? What made you think that the Cuts were so important to begin with? What about the echoing bang from the gun? Where's his . . . body now?" Dannie scanned the lobby. Not waiting for their answers, he rose, going around to the desk, and asked for the message he had been expecting.

The clerk handed him the folded paper. Dannie walked several feet away, reading it. Annette was at the W. She'd wait. She loved him, Dannie rocketed to Jupiter standing still.

"Let's go," he was edgy by the two striking, insidious storytellers. He handed Eve a tarnished key. "Go up to this room. Clean up, both of you. I'll be right up. Get going."

Dannie sat alone in the lobby.

He had pre-arranged a second room to finally isolate Eleanor for that overdue whack she had coming by spewing out "tramp" in reference to Annette.

Now the room came in doubly handy, getting both Eleanor and Eve out of sight *if* their outlandish short story were even remotely true. He tried to analyze the feasibility of certain points in their narrative.

The "trail" when he was in the taxicab after the *budella* with Muscles and pal. Before that the Park Theater to the St. George Hotel. Believable enough. The Cuts first . . . he had been there often enough.

They both had on their dirty jumpsuits. A woman. Stir up the wrath stored in her head and life's shit hits the ever-evil fan. A misunderstood kiss to Anna the Nose and bam! A beating.

Eleanor's foot patrolman beau had a few drinks too many, crazily loves the wrong sis, and slam! A career and purity go by the wayside.

Johnny sends his underlings to a pregnant beauty-witch and the mother instinct inspires a slug that tears apart the back of his head. Dannie still couldn't digest it. He should go to the Waldorf, grab Annette, and see if she would drop out of sight for twenty years with him. He had to know what had happened, which meant that he'd have to go up to the room to delve a bit more into their bizarre exploit.

Eve, the T.V. set on low, was sitting towel-robed, on a hard-backed dining chair. Eleanor was bathing.

He drilled Eve about Pop the city watchman. She had known of that old hermit for many years. After all they had lived for so long less than fifty yards from his terrain. He was truly part of their backyard. It was only assumed that he was a link in the horrendous Schuster slaying. Or at least his grassy Cuts were. After all, it was only a minute away from where Arnold was gunned down. Add to that Dannie himself taking off from Los Angeles so unexpectedly, turning up in Brooklyn of all places, by the freight yards to boot, and John saying on the "fake" phone that Dannie was here on "business." Why the rendezvous with that city-nobody? But that was not the imperative aspect to attempt to sort out. The meat of the situation was that where Dannie would be, Johnny would be also. For the main *kill!*—so the infamous Sutton-Schuster affair would be buried forever. And, if need be, two women and a child along with it!

He had never heard Eve speak like a sleuth before and he had to admit he was impressed. As for Pietro M. and Benny, she continued, they could have been told to stay away, not congest the deserted city dumps. Or perhaps the geep Benny stopped to eat Pietro M., he was that much the inhuman buzzard. Or both of them may well have knifed the treasure-chest-hoarding Pops just to stifle the boredom of that below-the-surface rail-hell hole.

Dannie's aunt towel-paraded by and sat on the bed. "Where's the *pisherkeh* that was in your other room," she said with disgust. "The short girl that you spent a fortune on shopping? She couldn't harden you?" she goaded.

Dannie held her blow at bay, as she took off on Pietro M. and Benny.

"They could be out looking for *you*. They may well be circling my new apartment on Ninth Avenue, Borough Park, right now."

"Well let those carving knife fucks go around in circles," she spread out lazily on the bed. "Ruby is packed and ready at *her* home. With tiny Daniel. Any other 'details' dear nephew?"

She answered the question of the gun's explosion. Timing. She had shot the mobster just as the West End thundered into the station. Messy but complete. "Not bad for two unlicensed executioners."

"As to the body," she near seductively yawned, "Why don't you go see for yourself. Bury it if you must. I wouldn't break a fingernail over that flunky underworld stooge."

Dannie was on the solid brink of believing them. And the ramifications of the "defensive" act.

They weren't just fighting someone they felt threatened by. No, not at all.

There was Don Vitone Genovese to contend with. John had

saved that underboss from being volted to Kingdom Come in New York State's electric chair. And he had untold "soldiers" and associates who looked out cold-bloodedly for their Own.

Then, of course there was Uncle Frank Costello who controlled politicians, cops, and officials at every level—from here to the coast to New Orleans. How could anyone hide from that even if they had a mind to? Dannie sought to balance those negative thoughts with the doubts as to who would really find out just *who* had killed John, though he felt certain he would be prominent on the suspect list.

John's downfall, Dannie mused. His own words the cause of it, they haunted Dannie now: "When a woman touches your balls tenderly—even with her fuckin' eyes—she has you by the prick the rest of your life."

"Rah, Rah," said Eleanor, seemingly reading Dannie's mind, overheated from the *kill*. "Dannyboy is doing some clever deep-thinking. He's growing up. I don't knock it, but it's been history proven what a man will do for that unattainable, shall we say, piece of platinum ass. Or put it this way, his evensong of death."

"Like my father?" Dannie's voice acid, his fist clenched.

"Like your father," Eleanor quipped. "*If you dig deep enough you may find him.* Why do you think I chose the location you were reared? It overlooked his grave, a free city plot."

Before Dannie could lunge at her from his position, she barely revealed the muzzle of the bronze automatic, which was pointing dead at his groin from her high-toweled hip.

He froze on the tips of his toes. Anyone capable of slaying a man that had fooled more than half the curious, watchful world was no one to trifle with.

"Do you want to examine the chamber," she said. "Sniff the barrel?"

"Do you want to risk losing Daniel the Third," his throat was parched. "Pull that trigger again tonight and this time they'll take you away handcuffed."

"I could turn up the television's volume," she toyed with the idea. "Catch a shoot-em-up program. That'll help cover the noise if push came to shove."

Talk, Dannie told himself, talk. He was dealing with someone who had broken life's human ice by taking one human being's life, *no*, make that *two*—a third would hardly cause her to drown more so in that cold lake beside hell.

"You may have been seen with me in the lobby. And recall that *decent* young lady knows you came to this hotel. She's somewhere that you don't know of. You're looking at life in prison. What's to be of the child then?"

"You'll never know if I pull, would you?" Her crazed blue eyes were seeing Daniel, the original, all over again. The betrayal, torment, agonizing nights. "I named you on your circumcision. Daniel. Obvious? Smart? Now I have to live with you alive all over again. Knowing, at my back."

The unattainable, Dannie thought. Her voice sounded *insane*, but still like a luscious lyre, a siren calling him to treacherous shores. He still had Eve, in view though the gun commanded his faulty vision.

"If you pull," he said, "you kill the three of us. *In every way.*" He'd attempt anything at this stage, he was so close to being home-free from it all. His bowels were loosening. *Eleanor hated him.*

Eve sat aghast, Eleanor amused, fascinated.

"You're bluffing," Eleanor Cross smiled, shooting a glance at her sister. Eve's eyes were wary, glued on Daniel Huntingdon.

Dannie had his Dawn—Little Mike fantasy striking his eyes! He stepped slowly, warily over to Eve.

"Come with us, Dan," she barely touched the back of his right hand. "Eleanor and I. We don't argue any more. Something I could never take. There are no more lies between us, she's strangely given me peace of mind. She saved your life, Dannie." She stood up barefoot by him.

Oh, Lord, Dannie's spunk was waning. Eleanor had indoctrinated him expertly, and he knew her exact measurements from the curves of her buttery breasts to the nuances of her lipstickless lips. He turned to her, lounging risque, doubtful upon the oversized bed.

"I need a private minute with Eve," he said with overwhelming sincerity, she hesitated, her man-eating blue eyes lit with skepticism, her svelte Astor cloth-wrapped body unmovable, her laugh beginning mildly, pulsating quickly from right out of an Edgar Allan Poe B-picture.

Nutso Eleanor was dreamy on the bed, making the mistake of facing the opposite wall. Eve's cat-eyes were suddenly a green-alert, she gestured silently to Eleanor's bare back. Dannie managed a quick half-tackle on the bed, grabbing her long hair and crunching her wrist till he had immediate control of the automatic.

"Game time," he told her, backhanding close-fisted her right temple. He was a coward for hitting her. *So what?* He emptied the automatic, tossing it on the bed, and smashed her again on her fragile chin.

"So you couldn't ruin Daniel," his brain was a haywire windmill. "But you wrecked your sister and me over your fuckin' lifelong lies," he wanted to kick her deranged brains in. "You miserable mother fucker! You kill 'cause you're dead." He was about to break her nose, but Eve was on him, and he had to gag her scream before the whole Hotel was down upon them.

He pocketed the unused bullets.

"*You* broke her hold on you," he said to Eve.

"I love you," she whispered.

"I love you too," he wasn't sorry for helping to "cure" her in California. She had lived for so long with so many lies that were not part of life.

"Patch that *basso-vita* up on the bed," he said. "And have my grandmother . . . and my . . . son . . ." a tear stung his eye ". . . have them out of this city before the sun shines." He turned to go, but turned back.

"Have better dreams from now on. And *thank you*, Mom. Don't crucify yourself. There are too many standing in line waiting to do it for . . . us." It was time to go. He had a real night burial to attend to.

As he left, he could have sworn he heard eerie, inscrutable . . . laughter? coming from the room. He shrugged it off. No doubt par for Eleanor's course.

He was out of the Astor, crossing the Brooklyn Bridge in a cab, and at the Cuts by 3:30 a.m.

He stopped at a telephone booth to call Annette.

She was drowsy, but attentive.

He told her he had a chore to perform. After it was over he'd see her and get her home.

"Then what?" she said in his left ear.

"Trip time again for me," he answered wearily.

She asked where he was going, why, and for how long? And where was he now?

He told her he was by the place where he used to live. "Do you remember where?"

"I do."

"Sounds like a marriage ceremony."

"It sounds like you're up to your neck in deep trouble." She went silent, but he could hear the striking of a match. Even at this ghostly hour, she was puffing away. "Your aunt's words from behind the door. About someone being internationally . . . sought. You're going but you're . . ." she was getting so mixed-up . . . she'd see him come daylight. "*Io amore tu, fidanzato.*" Then the pay phone clicked his coin away.

DANNIE MADE HIS WAY THROUGH THE BLACKENED, sloping weedy Cuts and up to the rocky incline to the gory shack.

He paused a moment, his thoughts racing to Annette. Funny, it had been Chappy who had first blocked their seeing each other because of the constant territorial struggles. He shook off the heavy thought and pressed on.

Entering the shack, he nearly stumbled over a bulky form hidden in the shadows. It was Johnny. Trembling, Dannie sat down, his bowels on the verge of busting.

He tried to get a grip on himself.

This was the end.

All those years ago hanging out by Pete's Radio Store . . . all those dreams of Johnny Squint being his father. It all added up to nothing.

The burial. It had to be done.

Let Hugo Duce in California, Don Vitone in Miami Beach, and all the rest of their breed do the guesswork as to what happened to their prize Button Man.

Straining under the weight, Dannie carried his *amico* under the Ninth Avenue trestle-bridge—a sheltered place to dig. But with what? Dannie slithered back to the raunchy hut and found a shovel. *Where* was Pop? he wondered, feeling the sweat drip down the sides of his body. Stumbling through the debris, he heard the sound of clinking metal. On a premonition, he picked it up . . . the Sacred Heart! Kathleen's gift. Pop had found it for him.

Stunned, he managed to scramble back to the burial site, as the reverberating, rattling trains pulled into the nearby station.

He ducked under the bridge, away from their shooting window lights.

With a sense of determination, Dannie plowed into the ground with his shovel and dug. He thought of the gold-red ruby ring that he had given Johnny as a gift. Damned memories. A long time ago, Johnny had called him "son." It was a figure of speech, sure, but it had caused church bells to resound in his heart. Dannie was digging from a bent position atop the solid brown-dirt hill, just below the overpass's cement foundation supports. The grave grew deeper, the dirt not granite-hard as in winter. Wiping his brow, Dannie took a break.

Sidetracked. Eleanor had sidetracked him on every turn of the sexual wheel. John now had a gaping, sickening bullet hole in the back of his head because of Eve's feigned rapture. Dannie resumed his efforts, outlining the grave's length.

The most intensive investigation in the annals of crime had come to an abrupt, unforeseen conclusion. He dug furiously.

Then, it was finished—long and deep enough.

He knelt and dragged John into the hole. Rolling him in, face up he began shovelling madly. Until he stopped dead.

THE KEY! It hit him as though the trestle above had fallen on his head.

He stood perfectly still in the frightening dark, the ominous silence broken only by the sound of crickets chirping and the occasional vehicle passing overhead.

The key. Where did Eleanor get the key to his room? Slowly he pushed aside the dirt from John's left hand. The pinky finger was bare. "Kinda loose, but it'll do," were Johnny's words in Fiola's when he had given him the ring.

Dannie scraped pebbles, damp dirt from the shoes. Patent leather. John had usually worn Brito brown-on-brown.

Dannie clawed for the face. The right eye . . . *no* scar. As he pulled at his face, the cold skin seemed to come off in his hands. Catching his breath, he realized that it was *putty* under his fingernail. *Jesus Christ in Jehovah's Sky* . . . Eleanor and Eve had mistakenly murdered *Angel "St. John" Tenuto*. The livid scar all but blinked at him!

"You can quit shovelling, kid," the voice *with the Brooklyn accent* came from behind Dannie. "You got a minute to tell me about it." It was the cold, calculating voice of none other than *Johnny Mazziotta*.

They were ten feet apart, Dannie gauged; both a minute away from where Arnold Schuster had lived, died! He was on one knee, his body shivering, his mind darting in different directions—a minute to a professional meant just *that*, probably no matter what he would try to say or explain. Did Augie still have a heater on him? Was Johnny off balance on his haunches due to the incline? He thought of Annette now—his sixty seconds ticked away. What did it matter? There was nothing he could say that Johnny would believe. When it came to battle, there were no inbetweens, and Dannie decided to take the *last* ditch chance. Wheeling the shovel around and up, he swung it in front of him and to the left. The bullet exploded into the implement as he dove headlong.

His head hit Johnny's gut, and he felt an immediate mule-punch to the side of his head from the toughest *cop-fighter* Borough Park had ever known. His head down, staggering from the swift punch to his skull, Dannie managed to right elbow Johnny's kidney, grasping at John's pants' waist. They both fell, rolling down the bumpy grave-mound, body-to-body, to the freight tracks below.

"Little motherfucker," Johnny ground the words, as he instinctively got back up on his feet.

"You only wished," Dannie responded, scrambling to all fours as Johnny's kick caught his hip. He rolled over, and was up again, blocking Johnny's power-driven right cross with his hooked left arm. Dannie stumbled backwards but stood pat, as Johnny came at him madly, eyes glazed, fists set.

The jaw. That was the target. Dannie tried to focus as he sidestepped, pivoting away from hammer-blows which whisked his jawline. Whoever got the pressure points first could get the knockout. Johnny was going for it, fighting like a street-experienced, sun-struck horned bull. Dannie caught John's abdomen with a stinging left uppercut. He had the height, the youth, and the reach, but it didn't stop him from catching a pile-driven punch to his chest which caused him to breathe in short, wheezing spurts. "All over a *matza Chreester*—Christ fuckin' killer," Johnny spit out the words, banging Dannie's forehead with an all too solid whack! "A fuckin' *schmuck* nobody cares about!" John swung rashly, missing Dannie's chin. Slowly getting into a groove, his bar-bouncing days coming back to him, Dannie managed to crack Johnny's nose with two successive left jabs. Johnny's blood spurted as Dannie's chest heaved exhaustedly.

They were fighting for the only thing they truly owned—their *lives.* John fought like a mad animal. If just one of his insane straight rights landed on Dannie's jaw it would bury Dannie in Greenwood Cemetery. Dannie hit, hit, aiming for the jaw. Johnny weaved, ducked, and bobbed, before hurriedly smashing Dannie's temple again. Dannie belted Johnny's jaw. Johnny, wavering, charged back, kicking Dannie's shins, belting for the knockdown. Ramming forward two-fisted, Dannie warded off the raging attack. Finally, he managed to rap John's jaw with a solid blow. Johnny Squint, staggering, going down, elbowed Dannie's abdomen as Dannie clipped John's jaw *again.* Then Johnny Squint went *down*— and stayed there. Dannie, on his knees, pounded him for dear life, his hands like two bloody stubs.

Johnny's face was a bloody pulp, but it wasn't the pain of the blows which was registering on his face. His mouth strained to open and his face filled with fear, like he had just suffered a stroke and was trying to say something.

Dannie, exhausted and beaten to within an inch of his life, keeled over on the silver track. He lay there, sucking wind, thinking that his heart, his lungs would burst, killing him.

He had . . . loved Johnny. Wasn't that strange.

He looked up at the overpass. A huge sepulcher. If John moved and struck him, it would be the *fatal blow*.

The dim orange glow on the horizon made him aware of another danger: daylight. Oncoming daylight was the enemy now. Dannie had to *move*.

Somehow, he amassed the strength to move. From previous experience he knew that the aches, pains came later, after the adrenalin had settled down. His eyes focused on the crumpled, beaten figure next to him—his *hero*. You took a life because of ambition . . . your ticket to the top, Dannie said to the lifeless man without moving his lips.

You should have bothered to listen to your own niece, Kathleen. T.E.H.M.A. She would have told you what the sum of life is—the individual. That the nefarious thief, repenting at the last minute on a cross, atoned in time; that somebody does care about that *schmuck*.

I cared, Johnny. *I cared*.

Payback—just sixty seconds away from where Schuster had fallen *on his back* with that same dumbfounded expression.

Dannie knew that he could never drag John up to the top of the steep mound where Augie lay uncovered. He felt shattered, alone—as if life was only a small wait and the earth just a big waiting room. He swallowed a fragmented tooth and gazed around, his swelling eyes foggy on three metal barrels. Pop used ones like that to burn refuse.

Dannie made his plans. It took him over a bone-inflamed, rib-busted hour to carry them out.

He side-wheeled and pushed the perforated barrel over by the tracks to a trench. Then, he stuffed Johnny Squint in one barrel, upside down, heaving the refuse can upright with his shoulder.

The cremation had the help of strewn newspapers, discarded pint sized oil cans, and shredded rags.

And a book with one match in it.

The Last Rites came along with the skin-fumes, flesh-smoke. Dannie kissed, then tossed in the inscribed Sacred Heart medal—it would melt along with the Alexander engraved pinky ring. Urging on the flames, he pitched in more cardboard, transmission fluid-fumed quarts.

Next, Dannie managed to crawl up the mound and finish Augie's gravesite, first covering the face with the suit jacket.

We all get that moment, Augie, to answer for this moment—life. God'll tell you if Willie Sutton was worth it.

Dannie threw in the black revolver that had been five feet from the hurried, inner rock piled grave. He wondered if it was the Schuster weapon, or was that all a set-up to begin with? Sliding inch by inch down the hill, he fueled the barrel again, and then, using rock-dirt he topped off the remains with his raw hands, before sidling painfully up to the side of the Cuts wall.

Looking back, he saw Johnny's glorious reputation smoking its way toward the adjacent Greenwood Cemetery. It was vanishing on a spring breeze. Dannie saw it graduate from a corner of the world, a block and a half from the 40th and Eighth kingdom, into oblivion . . . for that minute.

"Those who take or use a life shall enter heaven a minute apart/God's minute—not man's," Dannie repeated Kathleen's benediction as daylight came.

Would Pietro M. and Benny Napanack be waiting? Dannie peeked through the snaky-crack in the cement wall. A beginning army of John's *schmucks* were converging on the Ninth Avenue BMT station. Train time. Most of them lunch-pailing it to the business commercial-hub, Manhattan. For their decent, daily bread.

Dannie's blood coughed up against the beige, weathered concrete wall. His two top front teeth loosened. In a frenzy, he pushed endurance to the limit. "Finish what you start out to do and you've got a heck of a start in life," Johnny's own words pushed him onward. He crept along the wall away from the side of the station entrance. He felt glass cutting into his aching chest, his green-tint glasses, smashed.

Had someone seen the smoke before? Had they assumed that it was Pop performing his everyday garbage ritual? Dannie had to move further away from the direct, immediate scene. Shoving himself upwards, he brute-ached himself over the four foot wall.

Piss Alley stenched twenty feet away. Blessedly, he was partially sheltered by the concrete blocked-grass foot-high islands separating the station proper from the Cuts wall.

He lay in the narrow, urine haven, the place where he had dared Eleanor to go with him when she gave him kissing lessons.

Eleanor. She had managed to lift Augie's Astor Hotel key, thinking it was Johnny's. She was a stone patient trickster who had receded from reality, making Eve follow a close second. He heaved phlegm—blood.

A hospital. That's what he needed. Eleanor's beating in the hotel was peanuts compared to the one he had just received. The beautiful bitch and a half must be laughing her swollen head off, he thought. Gasping, he made it to the alley's far edge.

He peeked to the corner where he used to live. Annette had said on the telephone that she'd see him there come daylight. He could barely make out the blurred figures scurrying up the Ninth Avenue hill. He hoped to heck one of the school kids wouldn't decide to come back here and take a private leak. Inching away from the edge, near blacking out, spots flooding his vision, he hoped desperately that his busted ribs hadn't punctured his lungs.

So close. He was so close.

There was a telephone inside the station that he couldn't risk attempting to get to. What a spot to be in. Augie, too, had put himself in an ironic spot. Killed, probably trying to speed-up the Pop process. He had been looking to ice him, nail him for information, for the gun. But the ones Angel had always packed had done him no good at all when he had gotten caught flat-footed. Dannie bent over, his body wracked with pain. He had to try and stand, be seen a foot from the alley's edge. Praying Annette would spy him, he made it to his feet, barely noticing a bone bulging from the back of his right hand. He stood, back against the station's brick wall, exposed in the cursed, or was it blessed, daylight.

There were cops. A passing squad car. If someone spotted his grotesque condition, he would be hard pressed to explain. They'd take him to the nearby Tenth Avenue Israel Zion Division of Maimondes Hospital where he'd lay till a convoy of connected-hoods came to pay their final *respects*. He tensed, seeing colors. A short coat, contrasting cape—charcoal with gold. Dannie recognized it. He had bought it for Annette! He was *home free* as she ran towards him.

Looking him over, she was horrified, but helped him back into the smelly alley. She'd hail a cab, call an ambulance, get him to a doctor's. Dannie shook his head. "We have . . . to get . . . far away." His words came out of his mouth along with a trickle of blood.

"Can . . . you . . . drive?" His throat was one fat lump.

Yes, she had a permit. She could get a car. She had a shoulder strap full of money, which she had taken from the Astor and refused to leave at the Waldorf. The situation was so muddled, so scary, that she couldn't control the tears, the fright. He begged her to get a hold of herself and *"get going. Please."* Finally, she tore herself away from him and dashed off.

Dannie peered around the wall, looking for Pietro M. or Benny. They must have seen her shopping with him by Bickford's restaurant, on Fulton Street. Had they followed her as well?

She had taken everything from the room at the Astor, including Augie's loot. He waited on the threshold of escaping hell on earth, promising God, and himself, that he'd respect human decency, and try to make his moment worthwhile in Thy sight. He looked for the time. His Picard wrist watch was bits of metal and crystal, used junk now. It reminded him how he had been used as a pawn, used to waylay. *Used* to create his . . . father all over again.

The time wouldn't pass, seconds seeming like full days. *Arnold! Believe me.* I told you to *RUN.*

Then, Annette was back *beside him!*

There was still one thing he had to do before they drove to New Jersey—to a hospital, a doctor. Annette could handle the hydramatic car she had bought off a highway robber car dealer, and drove at Dannie's obsessed command, to 45th Street between Ninth and Tenth, double parking by 941.

It only took a minute.

He got out of the car, the black and blue movement, the pain excruciating, and made it to the patch of grass, the tree, by Arnold's home. Painstakingly, he took the six-pointed Star from around his neck, and stuck it three-quarters beneath the grass, its face pointing squarely to where Arnold had fallen.

Annette wheeled the length of Manhattan's Interstate Lincoln Tunnel, Dannie shading his face until New Jersey was fully theirs.

"Huntingdon," she said. "Could you spare two dollars so I could buy that 'royal' name?"

"You . . . got . . . it," he was afraid to smile for fear his teeth might fall out.

"And when you get a minute," she steered toward the beckoning hospital. "Could you tell me what this nightmare is all about?"

"I'll . . . tell you," he said, thinking of Kathleen. "I'll tell . . . ALL . . . about it. In a minute."

EPILOGUE

Twenty-five months after the brutal "execution" in the Cuts, Uncle Frank Costello was dethroned. Dannie was serving in the U.S. Army—May 2, 1957—when Vito "Don Vitone" Genovese made his move.

Hugo Duce felt sure that it was Al-bert Anastasia who had caused the *disappearance* of Chappy Mazziotta, Angel Tenuto, and "the kid." Other Captains of the Costello Group (Salvatore "Sally Burns" Granella, Salvatore "Pedro" Di Pietro, Frank "Frankie Dee" De Simone) joined Hugo in urging Uncle Frank to take vengeance on the Madhatter, Anastasia.

They heartily believed that Albert's culpability stemmed from not only the final quelling of the Schuster case, but the demise of his men—Al Rispone, Tony-boy, Gretti.

The brainy, corrupt "President Maker" did nothing. Frank Costello was too dependent on Albert and his outside muscle to help control the inner workings of his own Group.

But Vito Genovese sent a "message" to Costello by way of a grazing bullet to the docile leader's head as he walked into the lobby of his swank Manhattan, Central Park West apartment building.

Never one to overstay his welcome, Uncle Frank graciously stepped down.

Vito became the Boss. His next step (five months later) was to eliminate Al-bert.

(Albert was shot eleven times by two men as the would-be Boss of Bosses sat in a barber chair in the midtown Manhattan Sheraton

Sheraton Hotel. 10/25/57. He was fifty-four when slain.)

Johnny Squint's death, Frank Costello's downfall, and Albert Anastasia's "extermination" were all ironically linked to the horrible "hit" on Arnold Schuster!

Arnold's one precious life had indeed affected the fate of Mr. Murder Inc. Vito Genovese was convinced that Albert Anastasia had had Johnny killed. Albert's B.B.-eyed gentle spokesman, Carlo Gambino, was already secretly aligned with Don Vito. Carlo "subcontracted" the Gallo Brothers to do away with the Anastasia menace. Joey and his brother were Profachi men who also stood to gain from the death of "The Octopus" whose arms were reaching into that Crew as well.

Dannie's first thought was of Al-bert slapping Willie Sutton. Then a John Garfield movie title came to him: *The Postman Always Rings Twice*. Al-bert had heatedly, yet indirectly, instigated the death of Arnold Schuster and it was indirectly because of Arnold that Al-bert himself was shot!

Dannie, married to Annette, moved to Los Angeles. But he didn't stay for long. It was there that he ran into the temperamental Downey Dunsky, Frank De Simone.

Frank was being plagued by a Federal Grand Jury over his alleged attendance at the infamous upstate New York Appalachian Convention, November 1957. (The alleged "meet" was to sanction Don Vitone as BOSS OF BOSSES.)

Frank De Simone was at first surprised, then pleased to see him. He commented that two of the Gallo Brothers—Joey and Larry— had been "contracted" to do away with Al-bert. Dannie's mind raced with visions of Joe the Blond, his wispy blond hair combed straight back the last time he had seen him in Brooklyn.

Who else would want John gone to seal the Schuster case but Al-bert? Frankie Dee ran down Al-bert's Top Men: Pisano shot in his caddy along with a comedian's wife, The Mortician gunned down outside his Brooklyn nightclub, all to secure Carlo's smooth transition in holding tight the reins to Mangano's old Crew.

When Frank brought up the subject of Chappy and his mysterious disappearance, Dannie lamented the loss, cursed Al-bert, and within the space of half a day was back to his old habit—packing suddenly and hightailing it from sunny southern California. But Dannie knew that Vito Genovese would know "that the kid was alive." Dannie and childbearing Annette settled in Tampa, Florida. He told Annette, during the trip, "that the minute to 'explain' had to be postponed."

In Florida he saw Eleanor.

They met in a motel dining room in Clearwater, Florida. 1958.

She was the epitome of middle-age grace and loveliness. And as shrewd as ever.

They reviewed the events which had passed: Willie Sutton still in a penitentiary, Frank Costello made to relinquish his post as Prime Minister of the Underworld, Albert Anastasia murdered by "his own," and most of all, Johnny Squint sent to hell! Dannie didn't tell her of the blunder committed by her and Eve, that they had sent the wrong man to hell.

She staunchly agreed how much this nation owed a debt of gratitude to Arnold Schuster, that must be paid. She gloated about Benny Napanack and his sister Connie both being stabbed to death in Borough Park by an irate landlord. "The drooling butcher wanted to harm *my child*!" she tongued her palate, smiling blue-eyed. He was struck with the twist of Benny and his other sister Connie butcher-knifed.

She inquired if he had run into Roscoe in California.

No.

Did he want to see Ruby in her home in St. Petersburg? But not little Daniel, four years old, in pre-school.

He said nothing.

Eve? The . . ."therapy" had . . . worked. Her nightmares, thank the Lord, had diminished.

He sat mute, knowing it wasn't *safe*.

Eleanor's ice-blue eyes glimmered.

Did his wife surpass *her* in their Floridian bed?

"We have a daughter," he wouldn't dignify that. "We named her, Eleanor," he laughed this time, an inscrutable laugh, thinking—God forbid—*another her*. He wondered whatever happened to Rocco Bruzzese, and Willie Sutton's grand stash. She had no idea. Within a month, he moved to Fort Lauderdale, the tip of southern Florida, far enough away from the criss-crossing Eleanor Cross.

Throughout the years Annette's family, while visiting them in Florida, would keep Dannie—with the prying, inquisitive blue eyes—apprised of the Kingdom of Brooklyn.

Joey Gallo, taking open credit for the Anastasia rub-out—his claim to fame—revolted against his boss, Profachi, the first in the history of the Clans. Dozens of Mob guys were slain in the grasp for power—the authorities called it a purge—the mob killing one another which benefits John Q. Public-at-Large. It was a theory which Annette's aging mom refuted.

After an eleven-year Crew battle, the rebellious Brothers lost, Joey being sent to Greenhaven Prison, Stormsville, New York, for extortion.

Vito Genovese died in Leavenworth Federal Penitentiary in 1969. While slowly dying, Vito was asked by a prison administrator how he felt about death in prison. Don Vito replied simply, "You got to die somewhere."

That same year, Willie "The Actor" Sutton was released from prison after serving seventeen years.

Willie sat on Brooklyn park benches, giving autographs, wondering why Angel had never shown for the escape. In time he would become a consultant to Connecticut banks. On security.

He often remarked that because of the tremendous "heat" over Arnold Schuster's death, an unwritten law had been put into effect: That no "citizen" shall ever be harmed. An ironclad rule never broken, intact until this day.

Joey Gallo, also released from prison, was beginning to fan the fires of war again within his Crew. Afraid he might win this time, his foes had him killed. Shot in Lower Manhattan, April 7, 1972.

Joey was buried in Greenwood non-sectarian cemetery. He had been slain not two miles from where Albert had been slaughtered. Now he lay not more than ten yards from where his old foe, Albert, was interred. They were both just a stone's throw away from the Cuts, where Johnny Squint's remains had fluttered away.

Shopping bag toting Uncle Frank, who filled his days visiting afternoon wiseguy hangouts and fancy eateries, died of natural causes February 18, 1973.

The affable Meyer Lansky lived only several miles from Dannie. Meyer had been seeking asylum in another country to avoid prosecution in the United States. He was perpetually collecting money for his homeland, Israel, to support them when they had become a recognized state, and to further fund them in their incessant wars against their Arab neighbors. But when he landed in Zion claiming his Jewish "right of the return," he was denied. Dannie kept in mind the phrase from Meyer on just what Payback is! *It's a motherfucker!*

In 1979 Dannie took a trip to see Roscoe in the San Fernando Valley, Los Angeles, California (safe, as Frank De Simone was deceased).

While dining in the Mr. H room at the Beverly Hilton Hotel he was "greeted" by a sophisticated, cigarette-holder biting man. The man had shocking gray hair and a crafty half-smile. His name was

Robert P. Lawton, an attorney from Brea, Orange County, southern California. An ex-FBI man who had worked assiduously on the Sutton-Schuster case!

He knew this tall "kid." From Brooklyn. Chappy's mascot.

Dannie smiled.

And returned to southern Florida.

In the beginning of 1980 he took a jaunt to Spring Hills, Florida, where Willie the Actor had "retired."

It took both of them some time before they could "place" each other, such was the physical toll of time.

Willie asked if Dannie had ever found John or Angel before they "evaporated."

"Angel thought of you right up until his last day," Dannie said, Willie beaming slyly.

Willie hoped that the blood of the "young fellow," Schuster, had not been shed in vain. His life of upright decency "was the truer lifeline of mankind." Soon after that, Willie died.

"The Actor," always the gentle man, had passed away true to form.

No mention of his marshland millions was made.

August 25, 1982. Hugo Duce, despondent over and besieged by financial problems, committed a documented suicide. Quiet, deadly, loyal Hugo, distraught over money. Dannie thought of the hunt that was still on for John.

In January 1983, Dannie saw Eleanor at the Thunderbird Motel on Collins Avenue, Miami Beach.

She commented on *her* Daniel being so tall, a university graduate.

As for Eve, the time was long overdue for Dannie to insure her seeing her *other* grandchildren.

He agreed, tearful, but smiling warmly. It was safe for *her*, now!

As for Eleanor herself, she wasn't young any more, but she was stately, looking sensational for a woman in her early sixties. She still had the whistle bait legs, and ravishing eyes. She fiddled with the sleeve of her fustian outfit, coming on without coming on. Her sexual organs still did most of the talking for her.

She spoke of Hugo Duce, that filth, who had threatened her unborn child. She had purposely sought Dannie out. He was free now to travel wherever he wanted. Dannie heard, saw in the glint of those blue eyes that HUGO DUCE DID NOT COMMIT SUICIDE. She had blown his brains out in a card club in Borough Park.

That creeping fear in her that her son was living under the threat of a violent death-cloud had caused the Black Widow to *eight-leg* it east for the final kill.

Dannie traveled. To Brooklyn. Arnold's store was no more. But there was a haberdashery store on the corner of 57th and Fifth. A block away. The name of it was Arnold's. Coincidence?

He traveled to Queens. Montifiore Cemetery, Springfield. Arnold's gravesite. He was stricken by the carving on the seven-foot headstone. A tree with overhanging, leafy branches, a Star of David beneath them.

It resembled exactly what he had done by Arnold's home in April 1955.

Paid in full, Arnold? God, let it be so, Dannie *hopefully* prayed.